Indiana

Finish Line ECA

Algebra I

Acknowledgments

Photo Credits: Front cover and title page: *Indianapolis 500, Indianapolis, Indiana,* www.flickr.com, Craig Stephen

ISBN 978-0-8454-5888-4

Contents

Welcome to Indiana Finish Line ECA Algebra I

One of the most important sets of skills you can acquire while in school is a strong ability to deal with mathematical situations. This ability goes beyond understanding magnitudes of numbers and performing operations such as subtraction or multiplication. A solid understanding of mathematics also involves a variety of other skills, including those listed below.

- judging the reasonableness of computations
- applying and interpreting formulas
- reading, interpreting, and making predictions from graphical displays
- using logic and reasoning skills to solve problems
- relating previously learned knowledge to help solve more complex problems

These skills, among others, are addressed in the Indiana Algebra I End-of-Course Assessment (ECA). The ECA is a final exam aligned with Indiana's Academic Standards and designed to test students' knowledge and ability upon completion of Algebra I. As a Core 40 course, Algebra I is a requirement for Indiana students wishing to graduate from high school.

In order to ensure consistency and accuracy in Algebra I courses, Indiana developed Academic Standards to clarify the topics and knowledge you are expected to have mastered at the end of the course. For Algebra I, these standards are:

1. Relations and Functions
2. Linear Functions, Equations, and Inequalities
3. Pairs of Linear Equations and Inequalities
4. Polynomials
5. Quadratic Equations and Functions
6. Rational and Radical Expressions and Equations
7. Data Analysis

Each standard is further divided into specific skills you are expected to be able to perform. The purpose of these standards is to clarify what essential mathematics skills you should learn inside the classroom so that you will be able to handle everyday situations outside of the classroom. The standards provide a guide to help your teachers prepare you for the Algebra I ECA. This book, ***Indiana Finish Line ECA Algebra I,*** is also intended to help prepare you for the Algebra I ECA by reviewing the topics you have already studied in class.

This book is divided into seven units. Each unit covers a standard and its subdivisions. Within each unit is a series of lessons, which review the main concepts of the standard. The features contained in each lesson are listed below:

- the standard number at the start of each lesson
- sections describing each review topic
- explanations of important concepts for each review topic
- examples to illustrate the explanations
- sample questions for each review topic
- complete explanations for each sample question
- strategy tips or formula reminders
- a section of independent practice questions referred to as *It's Your Turn*

At the end of each unit is a set of review questions for all of the topics covered within the unit lessons.

The Algebra I ECA consists of three question types: multiple-choice, gridded-response, and constructed-response. Multiple-choice questions have four possible answer choices. Each correct answer is worth 1 point.

Gridded-response questions require you to write and fill in a numerical answer into a bubble grid. The bubble grids allow for whole numbers, fractions, and decimals, as the examples on the next page show. Fill in the grids from left to right.

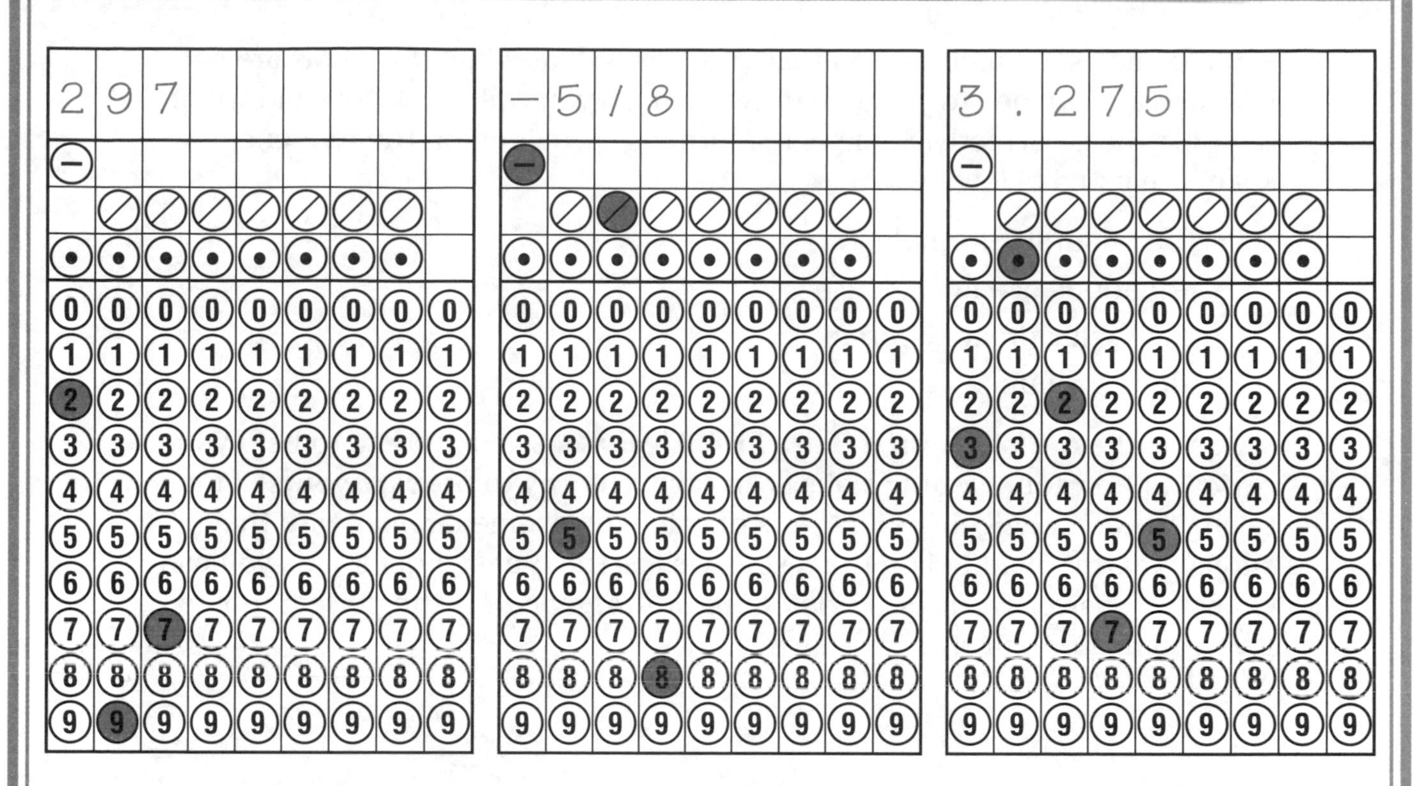

Notice that the bubble grid includes a negative sign, a fraction bar, and a decimal point. No other symbols can be used in the bubble grid. All mixed numbers must be converted to improper fractions before entering them into the bubble grid to receive full credit. You must write the answer in the answer boxes and fill in the appropriate bubble underneath.

Constructed-response questions require you to write your answer on a line. These questions may be divided into multiple parts. Each constructed-response question is worth 3 points. The exact scoring guidelines vary for each constructed-response question. It is possible to receive some points on a constructed response question even if your answer is not correct. It is always important to answer constructed-response questions completely, show all your work, and write thorough explanations whenever possible.

Calculator use is permitted on one session of the Algebra I ECA. It is not permitted on the second session. Most types of calculators are permitted; your teacher will have a list of those calculators that are not allowed. Be sure to verify that your calculator is approved for use on the Algebra I ECA prior to test day. It is also important that you are familiar with your calculator's features and abilities before beginning the test.

In addition to the use of a calculator, you will also be given a Reference Sheet. A sample of this is included in the back of this book. This sheet contains many important formulas that you may want to use when solving questions on the test. You can save yourself time by becoming familiar with what formulas are included on this sheet, as well as which formulas are not. It is also a good idea to practice using them so you will know how and when to apply them correctly. Some of the formulas provided on the reference sheet are listed below:

- the quadratic formula
- equations of a line
- the Pythagorean theorem
- slope formula

Using the ***Indiana Finish Line ECA Algebra I*** as a resource to help you review important Algebra I skills is an excellent way to prepare yourself for taking the actual Algebra I ECA. It is of value to become familiar with the subject matter included on the test as well as the types of questions you can expect to answer. ***Indiana Finish Line ECA Algebra I*** is the perfect tool to give you this practice.

Unit 1
Relations and Functions

You can find many different types of graphs in newspapers, magazines, and on the Internet. It is important to be able to understand the relationship represented in a graph. Relations and functions are types of quantitative relationships. They are often expressed in tabular or graphic form.

There are two lessons in this unit:

1. **Identifying Functions and Relations** reviews characteristics of a function and how to connect a function with its equation.
2. **Finding Domain and Range** reviews identifying the domain and range of a given relation.

LESSON 1

Identifying Functions and Relations

Standard A1.1.1

Identifying Functions from Relations

A relation that assigns a unique range value for every domain value is called a **function.** With ordered pairs in the form (x, y), the x-values are the domain and the y-values are the range. You can determine if a relation is a function using any of these methods:

- Check that no domain values are repeated.
- Analyze the graph of a relation.
- Use a mapping diagram.

> A function assigns each x-value to one and only one y-value.

A **vertical-line test** can be used on a graph to determine if a relation is a function. If a vertical line passes through no more than one point at a time on the graph, the relation is a function. For example, look at the two graphs below.

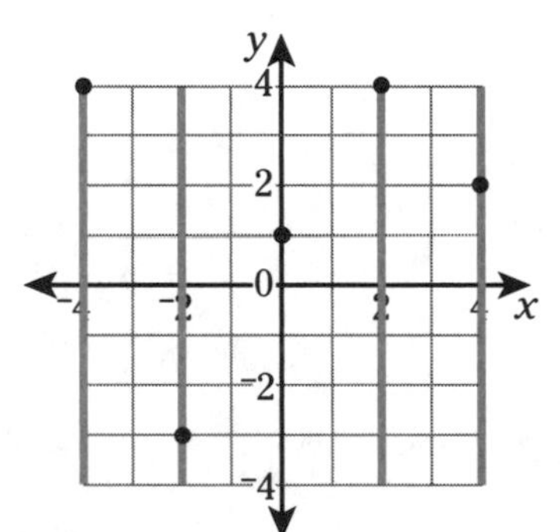

This graph is a function since each vertical line drawn passes through only one point.

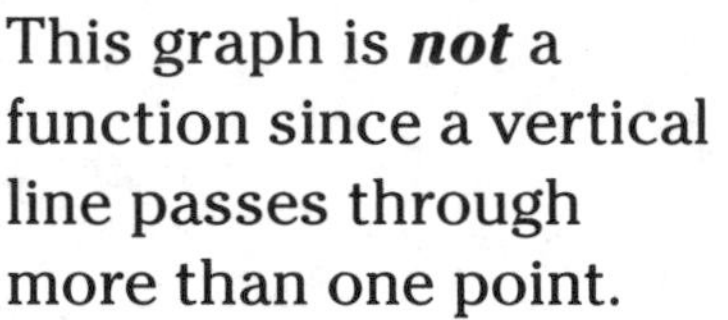

This graph is ***not*** a function since a vertical line passes through more than one point.

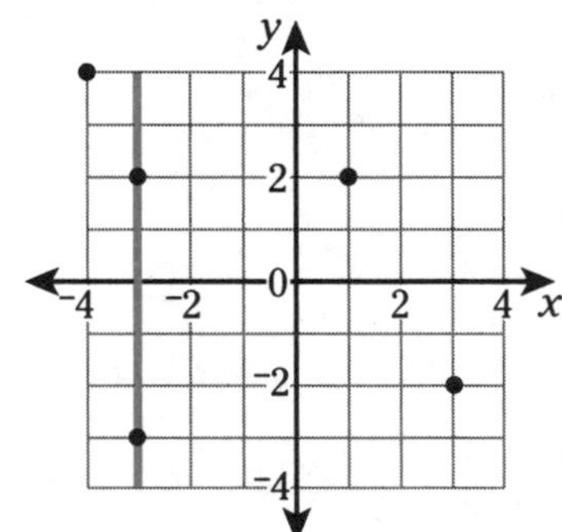

Some relations are graphed as a set of continuous points that form a straight or curved line or part of a line. For example, in this graph, data is continuous at all x-values from -5 to 5 except for at $x = 3$, where there is a break in the graph.

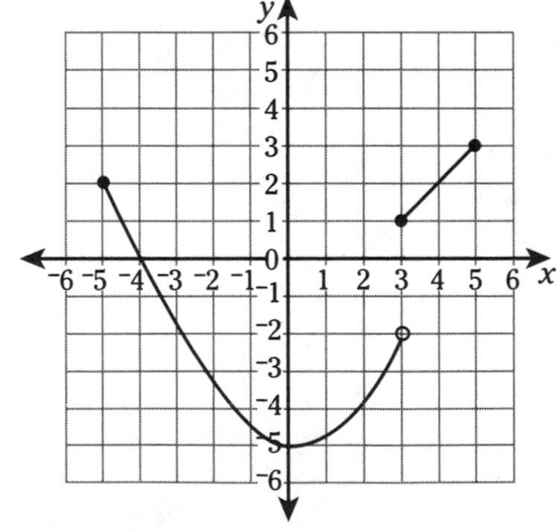

Notice the open circle at (3, -2), and the closed circle at (3, 1). The open circle means the point (3, -2) is ***not*** part of the graph. The closed circle means the point (3, 1) ***is*** part of the graph. Having one open and one closed circle at points when $x = 3$ means that x-value corresponds to only one y-value. Therefore, this relation is a function. The vertical line test can also be used to show this.

Try the sample question below.

S-1 Which statement best describes the relation graphed below?

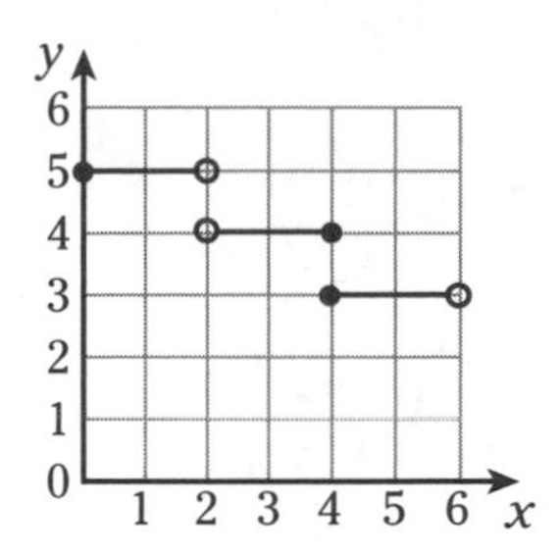

A The relation is a function since the x-value 2 does not correspond to any y-value.

B The relation is not a function since the x-value 4 corresponds to more than one y-value.

C The relation is a function since the x-values from 0 to 6 correspond to only one y-value each.

D The relation is not a function since the y-values 3, 4, and 5 correspond to more than one x-value.

In order for a relation to be a function, each x-value must correspond to no more than one y-value. The x-values in this graph include all numbers from 0 to 6, except for 2 and 6. The closed circles mean those points are part of the graph. The open circles mean those points are not part of the graph. In choice A, it is true that the x-value 2 corresponds to no y-value. But this only means the relation is not continuous. Since there are two closed circles at $x = 4$, this x-value corresponds to two y-values, 3 and 4. For that reason, this relation is not a function. You can also see that this graph does not pass the vertical line test at $x = 4$. Choice B is correct.

Mappings are another way of determining if a relation is a function. In a mapping, arrows are typically drawn from the domain of a relation to its range. If no more than one arrow is drawn from any domain value to a range value, the relation is a function. Otherwise, it is not.

The next sample shows if a relation is a function using a mapping diagram.

S-2 Which relation is also a function?

A 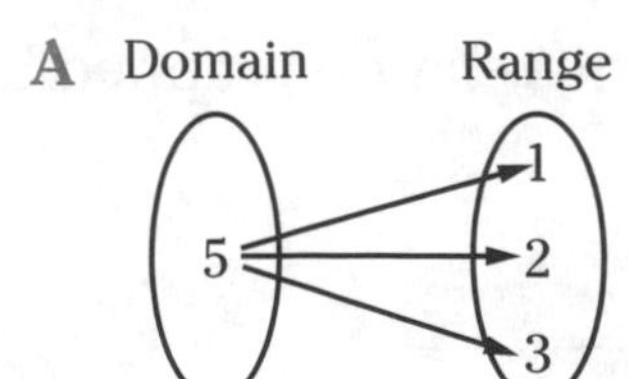

C 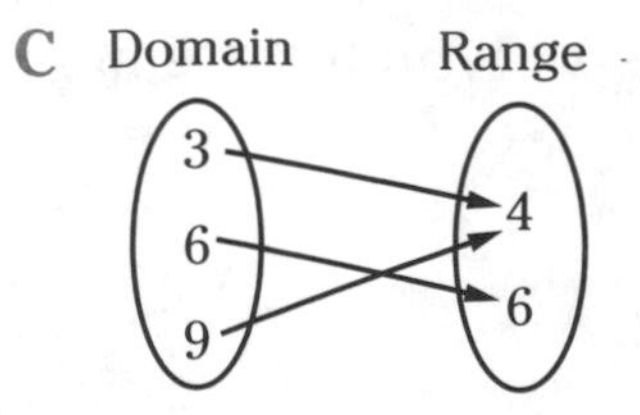

B 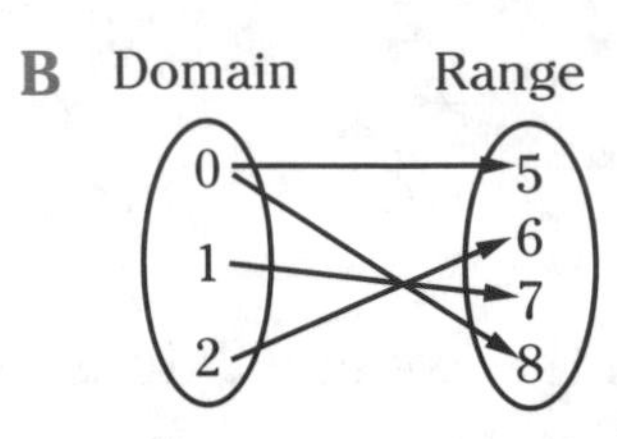

D 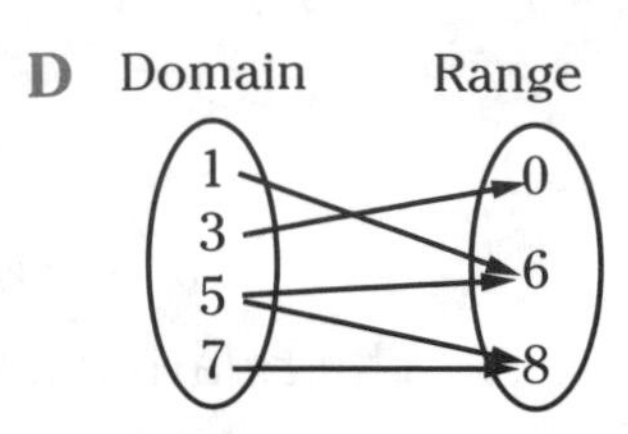

The arrows in these mappings show the domain values that correspond to the range values. In a function, each domain value corresponds to only one range value. So, the mapping that is a function has exactly one arrow from each domain value to any range value. Choices A, B, and D show at least two arrows pointing from the same domain value. Only choice C shows one arrow pointing from each domain value. Choice C is correct.

Matching Graphs of Functions

Functions can be represented using equations, tables, and graphs. Being able to identify different representations of the same function is a valuable skill to have.

One way to connect a function with its equation is to find some points that make the equation true. Then match these ordered pairs with the appropriate graph.

Two special cases to watch out for are vertical and horizontal lines. Equations of the form $x = a$ represent vertical lines, while equations of the form $y = b$ represent horizontal lines.

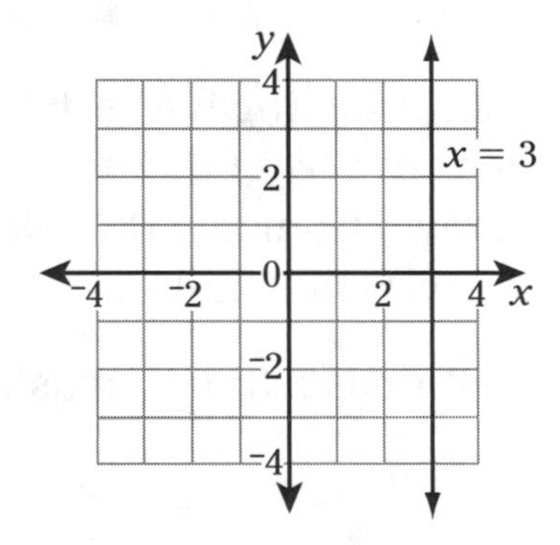

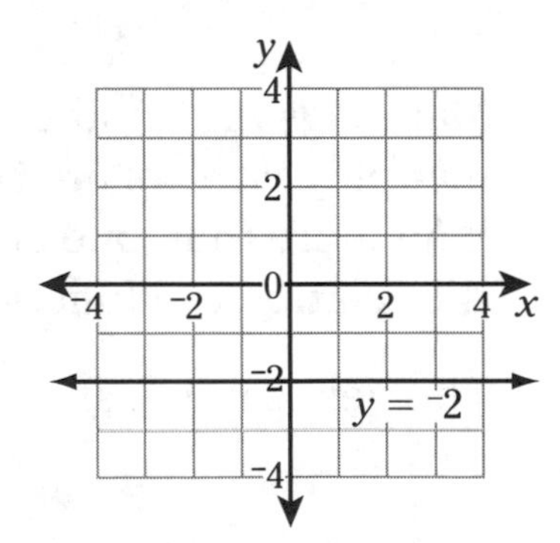

Try this sample question.

S-3 A company estimates its total monthly expenses using the equation $y = 4{,}000x + 4{,}000$. Which of these graphs shows this relationship?

A
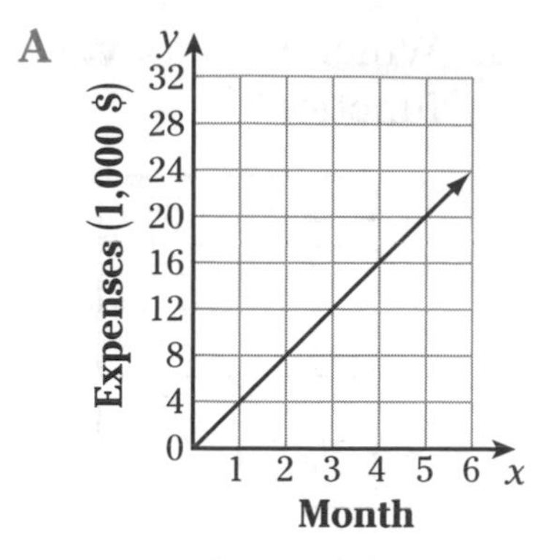

C
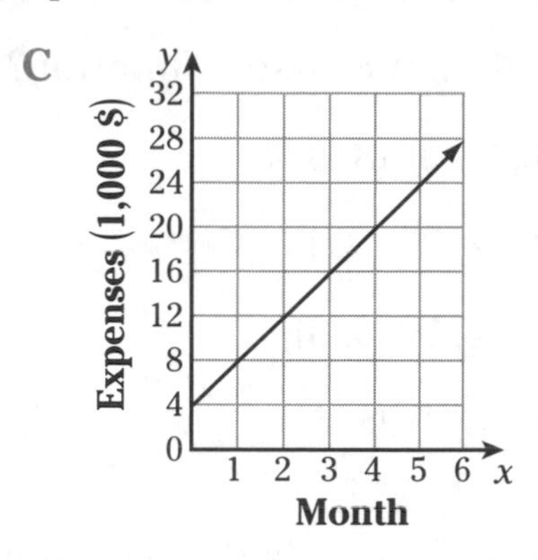

B
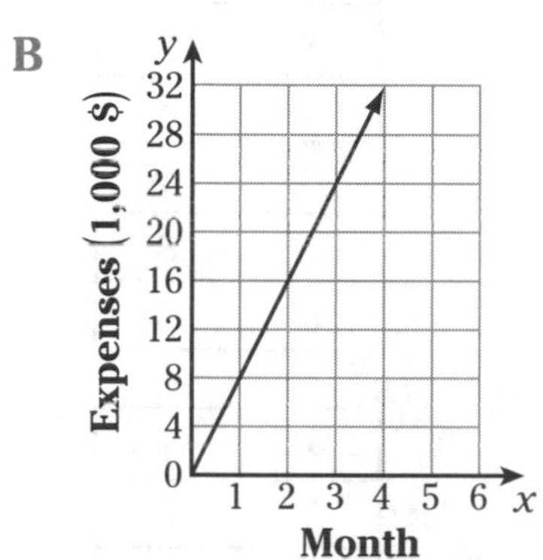

D
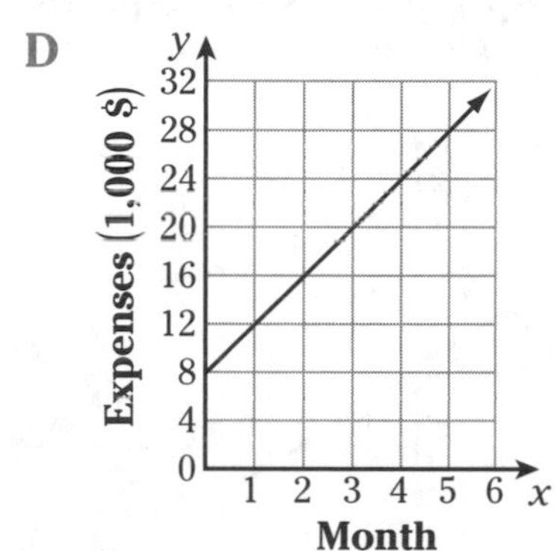

First choose some values for x and solve the equation for y. You can make a table to keep track of your pairs.

Month	1	2	3	4
Expenses ($)	8,000	12,000	16,000	20,000

Rewrite the points shown in your table as the set of ordered pairs (1, 8,000), (2, 12,000), (3, 16,000), and (4, 20,000). Look at each graph. Find the graph that contains these ordered pairs. Only the graph in choice C contains all of these points. Choice C is correct.

IT'S YOUR TURN

Read each problem. Circle the letter of the best answer.

1. Which relation is also a function?

   A {(0, 3), (4, 3), (8, 3)}

   B {(1, 2), (2, 3), (1, 4)}

   C {(4, 5), (4, 7), (4, 9)}

   D {(6, 0), (8, 1), (8, 5)}

2. Which graph models the equation $2x + 3y = -6$?

   A

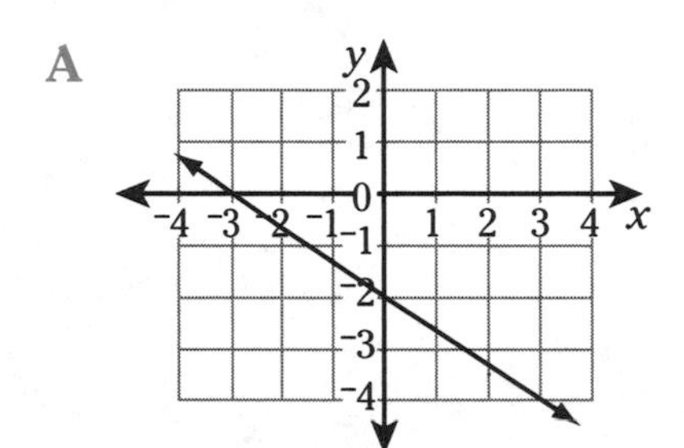

   B

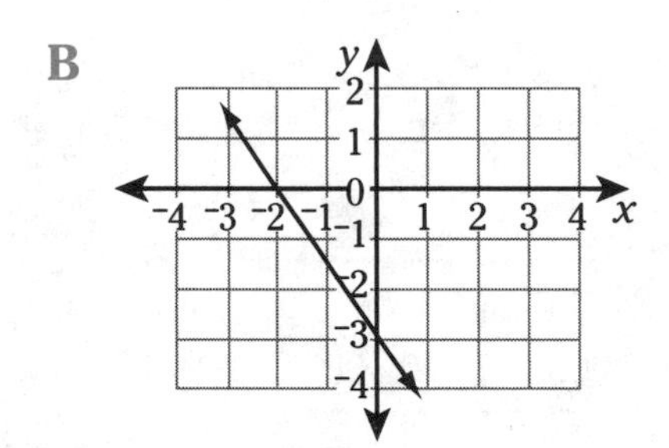

   C

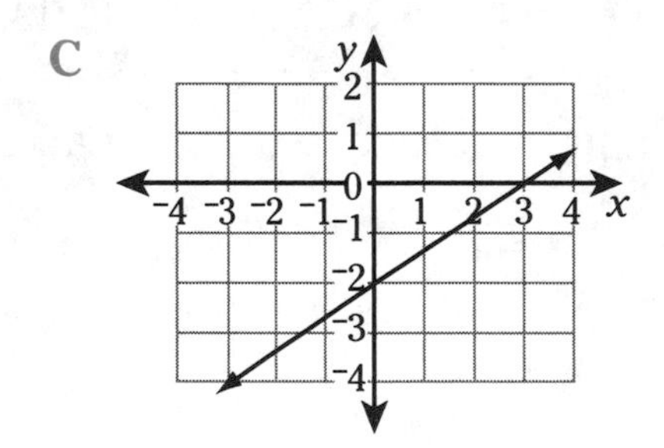

   D

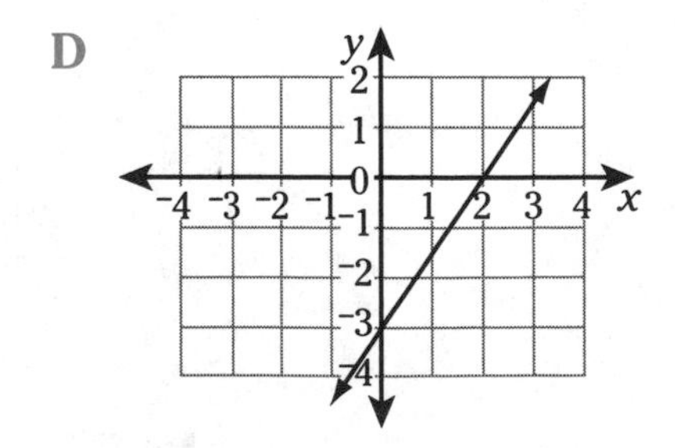

3. Which table of values represents a function?

   A

x	y
8	-2
0	-1
-1	5
8	-9

   B

x	y
-2	3
0	-3
-2	8
6	-1

   C

x	y
5	0
5	3
5	-7
5	-9

   D

x	y
7	-2
-3	-2
9	-2
-4	-2

Read the problem. Circle the letter of the best answer.

4. Look at the function below.

$$P = 500t + 5{,}000$$

Which graph best models this function?

A
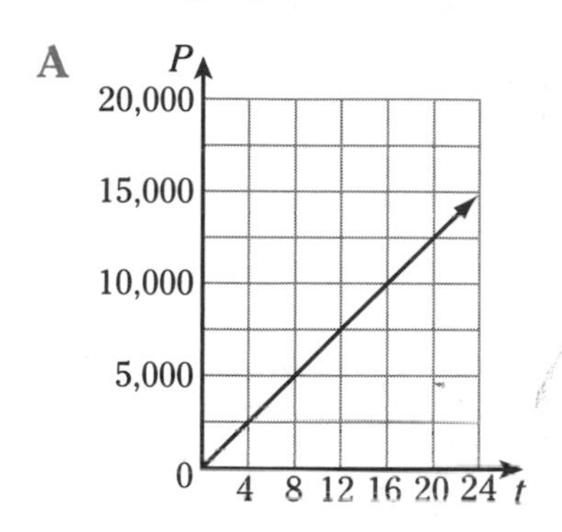

C
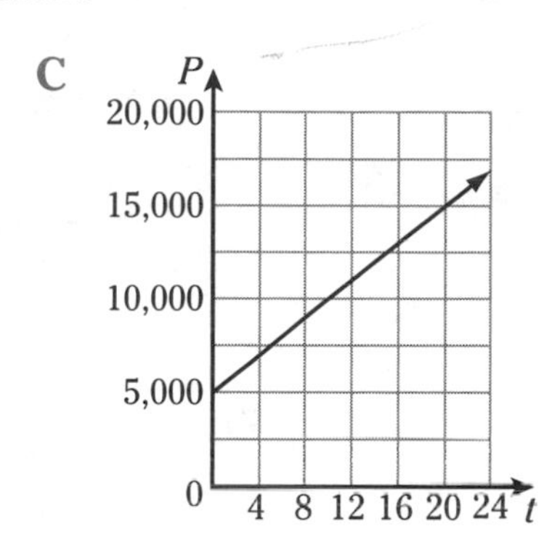

B
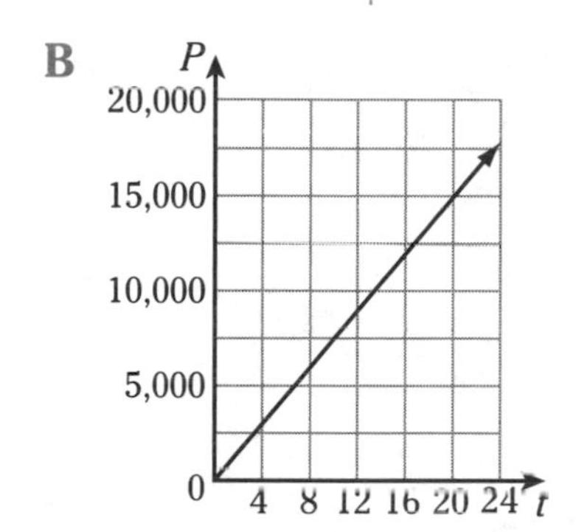

D
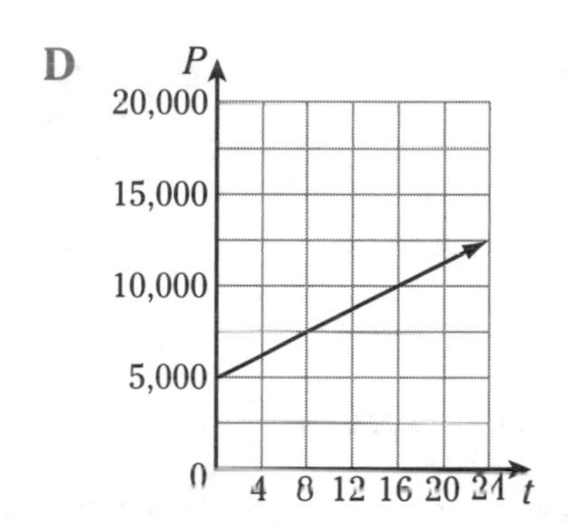

Read the problem. Circle the letter of the best answer.

5. Which graph represents a function?

A

C

B

D

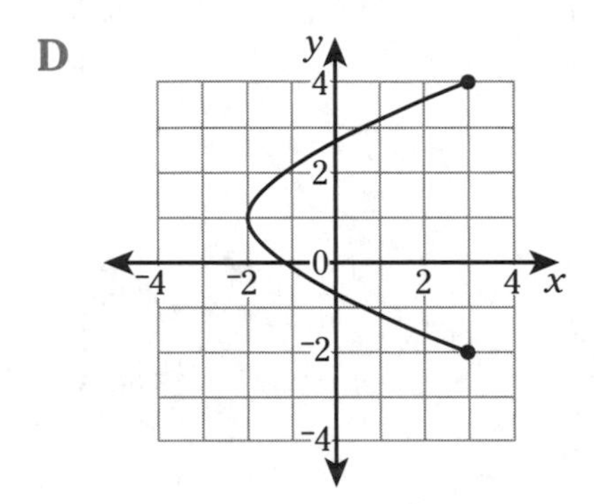

Read the problem. Write your answer.

6. During the summer, Kasey mows lawns to earn money. He keeps track of the number of lawns he mows and how many hours it takes him each day for five days.

Number of Lawns	4	2	2	3	1
Number of Hours	3	5	2	5	1

Explain how you know whether or not this relation is a function.

____

____

____

____

LESSON

2 Finding Domain and Range

Standard A1.1.2

A **relation** is a set of ordered pairs (input, output). These ordered pairs are often written within braces. For example, the ordered pairs for (age, height) shown below form a relation.

{(15, 65), (21, 70), (18, 73), (16, 62)}

Identifying Domain and Range

The **domain** of a relation is the set of all input values. The **range** is the set of all output values. The domain of the relation above is {15, 21, 18, 16}. Its range is {65, 70, 73, 62}.

In ordered pairs (x, y), the x-values are the domain and the y-values are the range.

Try this sample question.

S-1 The number of laps some students ran around the school track and the number of minutes they ran are shown in the table below.

Laps	3	8	5	6	4
Minutes	9	14	9	15	8

What is the range of this relation?

A {3, 4, 5, 6, 8}

B {8, 9, 14, 15}

C {3, 4, 5, 6, 14, 15}

D {3, 4, 5, 6, 8, 9, 14, 15}

The range is the set of output values. In the table, laps are the input and minutes are the output. So the range is the set containing the number of minutes {8, 9, 14, 15}. Repeated numbers are written once. Choice B is correct.

IT'S YOUR TURN

Read each problem. Circle the letter of the best answer.

1. The number of hours the wait staff at Emilio's Restaurant worked one day and the amount in tips each person got is shown in the table below.

Hours Worked	4	6	5	2
$ in Tips	40	45	36	16

What is the range of this relation?

A {2, 4, 5, 6}

B {2, 4, 5, 6, 16}

C {16, 36, 40, 45}

D {2, 4, 5, 6, 16, 26, 40, 45}

2. What is the domain of the relation graphed below?

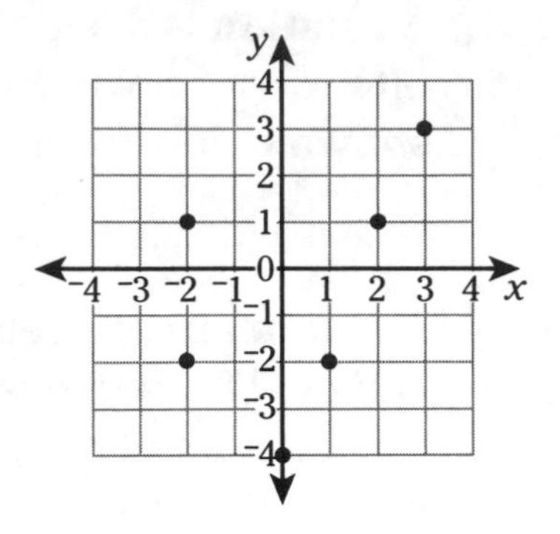

A {-2, 1, 2, 3}

B {-4, -2, 1, 3}

C {-2, 0, 1, 2, 3}

D {-2, -1, 0, 1, 2, 3}

Read the problem. Write your answer.

3. Look at the relation below.

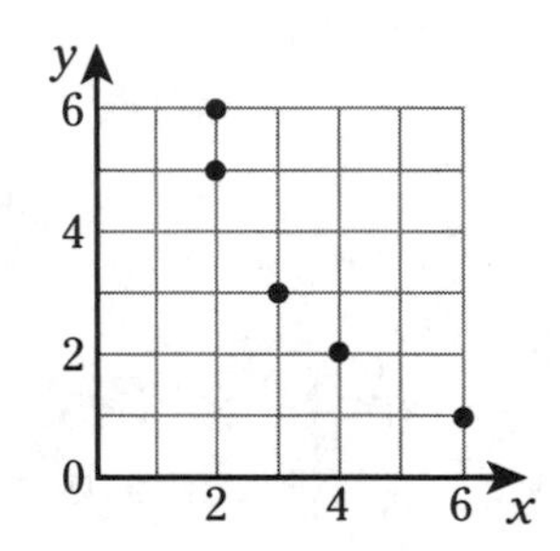

What are the domain and range of this graph?

Domain: ____________________

Range: ____________________

Relations and Functions Review

Read each problem. Circle the letter of the best answer.

1. The points below show the relationship between the number of hours some employees at a music shop worked one day and the amount of pay they received in dollars.

{(6, 55), (4, 40), (5, 50), (5, 60), (8, 108), (7, 60)}

What set represents the range of this data?

A {5, 60}

B {4, 5, 6, 7, 8}

C {40, 50, 55, 108}

D {40, 50, 55, 60, 108}

2. Which of these graphs represents a function?

A
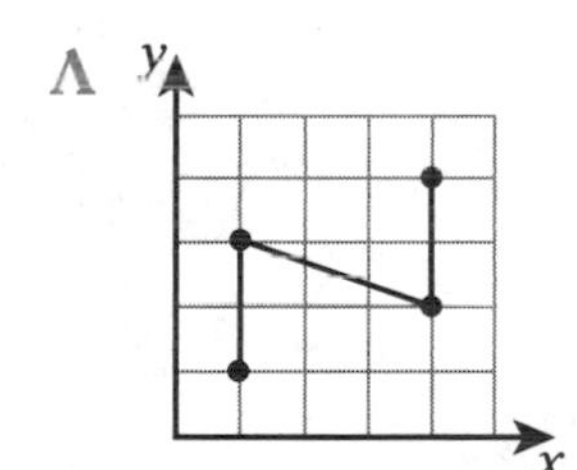

C
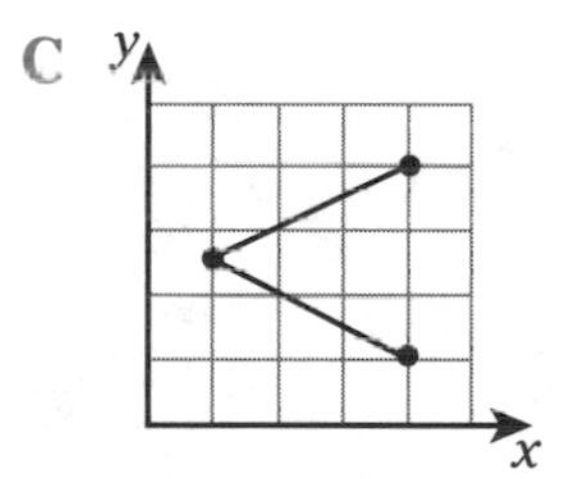

B
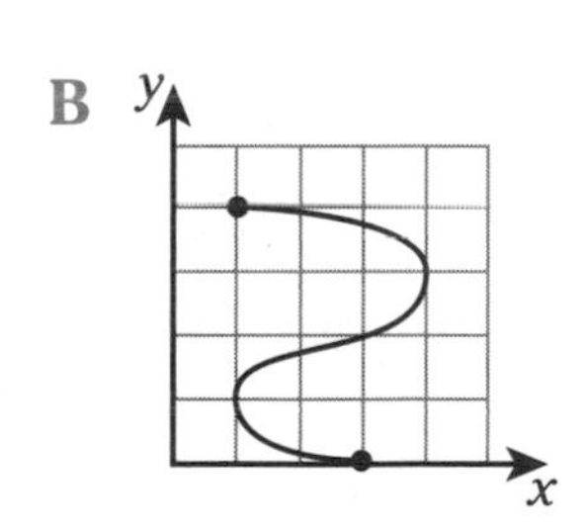

D
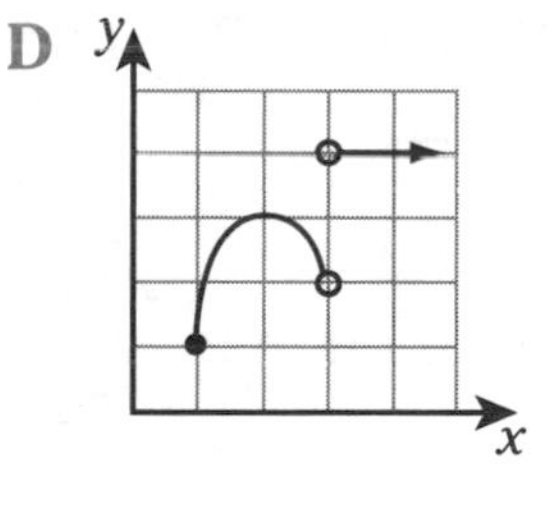

3. Which of the following is the graph of the line $y = -x + 2$?

A
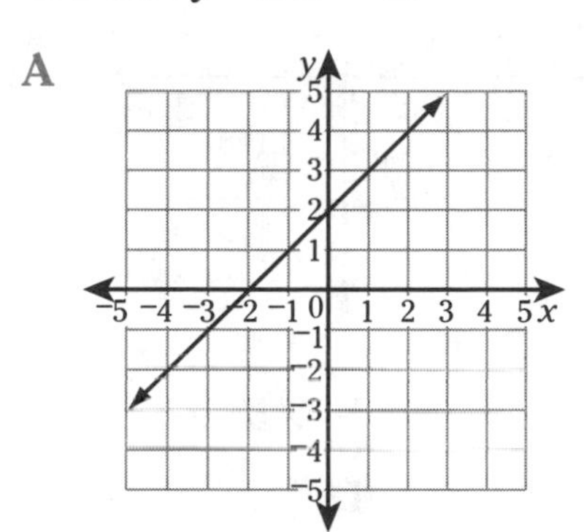

B
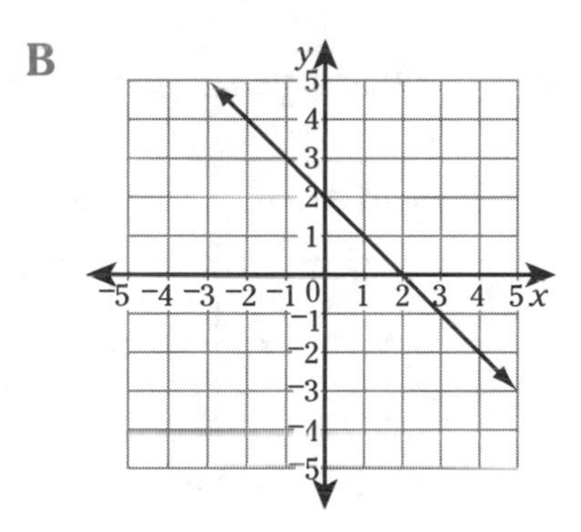

C
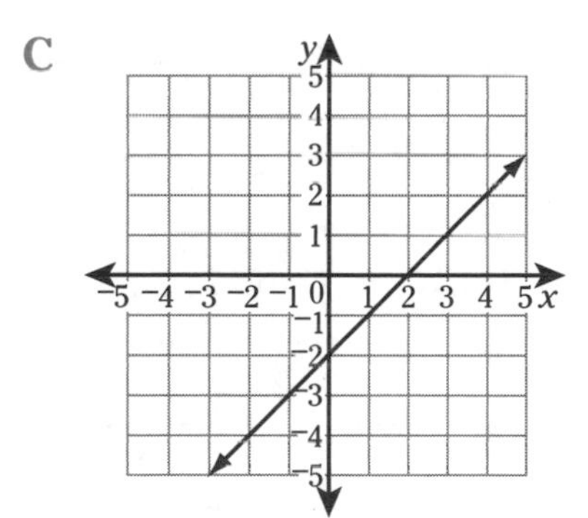

D
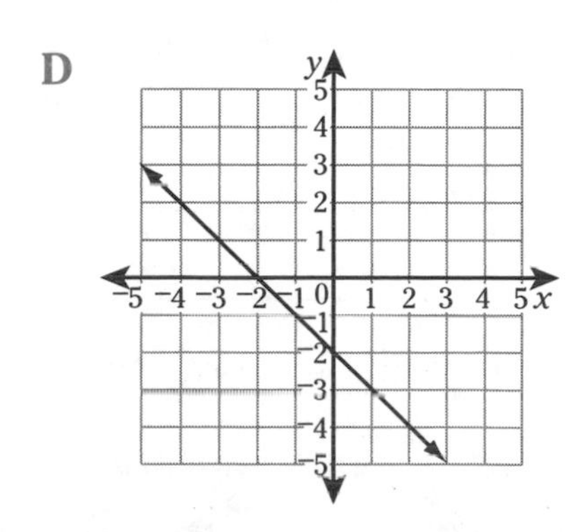

Read each problem. Circle the letter of the best answer.

4. Which of the following is an equation of the function shown graphed below?

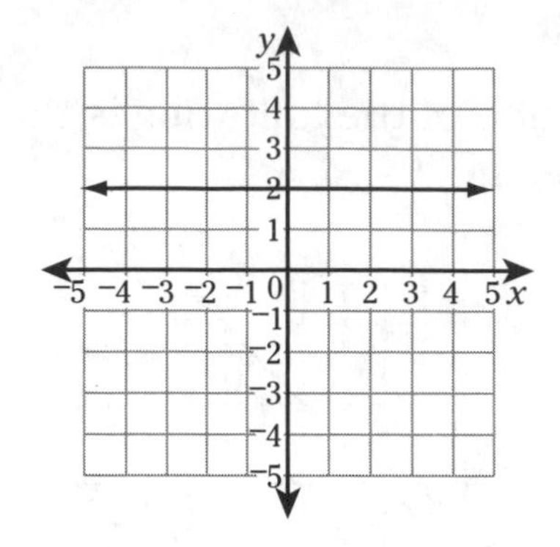

A $x = 2$

B $x = -2$

C $y = 2$

D $y = -2$

5. What is the range of the relation shown in the table below?

x	5	4	3	2
y	-3	-1	1	3

A {1, 2, 3, 4, 5}

B {2, 3, 4, 5}

C {-3, -1, 1, 2, 3, 4, 5}

D {-3, -1, 1, 3}

Read each problem. Write your answers.

6. Look at the relation shown in this table.

x	-2	0	2	4	6
y	-8	0	4	4	0

What are the domain and range of this relation?

Domain: ______________________

Range: ______________________

7. Look at this table of values.

x	-2	-1	0	1	2
y	5	2	1	2	5

Is the relation shown in the table also a function? Explain how you know.

____

____

What is the domain of the relation above?

Answer: ______________________

Unit 2
Linear Functions, Equations, and Inequalities

Many real-life situations and patterns can be described using linear equations and inequalities. For example, the linear equation $y = 2x$ can be used to describe the number of tires, y, on x bicycles. In working with and solving linear inequalities, you use many of the same rules as with equations. The solutions to linear equations and inequalities are often easier to comprehend in graphic form on a coordinate plane. Being able to solve and graph equations and inequalities is an important algebraic skill. Understanding the meaning of a line's slope and given points is useful when trying to make predictions about other points that lie on the line.

There are seven lessons in this unit:

1 **Solving Equations and Formulas** reviews solving two-step linear equations for a variable and solving formulas.

2 **Solving Linear Inequalities** reviews solving linear inequalities for a variable, as well as graphing the solution set on a number line.

3 **Graphing Linear Functions** reviews using a table of values to graph a linear equation on the coordinate plane.

4 **Slope and Intercepts of a Line** reviews how to determine a line's slope and x- and y-intercepts from its graph or equation.

5 **Writing Linear Equations** reviews writing or identifying the linear equation in point-slope, standard, and slope-intercept forms given the graph of the line, two points on the line, or the slope and a point on the line.

6 **Parallel and Perpendicular Lines** reviews finding linear equations that represent lines that are either perpendicular or parallel to a given line.

7 **Graphing Linear Inequalities** reviews graphing an inequality in two variables on a coordinate plane.

Solving Equations and Formulas

Standard A1.2.5

Linear Equations

Real-world patterns and relationships are often modeled by linear equations. A **linear equation** is any equation that includes constants and variables that are multiplied by coefficients. By working with linear equations, you will be able to understand many patterns and relationships in the real world.

The following are all examples of linear equations:

$2x - 12 = 10$

$x + y = \pi$ (Remember that π is just a constant.)

$5x - 4 = -3x$

The following are ***not*** examples of linear equations:

$2x^2 - 12 = 10$ (not linear because the variable is squared)

$x + |y| = \pi$ (not linear because one of the variables is inside absolute value symbols)

$\sqrt{5x - 4} = -3x$ (not linear because the first instance of x is under a square root sign)

To solve a linear equation, you need to write it as an equivalent equation with just the variable on the left side of the equation. Rewrite the equation by adding, subtracting, multiplying, and dividing, making sure to do the same operation to both sides of the equation. The properties you can use are shown below.

If $x = y$, then:	
$x + a = y + a$	Addition Property of Equality
$x - a = y - a$	Subtraction Property of Equality
$ax = ay$	Multiplication Property of Equality
$\frac{x}{a} = \frac{y}{a}$	Division Property of Equality

For example, here is how to solve the equation $2x - 12 = 10$ for the variable x.

$2x - 12 = 10$

$2x - 12 + 12 = 10 + 12$ Add 12 to both sides of the equation.

$2x = 22$ Simplify.

$2x \div 2 = 22 \div 2$ Divide both sides of the equation by 2.

$x = 11$ Simplify.

Now try these sample questions.

S-1 What value of x makes the equation below true?

$$3x + 1 = -23$$

A -8

B -6

C 6

D 8

The original equation is $3x + 1 = -23$. Subtract 1 from each side and simplify. This results in $3x = -24$. Next, divide each side by 3 and simplify. This results in $x = -8$. Choice A is correct.

S-2 What value of x makes the equation below true?

$$4x - (3x - 5) = 2x + 11$$

To find the value of x in this equation, first simplify the left side of the equation. Then combine variable terms onto one side, as shown in the steps below:

$4x - (3x - 5) = 2x + 11$	
$4x - 3x + 5 = 2x + 11$	Distribute -1 to eliminate parentheses.
$x + 5 = 2x + 11$	Combine like terms.
$5 = x + 11$	Subtract x from both sides.
$-6 = x$	Subtract 11 from both sides.

When $x = -6$, the equation is true.

Formulas

A **formula** is a type of equation the states a relationship between two quantities, often represented by variables. You are already familiar with many mathematical formulas, such as the area formulas for rectangles and triangles, from your studies in geometry. Similar formulas also arise in the sciences and other real-world situations.

Given a mathematical formula, there are two things you might be asked to do.

- Evaluate the formula by substituting numbers for one or more variables.
- Solve the formula for a variable.

In physics, a formula for energy is given by $E = \frac{1}{2}mv^2$. If you know the values of m and v, you can find the value of E. For example, when $m = 6$ and $v = 10$:

$$E = \frac{1}{2}mv^2 = \frac{1}{2}(6)(10)^2 = \frac{1}{2}(6)(100) = 300$$

You can also solve this same formula for the variable m:

$$E = \frac{1}{2}mv^2$$

$$2 \times E = 2 \times \frac{1}{2}mv^2$$

$$2E = mv^2$$

$$2E \div v^2 = mv^2 \div v^2$$

$$2E \div v^2 = m$$

The energy formula, solved for m, is $m = \frac{2E}{v^2}$.

Now try these questions.

S-3 The formula for the circumference of a circle is $C = 2\pi r$, where r is the radius of the circle. Which of these shows the same formula solved for r?

A $r = 2\pi C$

B $r = \frac{2\pi}{C}$

C $r = \frac{C}{2\pi}$

D $r = \frac{2C}{\pi}$

Divide both sides of the original formula by 2π. Then simplify.

$$C = 2\pi r$$

$$C \div 2\pi = 2\pi r \div 2\pi$$

$$C \div 2\pi = r$$

$$\frac{C}{2\pi} = r$$

Choice C is correct.

S-4 The lateral surface area LA of a three-dimensional figure is the surface area of the sides only. The LA of a right square pyramid with side length s and slant height l is given by the equation $LA = 2sl$. If $LA = 12$ and $s = 4$, what is the value of l?

A 2

B $\frac{3}{2}$

C $\frac{2}{3}$

D $\frac{1}{6}$

Substitute each of the given values into the formula and solve by isolating the variable l:

$$12 = 2(4)l$$

$$12 = 8l$$

$$\frac{12}{8} = l = \frac{3}{2}$$

Choice B is correct.

The following sample problem can be solved by using the distance formula, *distance* = *rate* · *time* $(d = rt)$, twice. First you must solve the equation to find the value of r. Then you can use this value of r together with a new value of t to find the new value of d.

S-5 A rocket traveled 12 miles in 4 seconds. At this rate, how far would it travel in 5 seconds?

A 13 miles

B 14 miles

C 15 miles

D 16 miles

You are given d and t, and can solve for r using the formula $d = rt$. Plugging in $d = 12$ and $t = 4$, the equation becomes $12 = 4r$. Solving for r gives the rocket's average speed $r = 3$ miles per second. Now you can use the equation $d = rt$ again, with $r = 3$ and $t = 5$, as follows: $d = 3 \cdot 5 = 15$. The rocket will travel 15 miles in 5 seconds. Choice C is correct.

IT'S YOUR TURN

Read each problem. Circle the letter of the best answer.

1. What is the value of x in this equation?

$$4x - 2 = 6$$

A 1

B 2

C 16

D 32

2. The formula *Interest* = *principal* · *rate* · *time* ($I = prt$) is used to find simple interest. Which shows the interest formula solved for r?

A $r = \frac{pt}{I}$

B $r = \frac{I}{pt}$

C $r = Ipt$

D $r = \frac{It}{p}$

3. What is the solution to the equation $-6z + 1 = 13$?

A $z = -6$

B $z = -2$

C $z = 2$

D $z = 6$

4. In the study of electricity, the formula $V = I \times R$ is used to relate the voltage (V), current (I), and resistance (R) of circuits. What is the value of I when $V = 9$ and $R = 0.2$?

A 1.8

B 4.5

C 18.0

D 45.0

5. What is the solution to the equation $\frac{3}{4}y - 5 = 10$?

A $y = \frac{15}{4}$

B $y = \frac{20}{3}$

C $y = \frac{45}{4}$

D $y = 20$

6. Toni is riding her bicycle at a constant speed of 18 kilometers per hour. At this rate, how many hours will it take her to ride 24 kilometers? Use the distance formula $d = rt$.

A $1\frac{1}{3}$

B $1\frac{1}{2}$

C $1\frac{2}{3}$

D $1\frac{3}{4}$

Read each problem. Fill in your answer on the response grid.

7. If $4 + 8a = 4$, what is the value of a?

−								
	⊘	⊘	⊘	⊘	⊘	⊘	⊘	
⊙	⊙	⊙	⊙	⊙	⊙	⊙	⊙	
0	0	0	0	0	0	0	0	0
1	1	1	1	1	1	1	1	1
2	2	2	2	2	2	2	2	2
3	3	3	3	3	3	3	3	3
4	4	4	4	4	4	4	4	4
5	5	5	5	5	5	5	5	5
6	6	6	6	6	6	6	6	6
7	7	7	7	7	7	7	7	7
8	8	8	8	8	8	8	8	8
9	9	9	9	9	9	9	9	9

8. A plumber charges $30 to visit a residence, plus $40 per hour for the amount of time he spends there. If the total bill for a visit was $210, how many hours did the plumber spend at the residence?

−								
	⊘	⊘	⊘	⊘	⊘	⊘	⊘	
⊙	⊙	⊙	⊙	⊙	⊙	⊙	⊙	
0	0	0	0	0	0	0	0	0
1	1	1	1	1	1	1	1	1
2	2	2	2	2	2	2	2	2
3	3	3	3	3	3	3	3	3
4	4	4	4	4	4	4	4	4
5	5	5	5	5	5	5	5	5
6	6	6	6	6	6	6	6	6
7	7	7	7	7	7	7	7	7
8	8	8	8	8	8	8	8	8
9	9	9	9	9	9	9	9	9

Read the problem. Fill in your answer on the response grid.

9. If Luke tries a certain skateboard trick twice, the probability he will be successful both times is given by the equation $P = (1 - q)^2$. If $q = 0.4$, what is the value of P?

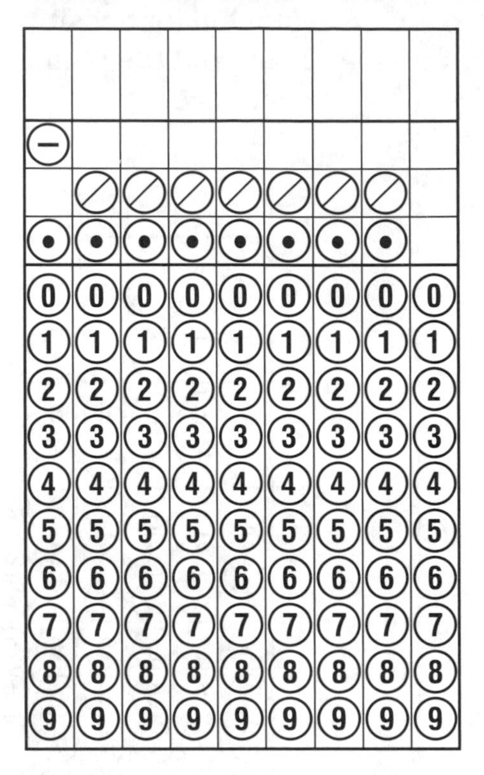

Read the problem. Write your answer.

10. The volume of a sphere is given by the formula $V = \frac{4}{3}\pi r^3$, where r is the radius of the sphere. What is the volume of a sphere that has a radius of 10 centimeters?

Answer: ______________________

Read each problem. Write your answers.

11. Leo uses the equation below to estimate the amount of taxes, A, he owes to the government.

$$A = 0.15(d - 7{,}550) + 755$$

Leo estimates that he owes the government $3,455 in taxes. What is d, the total dollars Leo earned during the past year?

Answer: ____________

12. The surface area formula for a sphere is $SA = 4\pi r^2$. Solve this formula for r.

Answer: ____________

Read each problem. Write your answers.

13. Trisha started out with 40,000 miles on her car and drove exactly 800 miles a week.

    Write an equation to determine the number of miles, m, on Trisha's car after w weeks.

    Answer: ____________

    After how many weeks did she have 44,800 miles on her car?

    Answer: ____________

14. The equation below was solved incorrectly.

$$3 - (k + 1) = -2$$

Step 1: $3 - k + 1 = -2$
Step 2: $4 - k = -2$
Step 3: $-k = -6$
Step 4: $k = 6$

What mistake was made in the work shown above?

____

____

____

____

What is the solution to $3 - (k + 1) = -2$?

Answer: ____________

LESSON 2 

Solving Linear Inequalities

Standard A1.2.5

A **linear inequality** is similar to a linear equation, but the equals sign is replaced by an inequality sign. For example, $-2x \leq 5$ and $5y + 2 > 0$ are linear inequalities. With a linear equation, there is one exact solution. A linear inequality, however, has a range of solutions.

A **solution set** lists possible solutions for a given inequality.

$<$ means "is less than"
$>$ means "is greater than"
$\leq$ means "is less than or equal to"
$\geq$ means "is greater than or equal to"

Solving Linear Inequalities

Linear inequalities are solved much the same way as linear equations. The properties that justify each step in the solution of an equation or inequality are given in Lesson 1 of this unit.

The steps used in solving the inequality $5(x + 2) > 6$ are shown below.

Step	Statement	Reason
1	$5(x + 2) > 6$	Given
2	$5x + 10 > 6$	Distributive Property
3	$5x > -4$	Subtraction Property of Equality
4	$x > -\frac{4}{5}$	Division Property of Equality

Try this sample question.

S-1 What is the solution to the inequality $3x - 9 \geq 6$?

A $x \geq -9$

B $x \geq -1$

C $x \geq 5$

D $x \geq 45$

Choice C is correct. Adding 9 to each side gives the inequality $3x \geq 15$. Dividing each side gives the solution $x \geq 5$. In other words, any value of x greater than or equal to 5 makes the inequality $3x - 9 \geq 6$ true.

An important difference between solving linear equations and solving linear inequalities is this:

- When multiplying or dividing by a negative number, the direction of the inequality symbol ***must*** be changed.

Try these sample questions.

S-2 What is the solution to the inequality $-\frac{y}{5} + 6 > 2$?

A $y < -20$

B $y < 20$

C $y > -20$

D $y > 20$

Choice B is correct. First subtract 6 from each side, giving the inequality $-\frac{y}{5} > -4$. Then multiply each side by -5 and reverse the inequality sign, and the solution is $y < 20$.

S-3 What is the solution to the inequality $4(y + 5) - 6(y - 1) \geq 30$?

A $y \leq -8$

B $y \geq -8$

C $y \leq -2$

D $y \geq -2$

Choice C is correct. Removing the parentheses gives the inequality $4y + 20 - 6y + 6 \geq 30$, which simplifies to $-2y \geq 4$. Dividing both sides by -2 and switching the direction of the inequality sign gives the solution: $y \leq -2$.

The solutions to inequality problems may be given in the form of a graph on a number line. Some examples are given below.

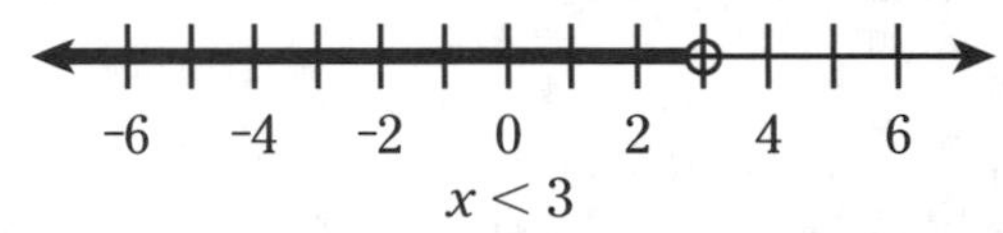

$x < 3$

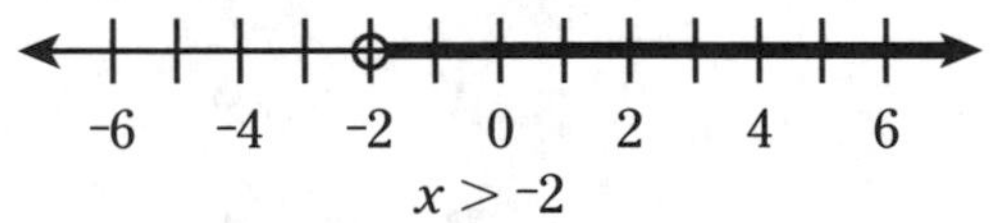

$x > -2$

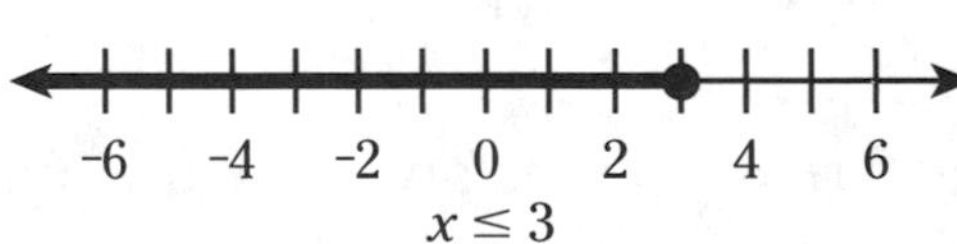

$x \leq 3$

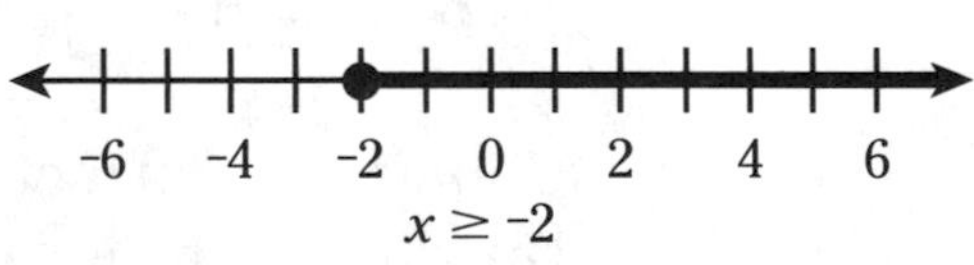

$x \geq -2$

Notice that open circles are used to symbolize the < and > signs, and closed circles are used to symbolize the ≤ and ≥ signs.

Some word problems must be solved using an inequality. If the inequality is not given you must be able to write one using the given information and then solve it in the context of the problem.

Try these sample questions.

S-4 Which graph represents the solution set for the inequality shown below?

$$9 - 2x \geq 1$$

A 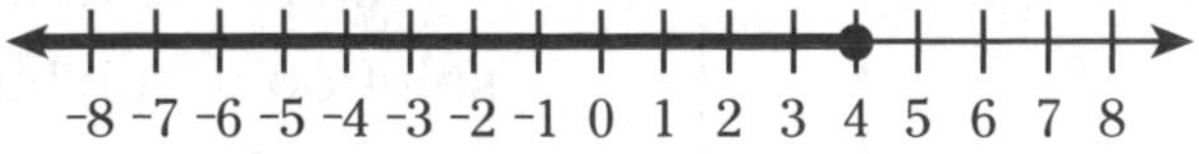

B 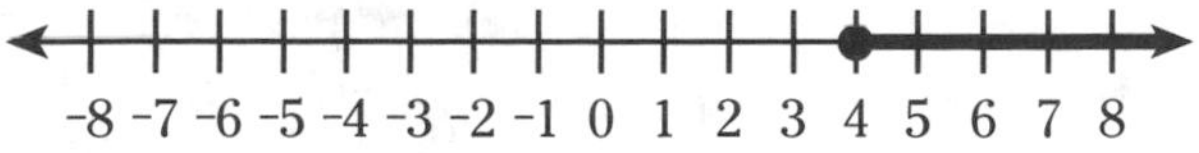

C 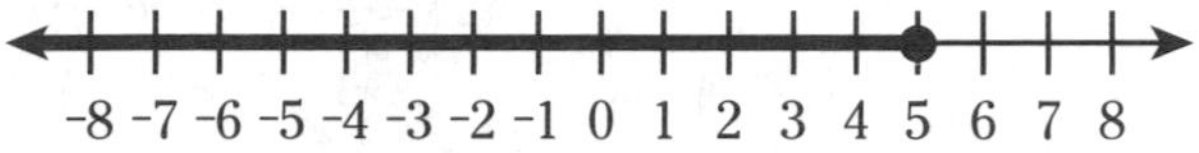

D 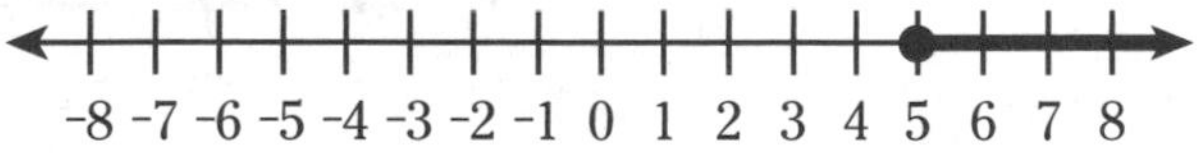

Solve the inequality using these steps:

$9 - 2x \geq 1$	
$-2x \geq -8$	Subtract 9 from both sides.
$x \leq 4$	Divide both sides by -2.
	Change the direction of the inequality symbol.

Choice A is correct.

S-5 Max brought $20.00 to the arcade. Each arcade game costs $1.25 to play. He used $6.50 of his money to buy snacks. What is the greatest number of arcade games Max can play with the money he has left?

A 5

B 10

C 11

D 16

Write an inequality to find the number of arcade games, *a,* Max can play. The amount paid for snacks plus the amount spent on arcade games should not be more than $20.00:

$6.50 + 1.25a \leq 20.00$	
$1.25a \leq 13.50$	Subtract 6.50 from both sides.
$a \leq 10.8$	Divide both sides by 1.25.
	Notice that the direction of the inequality symbol does ***not*** change when dividing by a positive number.

The number of games must be a whole number. Since Max doesn't have quite enough money to play 11 games, the most he can play is 10 games. Choice B is correct.

IT'S YOUR TURN

Read each problem. Circle the letter of the best answer.

1. What is the solution to the inequality $8x - 16 > 8$?

   A $x < -1$

   B $x < 3$

   C $x > -1$

   D $x > 3$

2. What is the solution to the inequality $\frac{2}{3}y + 2 \leq 3$?

   A $y \leq \frac{2}{3}$

   B $y \leq \frac{3}{2}$

   C $y \geq \frac{2}{3}$

   D $y \geq \frac{3}{2}$

3. What is the solution to the inequality $-4z + 1 \geq 10$?

   A $z \leq -\frac{9}{4}$

   B $z \leq \frac{9}{4}$

   C $z \geq -\frac{9}{4}$

   D $z \geq \frac{9}{4}$

4. Which of the following graphs shows the solution to the inequality $-\frac{1}{2}x - 4 < 0$?

   A 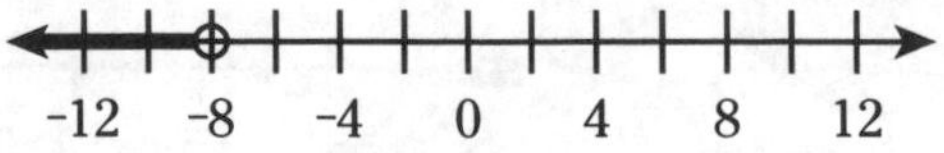

   B 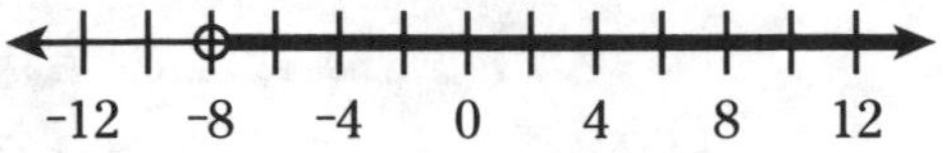

   C 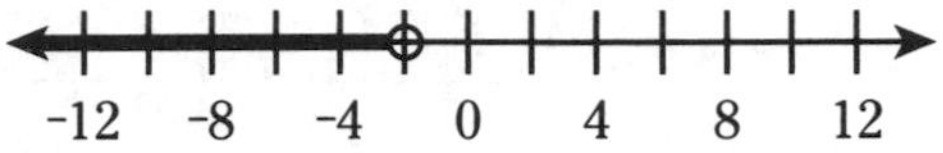

   D 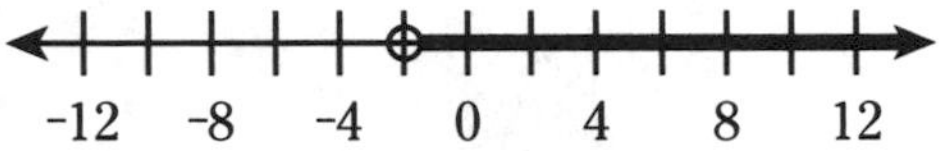

5. Solve for x:

   $$8x - 4(3x - 2) \geq 20$$

   A $x \leq -3$

   B $x \leq 3$

   C $x \geq -3$

   D $x \geq 3$

6. Which graph shows the solution set to the inequality below?

   $$3(3 - k) < -12$$

   A 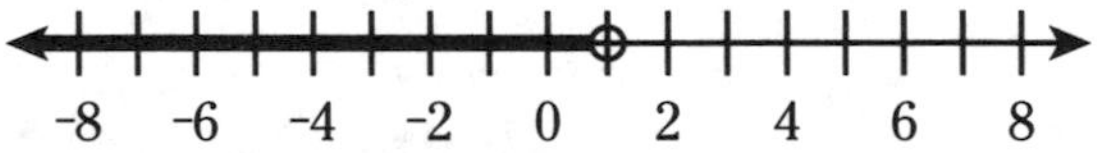

   B 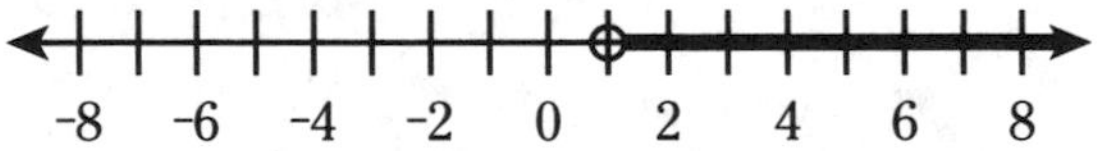

   C 

   D 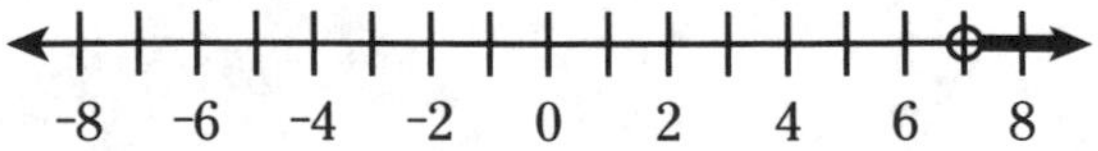

Read each problem. Write your answers.

7. An office manager budgets $1,600 to furnish a new office. She needs to buy 4 desks. She also needs to buy a table that costs $400.

   Write an inequality to show how much the office manager can spend on each desk.

   Answer: ______________________

   What is the maximum amount the office manager can spend on each desk?

   Answer: ___________

8. A freight elevator can hold at most 10,000 pounds. Martin needs to load the elevator with crates that weigh 300 pounds each.

   Write an inequality you can use to find the maximum number of crates that Martin can load at a time.

   Answer: ______________________

   What is the maximum number of crates that Martin can load at a time?

   Answer: ______________________

LESSON 3 

Graphing Linear Functions

Standards A1.2.1, 2

Graphing Linear Equations

In many real-life situations, the relationship between two quantities can be represented by the graph of a line. For example, the number of feet representing an object's length is always 3 times the number of yards representing the same length. You can use the equation $y = 3x$, where y is the number of feet and x is the number of yards, to represent this situation.

One way to graph a line is to use its equation to plot two or more points, and then draw the line connecting the points. For example, at the right is the graph of line $y = 2x - 3$:

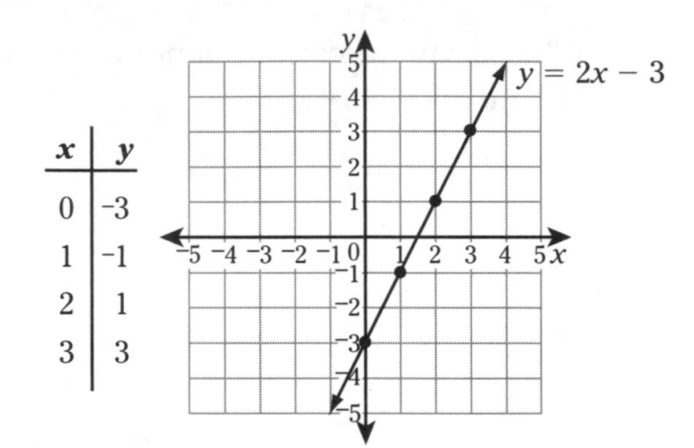

x	y
0	-3
1	-1
2	1
3	3

Try these sample questions.

S-1 Which of the following is the graph of the line $y = 3x + 1$?

A

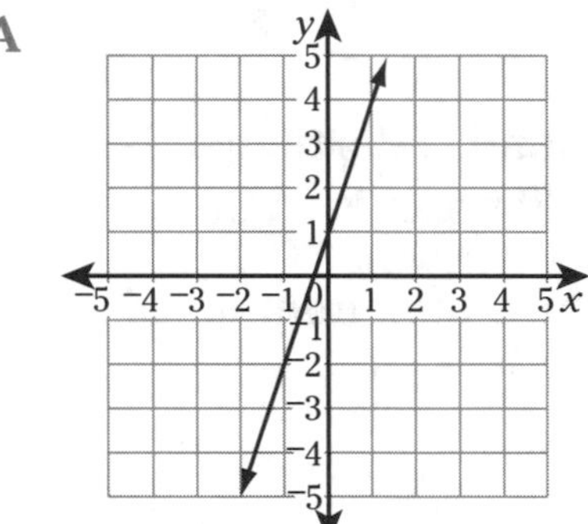

C

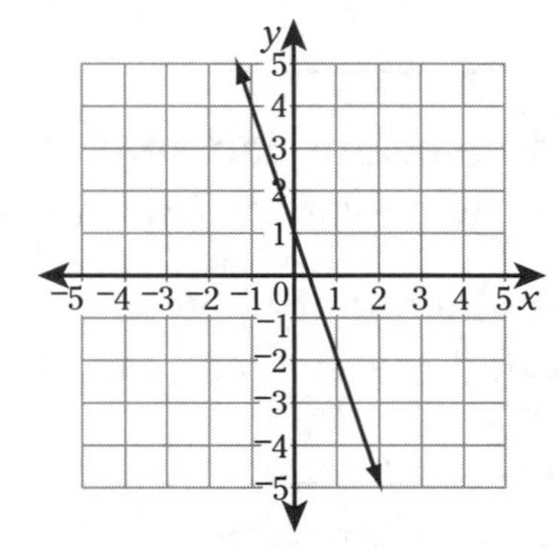

B

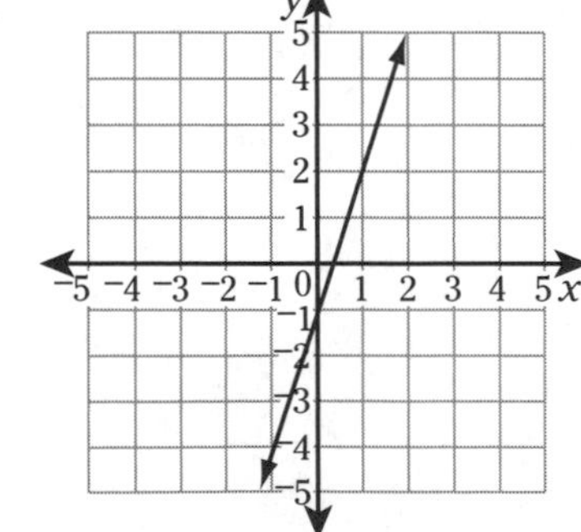

D

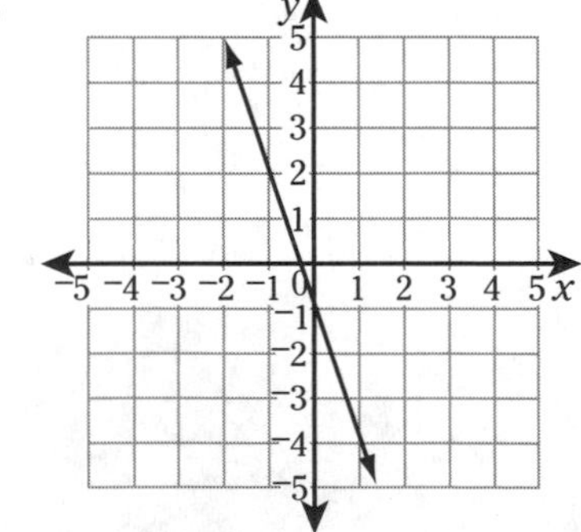

You can use the equation $y = 3x + 1$ to find the points (-1, -2), (0, 1), and (1, 4). The graph in choice A contains all these points. Choice A is correct.

S-2 The table shows the relationship between the number of tires purchased at a tire store and the total cost of the tires.

Number Purchased	Total Cost
0	\$0
1	\$60
2	\$120
3	\$180
4	\$240

Which of the following graphs best represents this relationship?

A
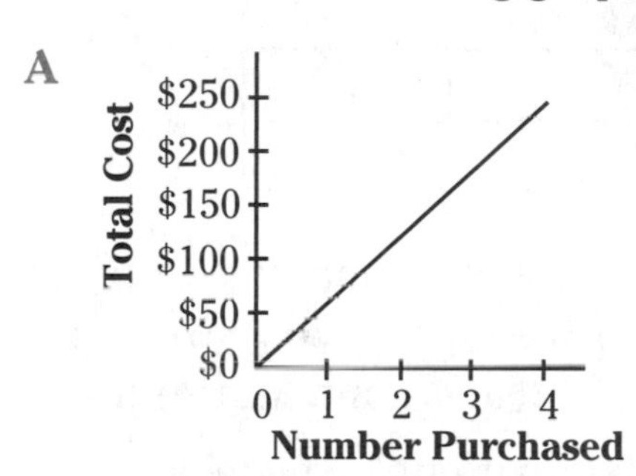

C
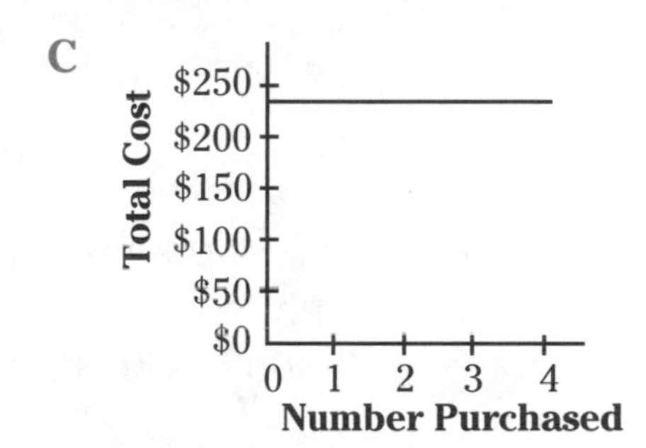

B
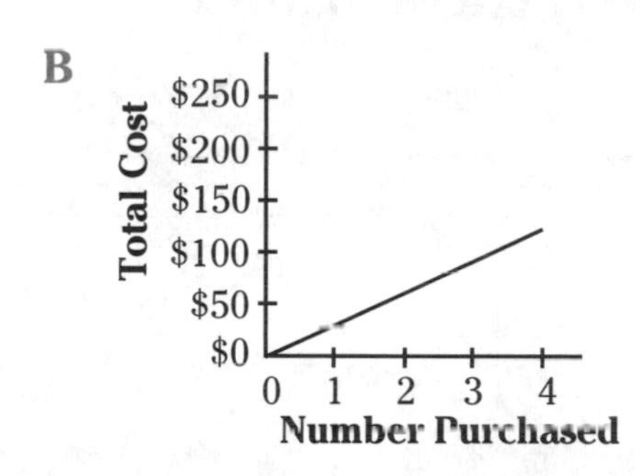

D
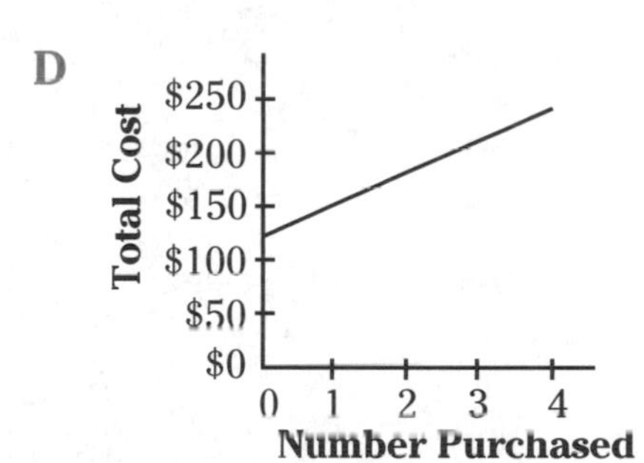

Choice A is correct. Its graphed line contains all the points in the table.

S-3 Scientists use the formula $F = \frac{9}{5}C + 32$ to convert temperature from the Celsius scale to the Fahrenheit scale.

Create a table of values that shows the temperature in degrees Fahrenheit when the temperature is 0°C, 20°C, 40°C, 60°C, 80°C, and 100°C.

Graph the relationship between temperature in degrees Celsius and degrees Fahrenheit on a coordinate plane.

Standard body temperature for humans is 98.6°F. Use your graph to estimate this same temperature in degrees Celsius.

For the first part, you can create a table of values by substituting 0, 20, 40, 60, 80, and 100 one at a time into the equation given. For example, at 20°C, the temperature in degrees Fahrenheit is $\frac{9}{5}(20) + 32 = 36 + 32 = 68$.

TEMPERATURE CONVERSION

°C	°F
0	32
20	68
40	104
60	140
80	176
100	212

Each row in the table gives you the coordinates of a point that will be on the graph for the second part. An easy way to graph the relationship is to plot the points (0, 32) and (100, 212) and connect them with a straight line.

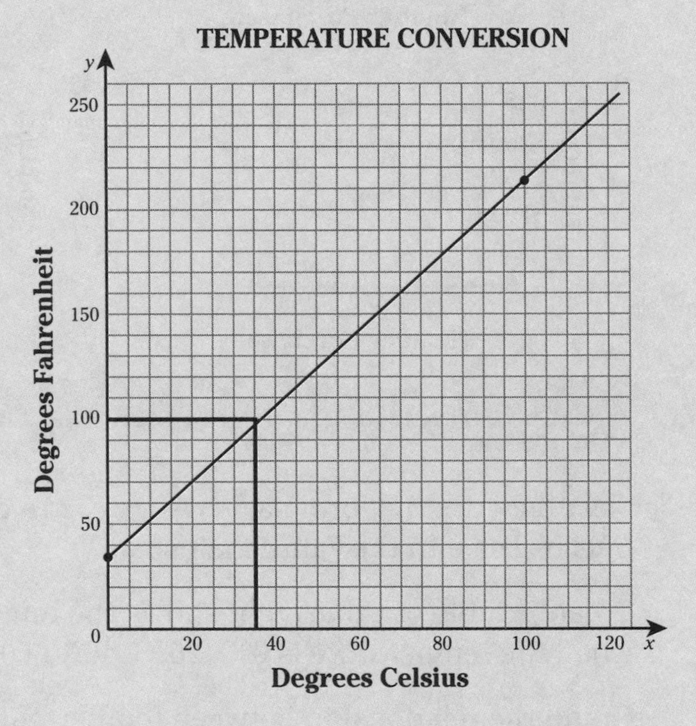

For the last part, round 98.6 to 100 and locate the temperature on the Fahrenheit scale. Read over to the line and then down to the Celsius temperature.

Based on the graph, body temperature is about 35° Celsius. (Note: The exact answer is 37°C, but your estimate is not expected to be exact.)

IT'S YOUR TURN

Read each problem. Circle the letter of the best answer.

1. Which graph best represents the data in the table below?

Number of Cartons	Number of Eggs
1	12
2	24
3	36
4	48

A
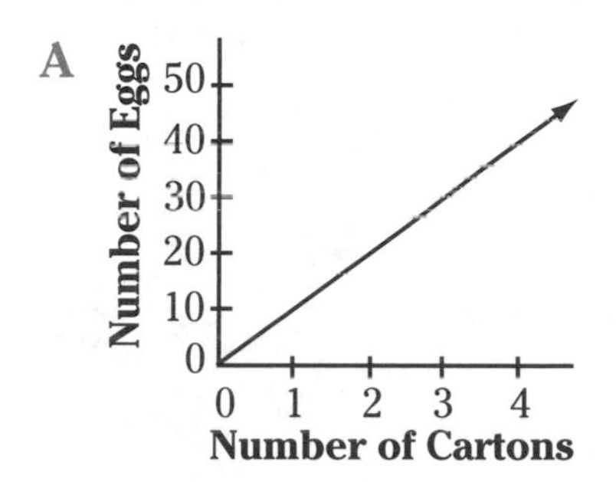

B
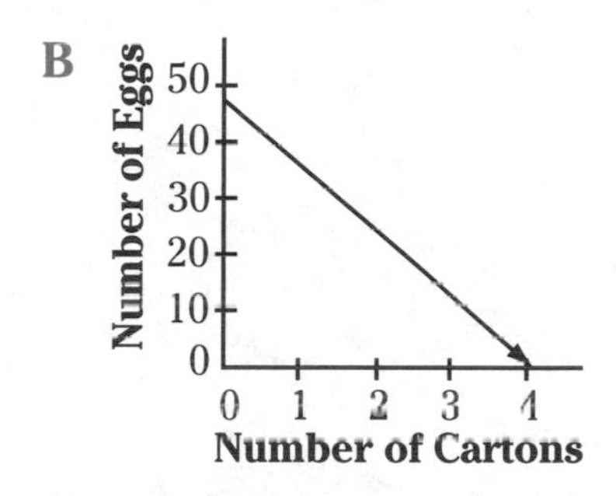

C
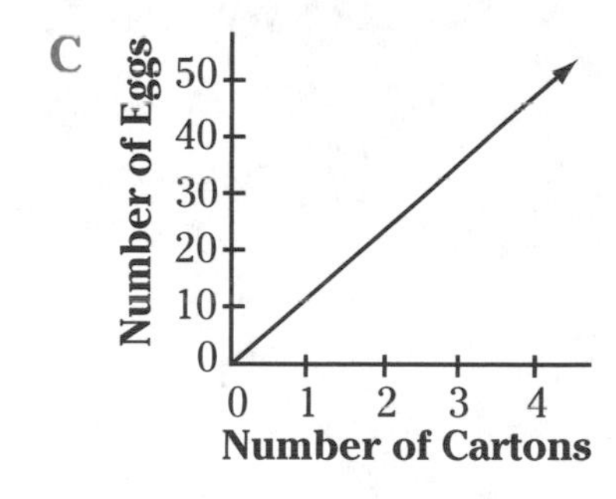

D
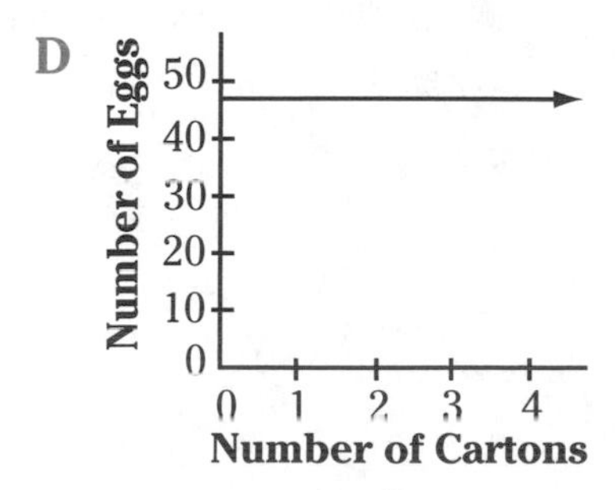

2. Mario created this table of values for the equation $y = 2x + 3$.

x	y
-3	-3
-2	-1
0	3

Which graph shows the line for $y = 2x + 3$?

A
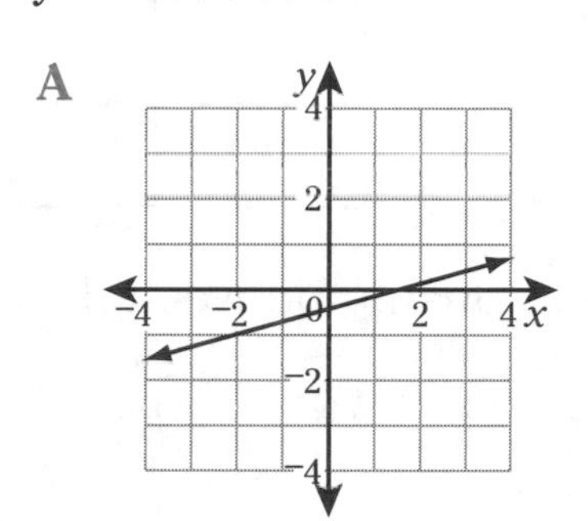

B
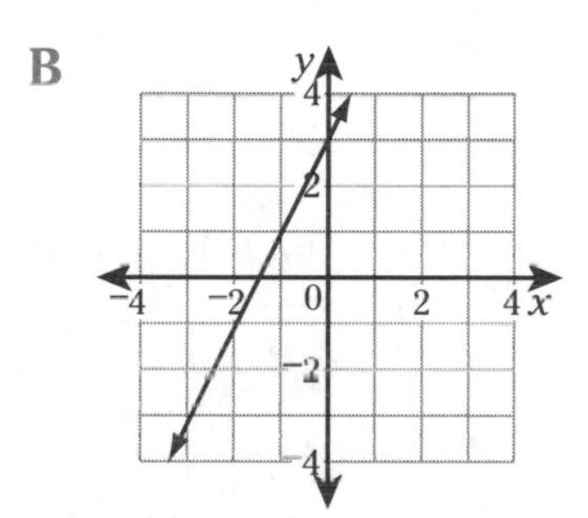

C
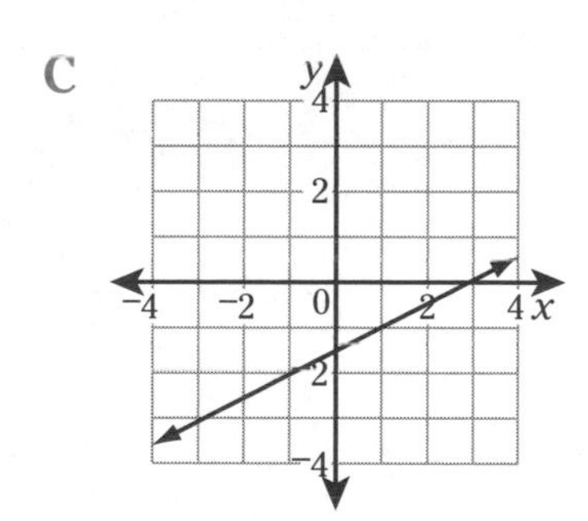

D
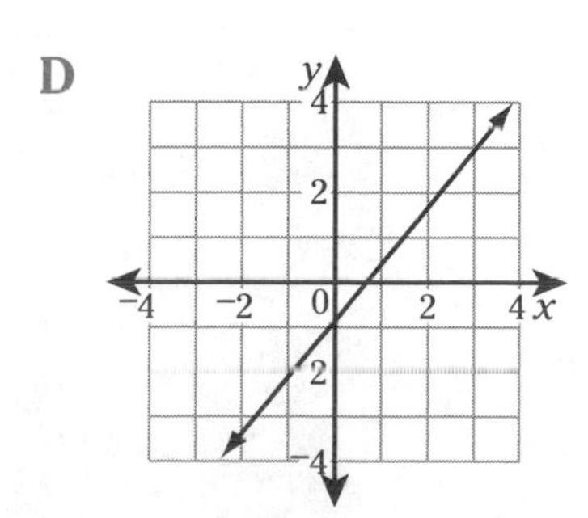

Read the problem. Write your answers.

3. The cost of a rug is given by the equation $C = 1.2A + 60$, where C is the cost in dollars and A is the area of the rug in square feet.

   Create a table of values that shows the cost in dollars when a rug's area is 20, 50, 75, or 120 square feet.

A	C
20	
50	
75	
120	

   Graph the relationship between the area of a rug and the cost of a rug.

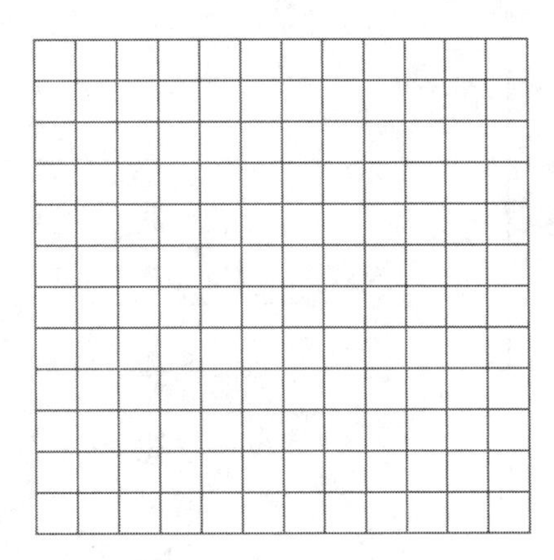

Read the problem. Write your answers.

4. The cost for a group to enter a museum is shown by the equation $C = 8N + 4$, where C is the cost in dollars and N is the number of people in the group.

   Create a table of values for this linear relationship. Find at least four ordered pairs. (Hint: Do not use negative numbers.)

N	C

   Graph the relationship between the number of people in a group and the cost of admission.

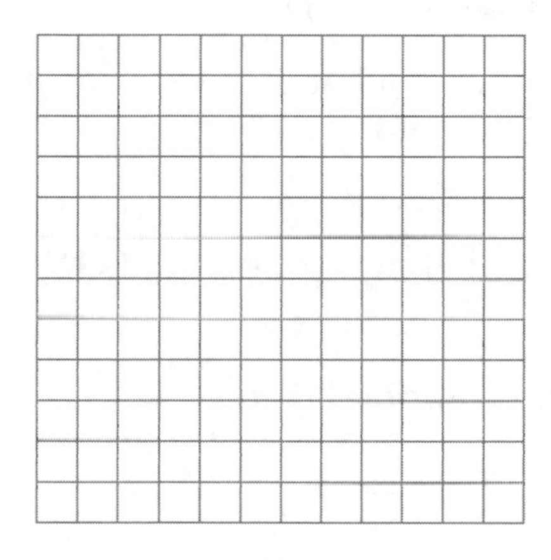

LESSON 4 Slope and Intercepts of a Line

Standards A1.2.3, 4

Slope

Slope is a measure of the steepness of a line. It describes a rate of change. The slope of a line can be found using either of these methods:

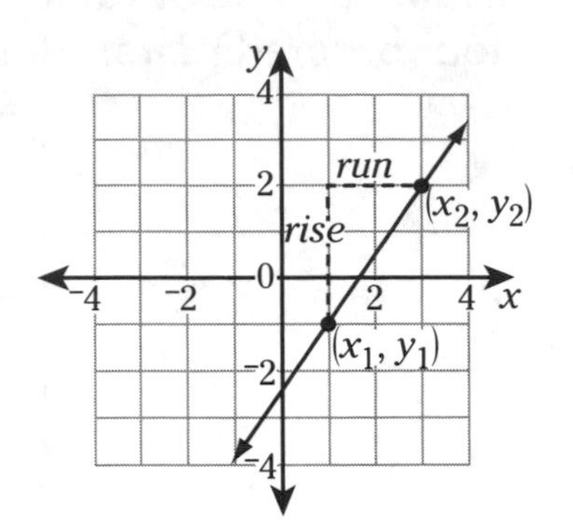

1. On the graph of a line, determine the vertical change (the "rise") over the horizontal change (the "run") from one point to another.

$$\text{slope} = \frac{\text{vertical change}}{\text{horizontal change}} = \frac{\text{"rise"}}{\text{"run"}}$$

2. Use the **slope formula.** For any two points on a line, (x_1, y_1) and (x_2, y_2) and $x_1 \neq x_2$, slope $= \frac{y_2 - y_1}{x_2 - x_1}$.

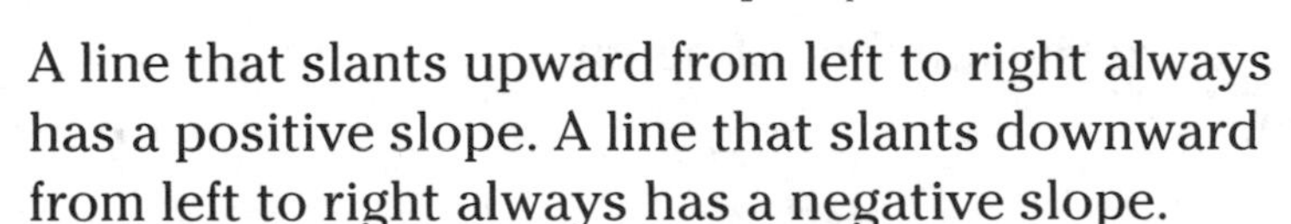

A line that slants upward from left to right always has a positive slope. A line that slants downward from left to right always has a negative slope.

Horizontal lines have a slope of 0. Vertical lines have an undefined slope.

It is a good idea to check the slope of a line found when looking at a graph using rise over run by also using the slope formula.

The sample question below shows how both methods for finding the slope can be used.

S-1 What is the slope of the line graphed below?

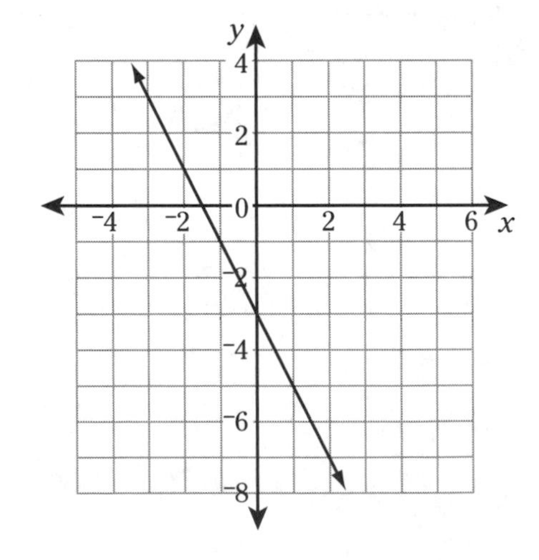

A -3 **B** -2 **C** $-\frac{1}{2}$ **D** $-\frac{1}{3}$

Find the slope using the rise over the run, or $\frac{\text{rise}}{\text{run}}$. By looking at the graph, you can see that the line has a rise of -2 and a run of 1, so the slope is $\frac{-2}{1}$ or -2. Verify this slope by using the slope formula with any two points on the graph.

$$\text{Slope} = \frac{-5 - (-3)}{1 - 0} = \frac{-5 + 3}{1} = \frac{-2}{1} \text{ or } -2$$

Both methods result in the same slope. Choice B is correct.

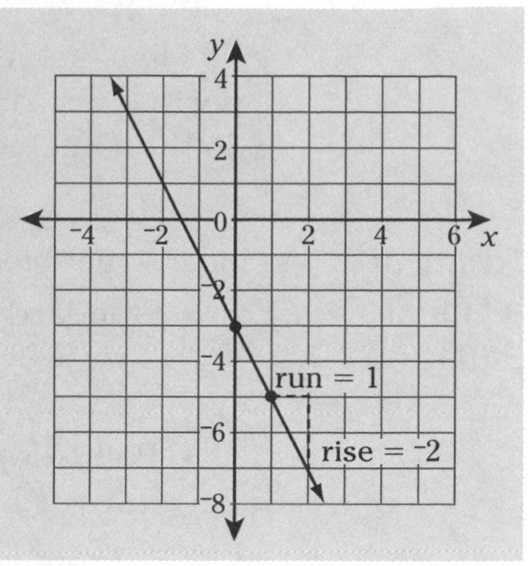

Finding Intercepts from Graphs

On the graph of a line, the point where the line touches the *x*-axis is the ***x*-intercept** of the line. The point where the line touches the *y*-axis is the ***y*-intercept** of the line.

For example, on the graph below, the line touches the *x*-axis at $x = 4$ and the *y*-axis at $y = -2$. The *x*-intercept of this line is (4, 0). The *y*-intercept is (0, -2).

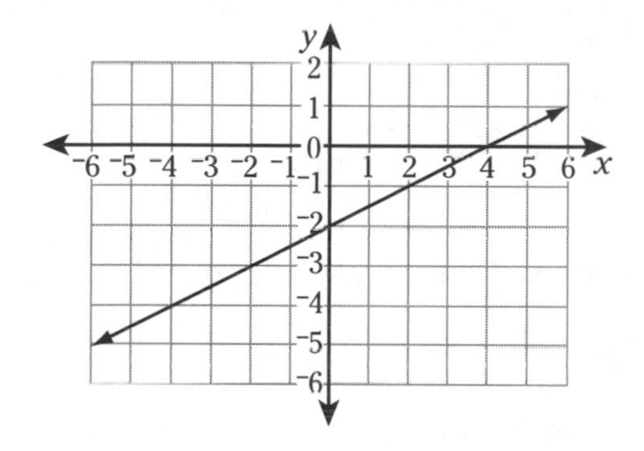

If a line touches the *x*-axis at $x = a$, the *x*-intercept is the point $(a, 0)$.
If a line touches the *y*-axis at $y = b$, the *y*-intercept is the point $(0, b)$.

Try this sample question.

S-2 Which statement best describes the graph of the line shown below?

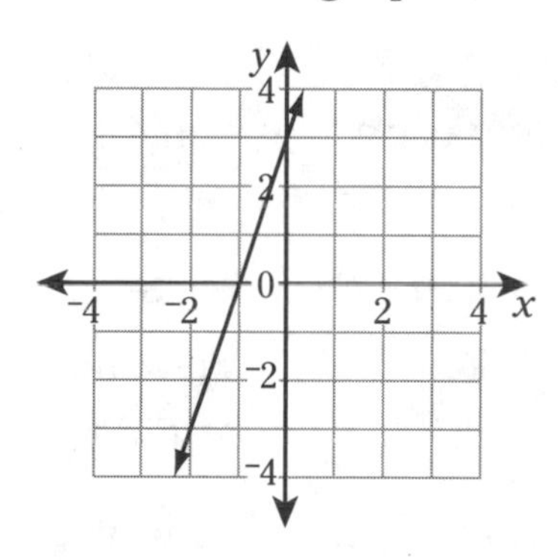

A The slope is positive and the *x*-intercept is -1.

B The slope is negative and the *x*-intercept is 3.

C The slope is positive and the *y*-intercept is -1.

D The slope is negative and the *y*-intercept is 3.

The line on the graph slants upward from left to right, so the slope is positive. The line touches the x-axis at -1 and it touches the y-axis at 3. So the x-intercept is -1 and the y-intercept is 3. Choice A is correct.

Forms of a Linear Equation

Linear equations can be represented in these ways:

- **Standard Form**
  $ax + by = c$, with constants a, b, and c
  Example: $4x - y = 3$ $\quad a = 4, b = -1, c = 3$
- **Point-Slope Form**
  $(y - y_1) = m(x - x_1)$, with slope m and point (x_1, y_1)
  Example: $y - 5 = \frac{2}{3}(x + 9)$ $\quad m = \frac{2}{3}$, point $(-9, 5)$
- **Slope-Intercept Form**
  $y = mx + b$, with slope m and y-intercept b
  Example: $y = -2x - 6$ $\quad m = -2, b = -6$

For an equation written in standard form or point-slope form, the slope and y-intercept can be identified by rewriting the equation in slope-intercept form. For example, $6x + 3y = 4$ can be written in slope-intercept form by solving the equation for y.

$$3y = -6x + 4$$

$$y = -2x + \frac{4}{3}$$

The slope of this equation is -2 and the y-intercept is $\frac{4}{3}$.

Try this sample question.

S-3 What is the y-intercept in the equation $y - 3 = 4(x - 2)$?

A -8

B -5

C -3

D -2

Write this equation in $y = mx + b$, or slope-intercept, form. Then look for the last value in the equation corresponding to b, the y-intercept.

$y - 3 = 4(x - 2)$	Write the original equation.
$y - 3 = 4x - 8$	Distribute 4.
$y = 4x - 5$	Add 3 to both sides.

The equation $y = 4x - 5$ is written in slope-intercept form. The last value in this equation is -5, so the y-intercept is -5. Choice B is correct.

Finding Intercepts from Equations

Recall that the x-intercept of a line is the point where the line touches the x-axis. The y-value at this point is 0. The point $(a, 0)$ describes the x-intercept. Similarly, the y-intercept of a line is the point where the line touches the y-axis. The x-value at this point is 0. The point $(0, b)$ describes the y-intercept.

To find the x-intercept of a line given its equation, substitute 0 for y and solve for x. To find the y-intercept of a line given its equation, substitute 0 for x and solve for y. For example, look at the equation $y = 2x + 8$.

x-intercept: let $y = 0$

$$0 = 2x + 8$$
$$-8 = 2x$$
$$-4 = x$$

x-intercept $= -4 = (-4, 0)$

y-intercept: let $x = 0$

$$y = 2(0) + 8$$
$$y = 8$$

y-intercept $= 8 = (0, 8)$

Try this sample question.

S-4 What is the x-intercept of the line having the equation below?

$$3x - 5y - -15$$

A $(-5, 0)$

B $(0, -3)$

C $(0, 3)$

D $(5, 0)$

The x-intercept occurs when $y = 0$. To find the x-intercept, substitute 0 for y and solve for x:

$3x - 5y = -15$	Write the original equation.
$3x - 5(0) = -15$	Substitute $y = 0$.
$3x = -15$	Simplify.
$x = -5$	Divide both sides by 3.

The x-intercept is the point $(-5, 0)$. Choice A is correct.

IT'S YOUR TURN

Read each problem. Circle the letter of the best answer.

1. What is the y-intercept of the line graphed below?

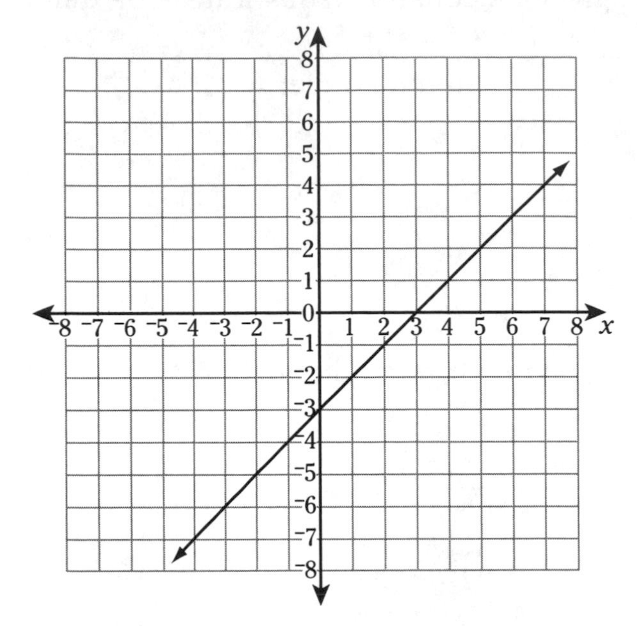

A -3

B -1

C 1

D 3

2. Which intercepts must be on a line with a negative slope?

A x-intercept = 0, y-intercept = 0

B x-intercept = 1, y-intercept = 6

C x-intercept = -4, y-intercept = 3

D x-intercept = 5, y-intercept = -2

3. What is the slope of the line shown below?

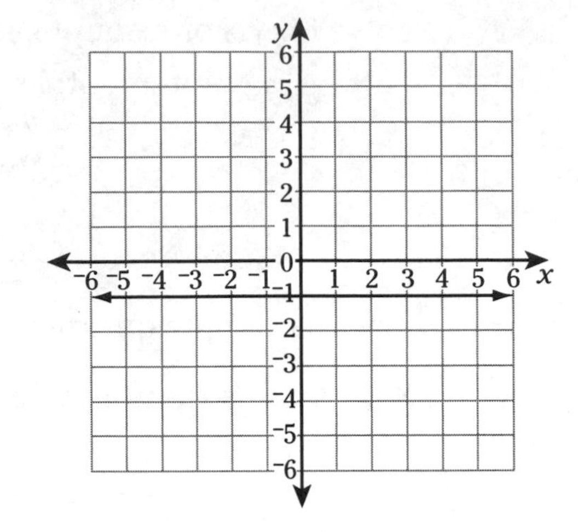

A -1

B 0

C 1

D undefined

4. Which statement is true of the equation below?

$$y - 6 = -3(x + 1)$$

A The slope is 3 and the y-intercept is 1.

B The slope is 3 and the y-intercept is -6.

C The slope is -3 and the y-intercept is 1.

D The slope is -3 and the y-intercept is 3.

Read each problem. Fill in your answer on the response grid.

5. Line p passes through the points (3, -2) and (5, 3). What is the slope of line p?

6. What is the x-intercept of the line $2x + 6y = 18$?

Read each problem. Write your answers.

7. What are the x- and y-intercepts of the line with equation $5x - 2y = 8$?

Answer: ______________________________

8. Look at the line graphed below.

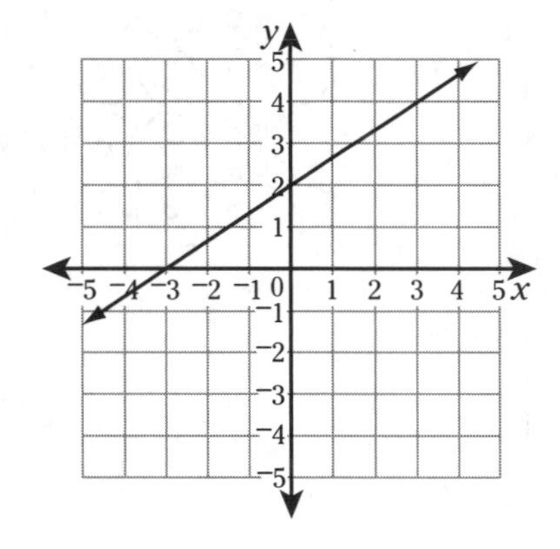

What is the slope of the line shown graphed above?

Answer: __________

What is the x-intercept of the line graphed above?

Answer: __________

LESSON 5

Writing Linear Equations

Standards A1.2.3, 4

Finding the Equation of a Line from a Graph

If you are given the graph of a line, the equation of the line can be found using the slope-intercept formula.

- **Slope-Intercept Formula for a Line:** If a line has slope m and intersects the y-axis at $(0, b)$, then the equation of the line is $y = mx + b$.

The three forms of a line are:
- standard form $ax + by = c$
- point-slope form $(y - y_1) = m(x - x_1)$
- slope-intercept form $y = mx + b$

When using the slope-intercept formula, you may also need to use the formula for slope.

- **Slope Formula:** If a line goes through the points (x_1, y_1) and (x_2, y_2) and $x_1 \neq x_2$, then the slope of the line is $\frac{y_2 - y_1}{x_2 - x_1}$.

For example, the line shown here intersects the y-axis at $(0, 3)$. Therefore, $b = 3$.

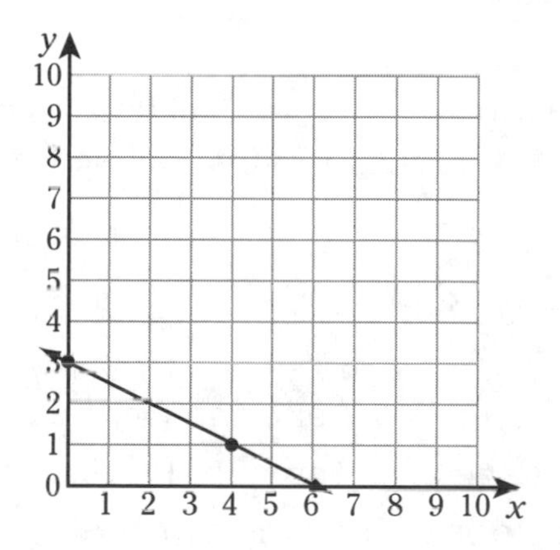

You can use the points $(0, 3)$ and $(4, 1)$ to find the slope.

$$\frac{y_2 - y_1}{x_2 - x_1} = \frac{1 - 3}{4 - 0} = \frac{-2}{4} = -\frac{1}{2}$$

Therefore, the equation of the line in slope-intercept form is:

$$y = -\frac{1}{2}x + 3$$

An advantage of slope-intercept form is that the equation of the line is already solved for y.

Now try this question.

S-1 Which of these graphs represents the line $3x + 2y = -2$?

A

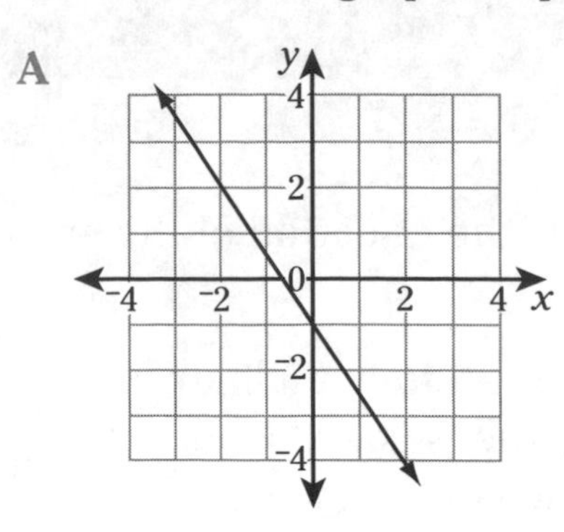

C

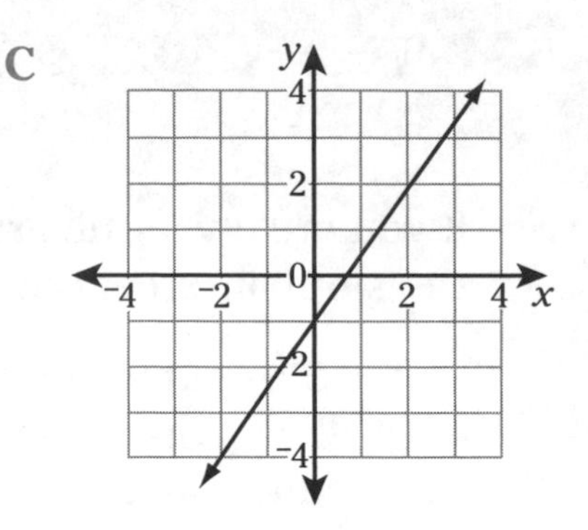

B

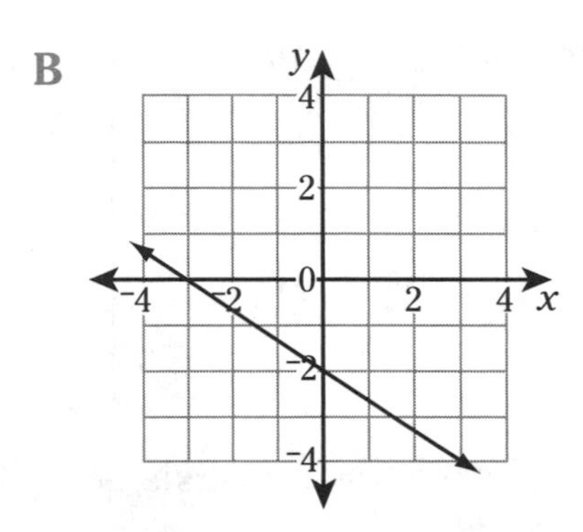

D

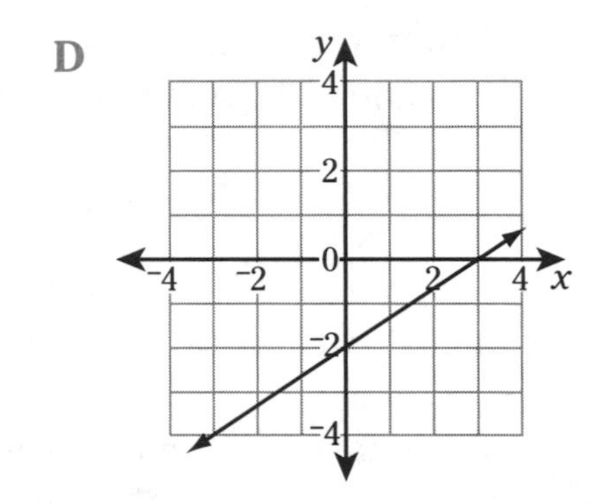

The equation $3x + 2y = -2$ is written in standard form. Rewrite the equation in slope-intercept form by solving for *y:*

$$2y = -3x - 2$$

$$y = -\frac{3}{2}x - 1$$

The slope, *m,* is $-\frac{3}{2}$ and the *y*-intercept, *b,* is -1. Only the graphs in choices A and C have a *y*-intercept of -1. The slope of the graph in choice C is $+\frac{3}{2}$, and the slope of the graph in choice A is $-\frac{3}{2}$. Choice A is correct.

Finding the Equation of a Line from Two Points

Between any two points in the coordinate plane, there is a straight line that connects them. Given the coordinates of those points, you can find the equation of that line using the point-slope formula.

- **Point-Slope Formula for a Line:** If a line goes through the point (x_1, y_1) and has slope *m,* then the equation of the line is $y - y_1 = m(x - x_1)$.

When using the point-slope formula, you will also need to use the formula for slope.

The slope formula is $m = \frac{y_2 - y_1}{x_2 - x_1}$.

For example, here is how to find the equation for the line that goes through (2, 3) and (4, 7), as shown on the graph.

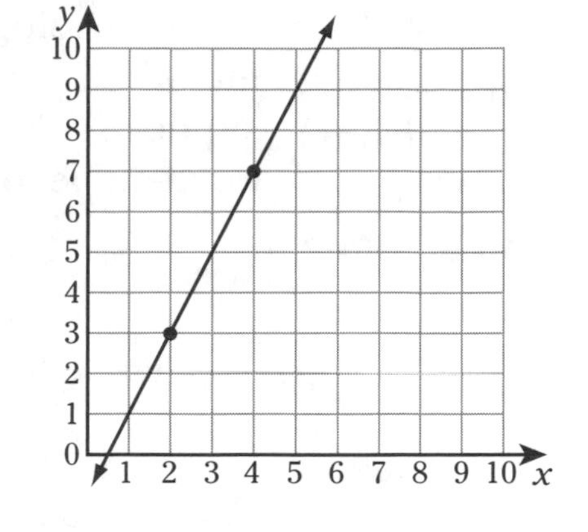

First use the slope formula to find the slope. You can let $(x_2, y_2) = (4, 7)$ and $(x_1, y_1) = (2, 3)$.

$$\frac{y_2 - y_1}{x_2 - x_1} = \frac{7 - 3}{4 - 2} = \frac{4}{2} = 2$$

Next use the point-slope formula with the known values of m, x_1, and y_1. The slope, m, is 2.

$$y - y_1 = m(x - x_1)$$
$$y - 3 = 2(x - 2)$$

Finally you can solve for y by rewriting this equation in the more common slope-intercept form.

$$y - 3 = 2(x - 2)$$
$$y - 3 = 2x - 4$$
$$y - 3 + 3 = 2x - 4 + 3$$
$$y = 2x - 1$$

Now try this sample question.

S-2 Which equation represents the line that passes through the points (2, -1) and (3, 3)?

A $y = 2x - 3$

B $y = 2x - 9$

C $y = 4x - 3$

D $y = 4x - 9$

First find the slope of the line:

$$m = \frac{y_2 - y_1}{x_2 - x_1} = \frac{3 - (-1)}{3 - 2} = 4$$

Next use the point-slope formula with slope 4 and known point (3, 3). So, $y - 3 = 4(x - 3)$. Rewrite the equation by solving for y.

$$y - 3 = 4x - 12$$
$$y = 4x - 9$$

Choice D is correct.

Finding the Equation of a Line from the Slope and a Point

The point-slope form of a line can also be used to find the equation of a line when the slope and only one point on the line are known. For example, suppose a line has a slope of 5 and contains the point (-1, 4). Using the point-slope formula, the equation of the line would be:

$$y - y_1 = m(x - x_1)$$
$$y - 4 = 5(x + 1)$$
$$y - 4 = 5x + 5$$
$$y = 5x + 9$$

Try this sample question.

S-3 The temperature of a liquid cools 4°F every minute. After 5 minutes, the temperature of the liquid is 175°F. Which equation best models the temperature of this liquid, y, after x minutes?

A $y = -4x + 155$

B $y = -4x + 195$

C $y = -5x + 155$

D $y = -5x + 195$

Slope represents the rate of change. The slope of this line, then, is -4 since the temperature decreases (cools) 4 degrees each minute. A point on this line is (5, 175). Use the point-slope formula with slope -4 and known point (5, 175). So, $y - 175 = -4(x - 5)$.

Rewrite the equation in terms of y, that is, in slope-intercept form.

$$y - 175 = -4x + 20$$
$$y = -4x + 195$$

Choice B is correct.

Applications of Slope

Many real-life situations can be modeled with a linear equation. You can use the equation or the graph of the equation to better understand the situation and to make predictions. In these situations, a **rate of change** shows the relationship between the two quantities that are changing. The constant rate of change in a linear relationship is the same as its slope.

Try this sample question.

S-4 A heater increases the temperature of a room at a constant rate. Before the heater is turned on, the temperature of the room is 46°F. After 10 minutes of heating the room, the temperature is 49°F.

What is the equation that relates the temperature of the room to the number of minutes that the heater operates?

What will the temperature be after one hour of operating the heater?

After how many minutes will the temperature be 80°F?

You need to find the equation of the line that includes the points (0, 46) and (10, 49). First find the slope, or *m* in the equation.

$$\frac{y_2 - y_1}{x_2 - x_1} = \frac{49 - 46}{10 - 0} = \frac{3}{10} = 0.3$$

The *y*-intercept of the line, or *b* in the equation, is 46 since the line includes the point (0, 46). Now you have the values of *m* and *b* needed to write the equation in slope-intercept form: $m = 0.3$, and $b = 46$. Therefore, the slope-intercept equation of the line is $y = 0.3x + 46$.

To find the temperature after 1 hour (i.e., 60 minutes), substitute 60 for *x*.

$$y = 0.3(60) + 46 = 18 + 46 = 64$$

After one hour, the temperature will be 64°F.

To find out how many minutes it will take the temperature to reach 80°F, substitute 80 for *y* in the equation of the line. Then, solve for *x*.

$$80 = 0.3x + 46$$
$$80 - 46 = 0.3x + 46 - 46$$
$$34 = 0.3x$$
$$34 \div 0.3 = 0.3x \div 0.3$$
$$113.33 \approx x$$

After about 113 minutes, the temperature of the room will reach 80°F.

IT'S YOUR TURN

Read each problem. Circle the letter of the best answer.

1. Which is an equation of the line that contains the points (0, 3) and (-2, 4)?

   A $2x + y = 3$

   B $x + 2y = 6$

   C $2x + y = 0$

   D $x - 2y = 6$

2. A line contains the point (-3, -1) and has a slope of $\frac{1}{3}$. Which equation represents this line?

   A $x + 3y = 0$ C $3x + y = 0$

   B $x - 3y = 0$ D $3x - y = 0$

3. Which is an equation of the line that contains the points (0, 2) and (4, 0)?

   A $x + 2y = 4$ C $2x + y = 4$

   B $x - 2y = 4$ D $2x - y = 4$

Read each problem. Circle the letter of the best answer.

4. The air pressure in a tire is 45 pounds per square inch. Air is released at a constant rate until the tire is deflated. The graph below shows the air pressure (y) in the tire after x minutes.

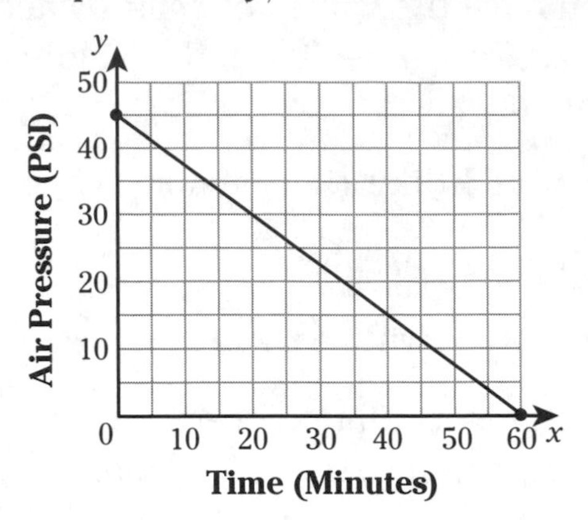

Which of these equations represents this relationship?

A $y = \frac{3}{4}x + 45$

B $y = \frac{3}{4}x - 45$

C $y = -\frac{3}{4}x + 45$

D $y = -\frac{3}{4}x - 45$

5. Which graph shows the line $y + 2 = \frac{3}{2}x$?

A

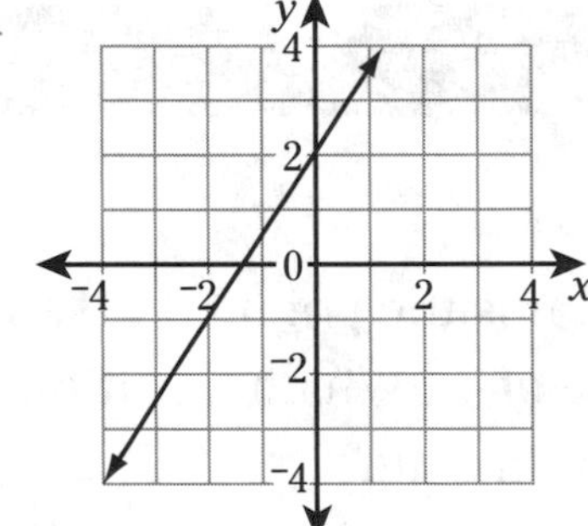

C

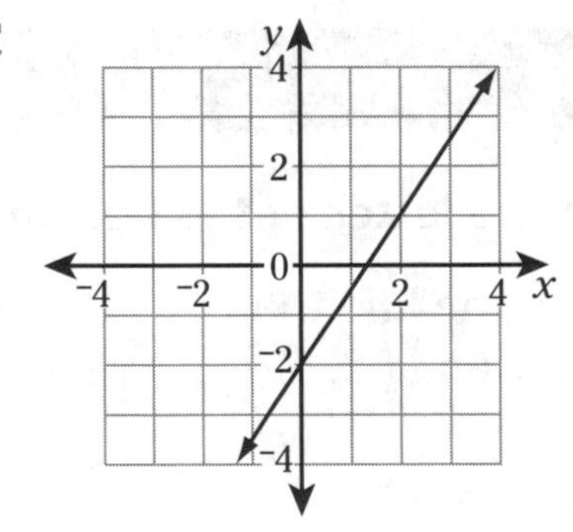

B

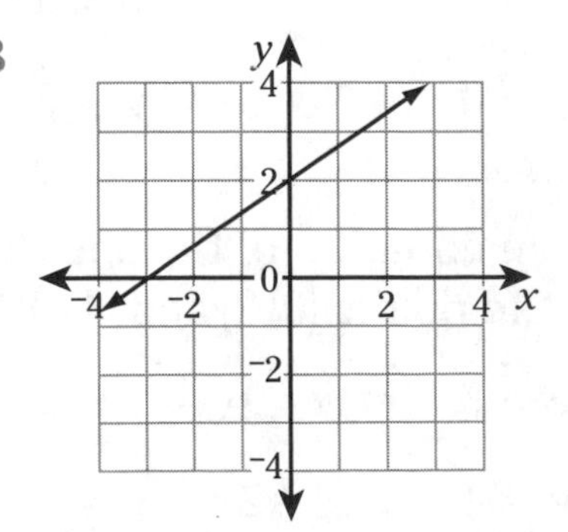

D

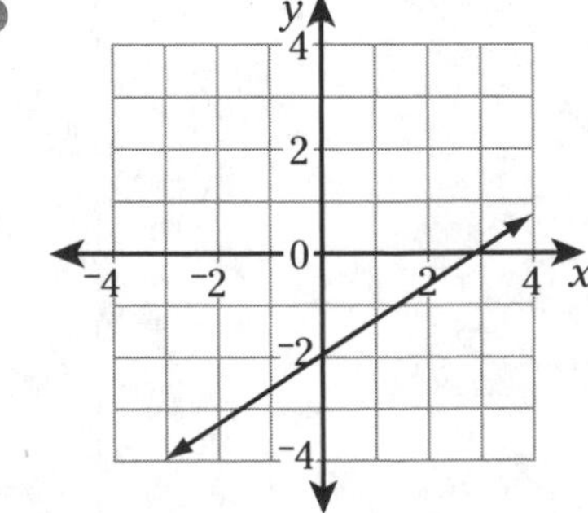

Read the problem. Write your answers.

6. The cost to ship each order from a mail-order catalog depends on the weight of the order. A 20-pound order costs $10 to ship. A 40-pound order costs $15 to ship.

   Write an equation in slope-intercept form that can be used to find the cost, C, to ship an order weighing p pounds.

   Answer: ______________________________

   Explain what the slope of the equation you wrote means in the context of the situation.

   ____

   ____

   ____

   ____

Read the problem. Write your answers.

7. A company noticed a linear relationship between the price of a luggage set and the number of luggage sets sold. At $100, the company sold 1,000 sets. When the company raised the price to $120, they only sold 800 sets.

   What is the equation that relates the price of the luggage sets to the total number of luggage sets sold?

   Answer: ______________________

   If the price of each luggage set were $150, how many sets should the company expect to sell?

   Answer: ___________

Parallel and Perpendicular Lines

Standard A1.2.3

Equations of Parallel Lines

Recall that the slope between any two points on a line, (x_1, y_1) and (x_2, y_2), is $m = \frac{y_2 - y_1}{x_2 - x_1}$.

Lines that are parallel never touch each other. The equations of parallel lines have the same slope, m, but different y-intercepts. For example, the line parallel to $y - 5 = 4(x - 3)$ has a slope of 4 since the slope of the given equation is 4.

> The three forms of a line are:
> - standard form $ax + by = c$
> - point-slope form $(y - y_1) = m(x - x_1)$
> - slope-intercept form $y = mx + b$

Try this sample question.

S-1 Which equation represents a line that passes through the point (-3, 5) and is parallel to $y = \frac{2}{3}x + 1$?

A $y = \frac{2}{3}x - 5$

B $y = \frac{2}{3}x - 3$

C $y = \frac{2}{3}x + 3$

D $y = \frac{2}{3}x + 7$

Parallel lines have the same slope. The slopes of both lines are $\frac{2}{3}$. To find the equation containing this slope and the point (-3, 5), substitute $x = -3$, $y = 5$, and slope $m = \frac{2}{3}$ into the equation $y = mx + b$ to find the value of b:

$$5 = \frac{2}{3}(-3) + b$$

$$5 = -2 + b$$

$$7 = b$$

So the equation, in $y = mx + b$ form, is $y = \frac{2}{3}x + 7$. Choice D is correct.

Equations of Perpendicular Lines

Perpendicular lines have slopes that are negative reciprocals of each other. For example, the line perpendicular to $y = 4x + 2$ has a slope of $-\frac{1}{4}$. The slopes of both lines, 4 and $-\frac{1}{4}$, are negative reciprocals of each other. The product of the slopes of two perpendicular lines is always -1.

> The reciprocal of a number $\frac{a}{b}$ is $\frac{b}{a}$.

An example illustrating the properties related to slopes of perpendicular lines is shown below.

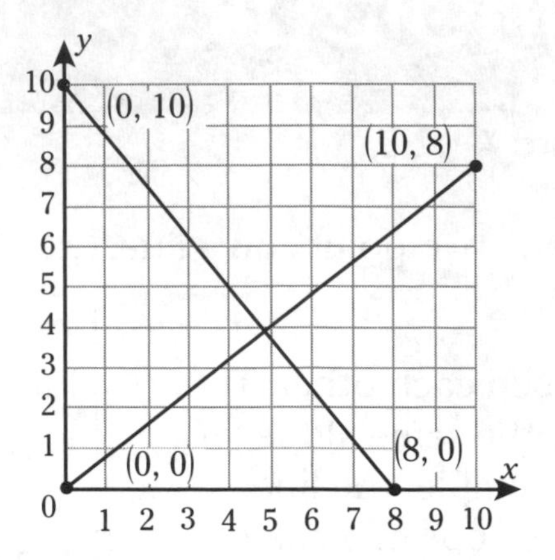

If two lines meet at a 90° angle (are perpendicular) and the slope of one line is $\frac{4}{5}$, then the slope of the other line is $-\frac{5}{4}$. The product of these slopes is $\frac{4}{5} \cdot -\frac{5}{4} = -1$.

Now try this sample question.

S-2 A line passes through the point (2, -1) and is perpendicular to the line with the equation $2x - 5y = 3$. Which equation represents this perpendicular line?

A $y = -\frac{5}{2}x + 4$

B $y = -\frac{2}{5}x - 6$

C $y = \frac{2}{5}x + 6$

D $y = \frac{5}{2}x - 4$

Perpendicular lines have slopes that are negative reciprocals of each other. Write the equation $2x - 5y = 3$ in slope-intercept form ($y = mx + b$) to find the slope of that line:

$$-5y = -2x + 3$$

$$y = \frac{2}{5}x - \frac{3}{5}$$

The slope of the given line is $\frac{2}{5}$, so the slope of the perpendicular line is $-\frac{5}{2}$. Substitute $x = 2$, $y = -1$, and slope $m = -\frac{5}{2}$ into the equation $y = mx + b$ to find the value of b:

$$-1 = -\frac{5}{2}(2) + b$$

$$-1 = -5 + b$$

$$4 = b$$

So the equation of the perpendicular line is $y = -\frac{5}{2}x + 4$. Choice A is correct.

IT'S YOUR TURN

Read each problem. Circle the letter of the best answer.

1. Which equation represents a line parallel to $4 - x + 2y = 0$?

   A $y + 1 = -2(x - 1)$

   B $y + 3 = -\frac{1}{2}(x - 2)$

   C $y + 5 = \frac{1}{2}(x - 3)$

   D $y + 7 = 2(x - 4)$

2. Which equation represents a line perpendicular to the line shown below?

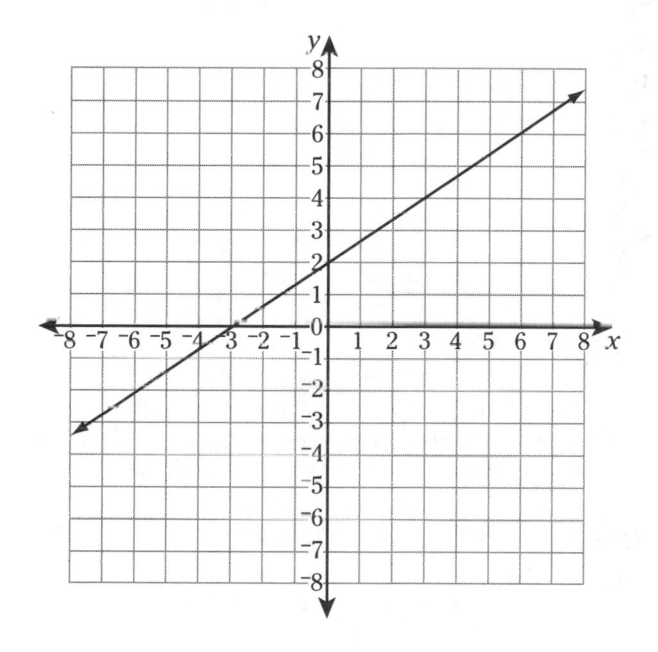

   A $y = -\frac{3}{2}x - 4$

   B $y = -\frac{2}{3}x - 3$

   C $y = \frac{2}{3}x - 2$

   D $y = \frac{3}{2}x - 1$

3. What is the slope of a line that is parallel to $y = 2x + 4$?

   A $-\frac{1}{2}$

   B $-\frac{1}{4}$

   C 2

   D 4

Read the problem. Fill in your answer on the response grid.

4. Right triangle *PQR* is drawn in the coordinate plane. The slope of one leg is $\frac{1}{7}$. What is the slope of the other leg?

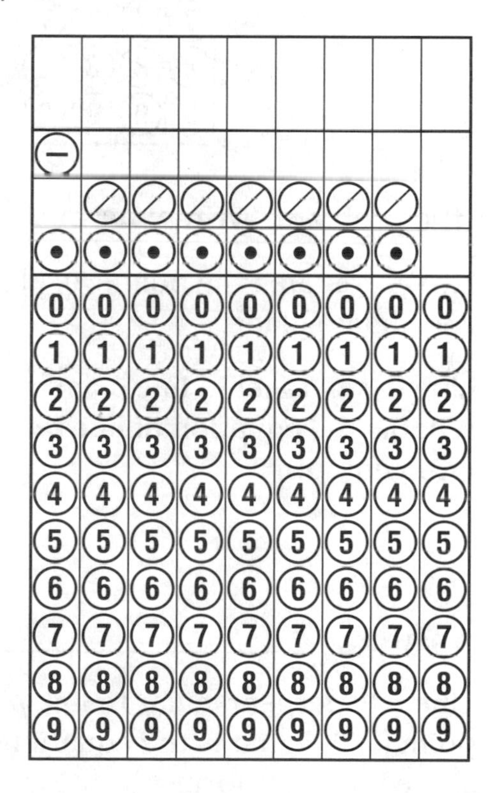

Read the problem. Fill in your answer on the response grid.

5. A line has a slope of $\frac{3}{4}$. A second line is drawn parallel to the first line. What is the slope of the second line?

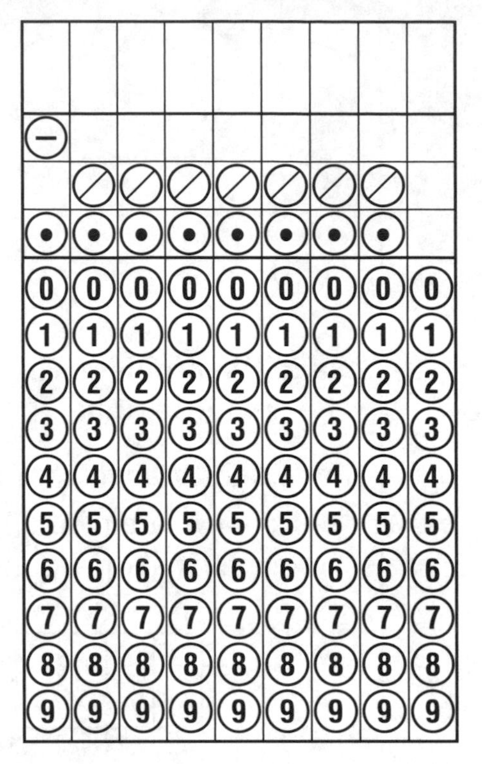

Read the problem. Write your answers.

6. Line p contains the points $(0, 6)$ and $(2, 0)$ and is graphed on a coordinate plane.

   Line q is parallel to line p and passes through the point $(5, 0)$. What is the equation of line q? Write your answer in slope-intercept form.

   Answer: ____________________

   Line n is perpendicular to line p and passes through the point $(5, 0)$. What is the equation of line n? Write your answer in slope-intercept form.

   Answer: ____________________

LESSON 7

Graphing Linear Inequalities

Standard A1.2.6

Graphing Linear Inequalities

Graphing inequalities in two variables is very similar to graphing equations.

Consider the inequality $y - 2x > 1$. By adding $2x$ to both sides, you can rewrite this same inequality as $y > 2x + 1$. To graph this inequality, first notice that the inequality is similar to the linear equation $y = 2x + 1$ (shown below), a straight line with a slope of 2 and a y-intercept of 1.

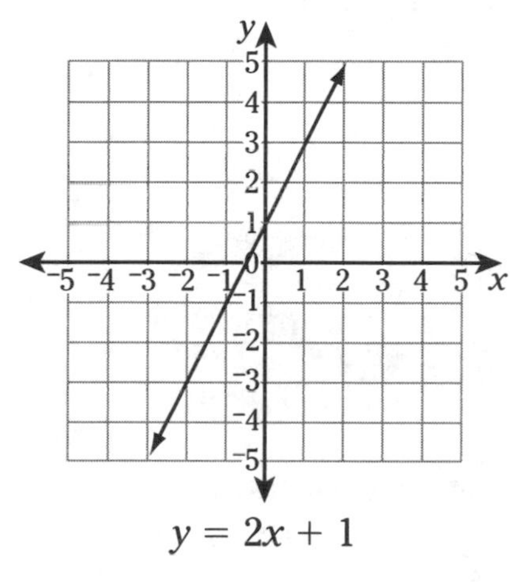

$y = 2x + 1$

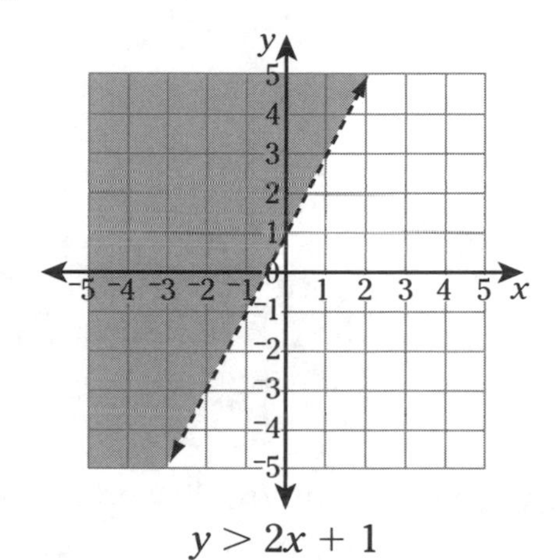

$y > 2x + 1$

The graph of the inequality $y > 2x + 1$ is exactly the area ***above*** the graph of the line $y = 2x + 1$, as shown in the graph above. Notice that when the line itself is ***not*** part of the graph, the line drawn is dashed.

> Graphs of inequalities with $\geq$ or $\leq$ include the line.
> Graphs of inequalities with $>$ or $<$ do ***not*** include the line.

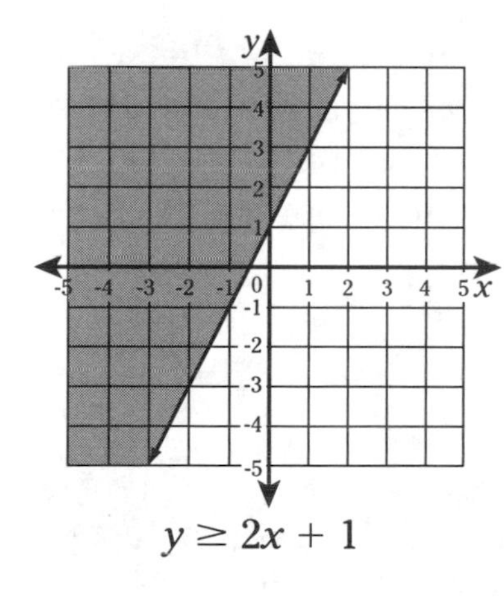

$y \geq 2x + 1$

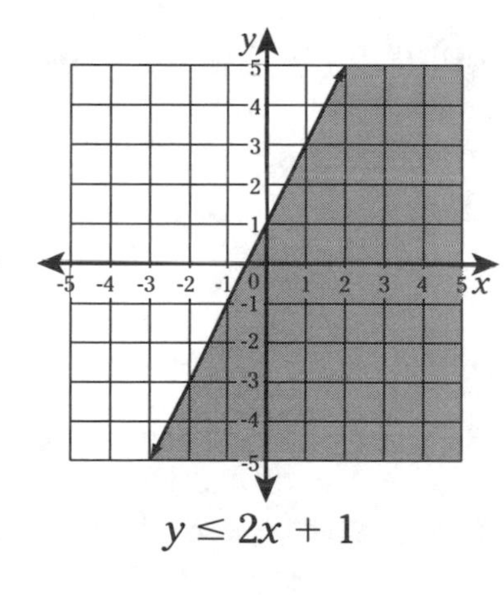

$y \leq 2x + 1$

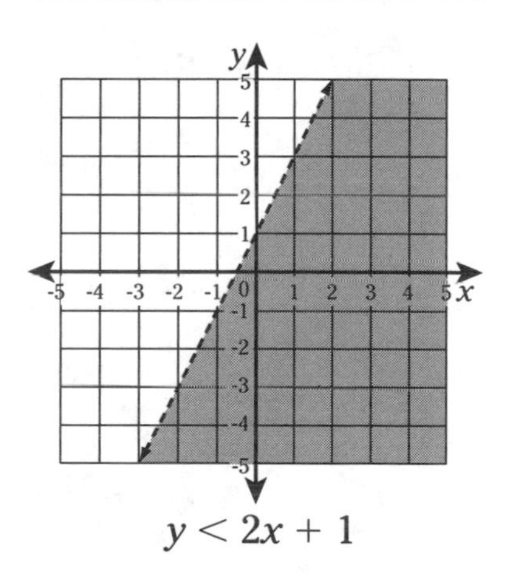

$y < 2x + 1$

Now try this question involving an inequality in two variables.

S-1 Which inequality is graphed below?

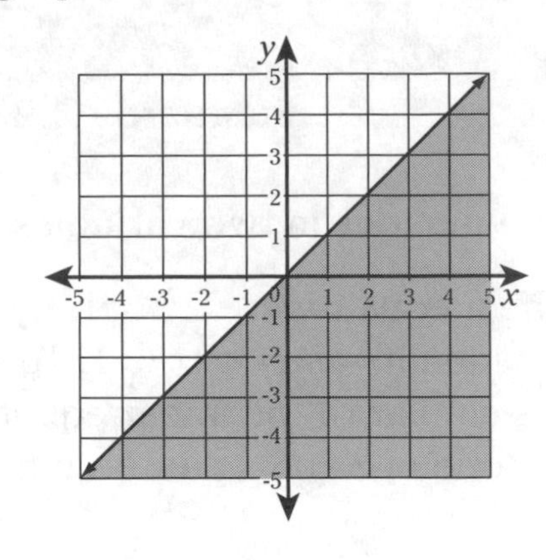

A $y > x$

B $y \geq x$

C $y < x$

D $y \leq x$

In this question, the area below the graph of $y = x$ is shaded. Also, the line itself is solid rather than dashed. Therefore, the graph shown is the graph of $y \leq x$. Choice D is correct.

Identifying Linear Inequalities

An inequality can model a real-world situation. Often, the real-world situation will involve more than one variable. Here is an example.

Jorge plans to save all the quarters and dimes he gets until he has at least \$5.00. To represent this situation as an inequality, begin by letting Q be the number of quarters and D be the number of dimes. The amount of money Jorge will have is $0.25Q + 0.10D$. Jorge will have at least \$5.00 when $0.25Q + 0.10D \geq 5.00$.

Now try this question.

S-2 Alex is applying to a cooking academy. As part of his application, he must take a test and submit an essay. His essay score (E) will be tripled and then added to his test score (T). The total must be at least 200 for Alex to be accepted at the school. Which inequality represents this situation?

A $3E + T \geq 200$

B $3E + T \leq 200$

C $3E \geq 3T + 200$

D $3E \leq 3T + 200$

Three times Alex's essay score is $3E$. When he adds his test score, the total score will be $3E + T$. In order to be accepted, this total has to be at least 200. In symbols, $3E + T \geq 200$. Choice A is correct.

IT'S YOUR TURN

Read each problem. Circle the letter of the best answer.

1. What is the equation of the inequality graphed below?

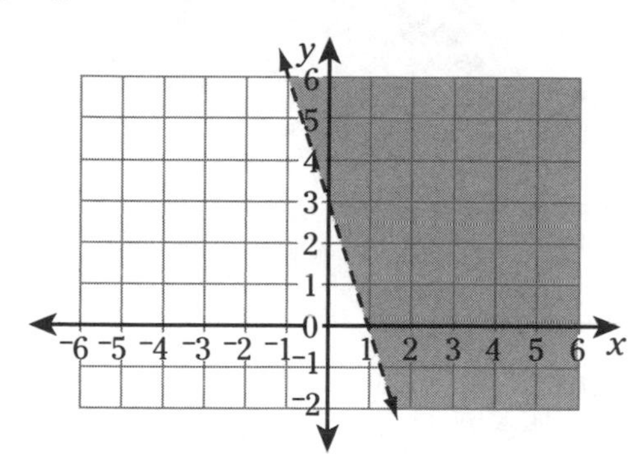

A $y < -\frac{1}{3}x + 3$

B $y > -\frac{1}{3}x + 3$

C $y < -3x + 3$

D $y > -3x + 3$

2. A television quiz show awards 4 points for each right answer (r), and subtracts 2 points for each wrong answer (w). Jeff wants to score at least 80 points. Which of these inequalities represents this situation?

A $2r - 4w \leq 80$

B $4r - 2w \leq 80$

C $2r - 4w \geq 80$

D $4r - 2w \geq 80$

3. Which graph shows the solution to the inequality below?

$$3x + y \geq 2$$

A

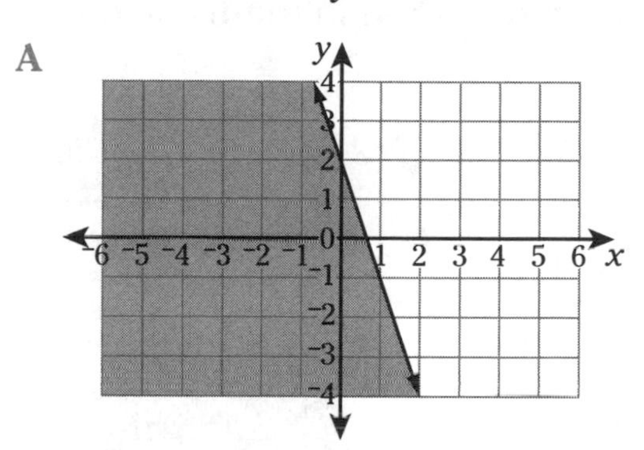

B

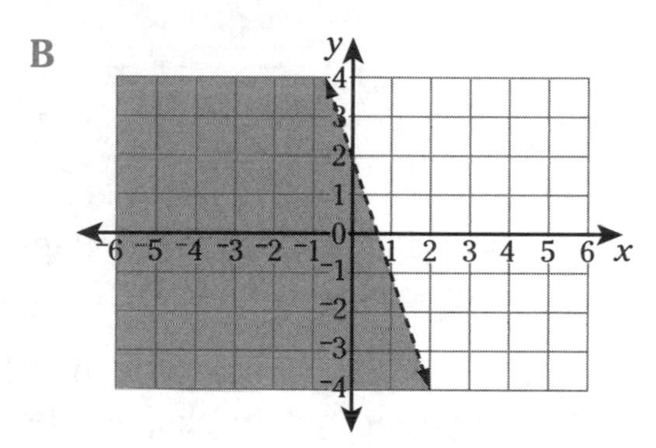

C

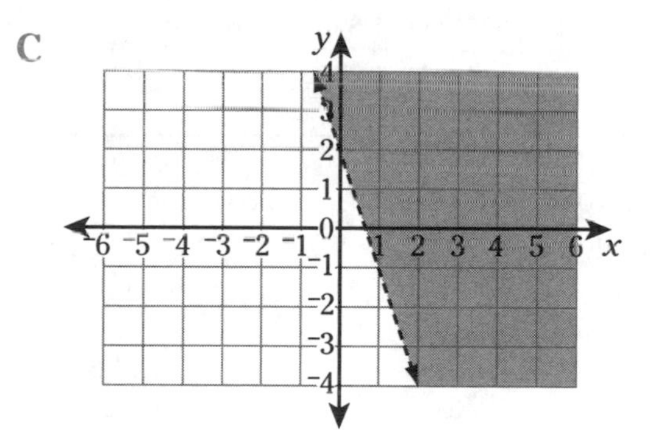

D

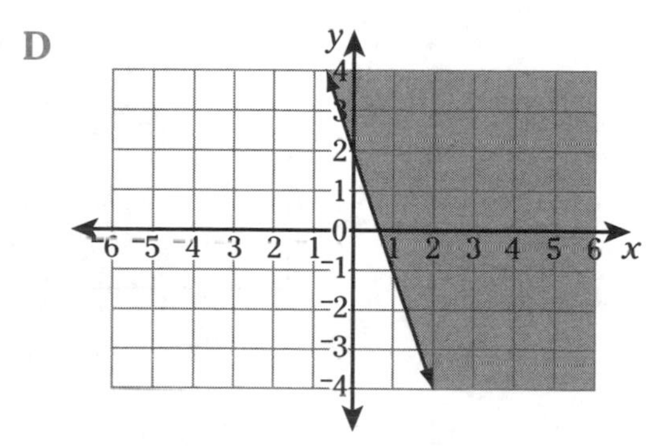

Read each problem. Write your answers.

4. Look at the inequality below.

$$-3x + y < 4$$

Graph the solution to this inequality on the coordinate plane below.

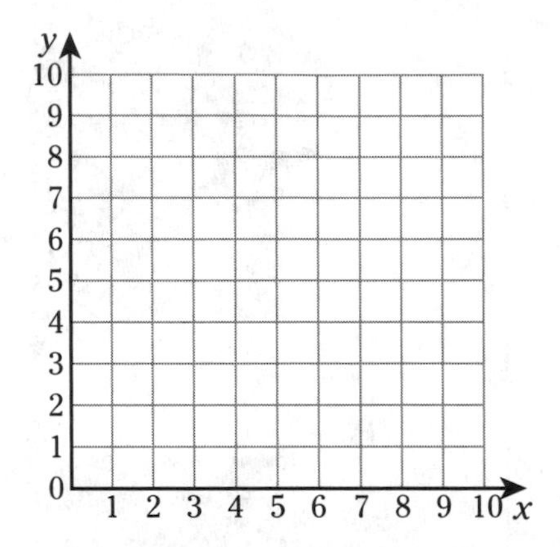

5. Carmen is at a used bookstore. Paperback books cost $1 each, and hardcover books cost $2 each. Carmen can spend up to $10 in all.

Write an inequality that represents this situation. Let x be the number of paperback books, and let y be the number of hardcover books.

Answer: ______________________

Graph the solution to your inequality on the coordinate plane below.

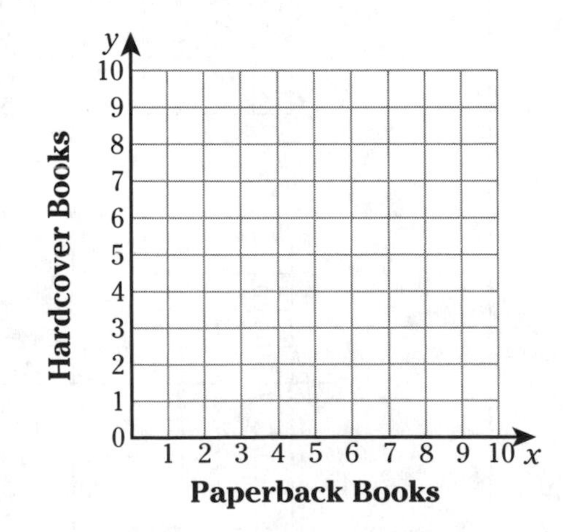

Linear Functions, Equations, and Inequalities Review

Read each problem. Circle the letter of the best answer.

1. An equation of a line is below.

$$y + 5 = 4(x + 1)$$

What is the y-intercept of this line?

A -4 C 1

B -1 D 5

2. What is the slope of the line graphed below?

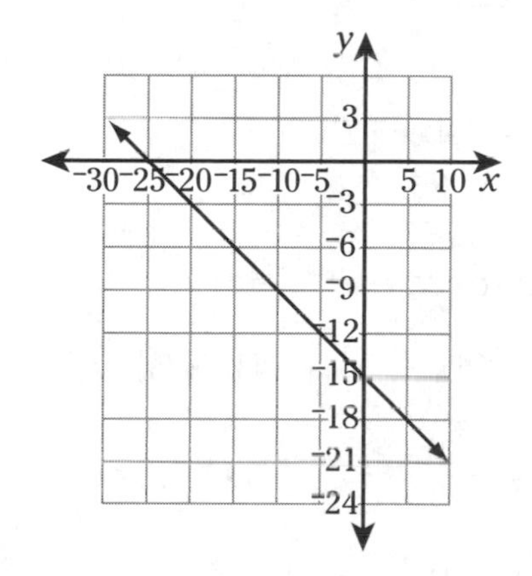

A $\frac{5}{3}$ C $-\frac{3}{5}$

B $\frac{3}{5}$ D $-\frac{5}{3}$

3. What is the solution to the inequality below?

$$8 > -7 - 3x$$

A $x > -5$ C $x < -5$

B $x > -\frac{1}{3}$ D $x < -\frac{1}{3}$

4. The equation below shows the relationship between the weight, in pounds, of a package, x, and the cost, in dollars, to mail the package, y.

$$y = 0.2x + 3$$

Which graph models the solution to this equation?

A

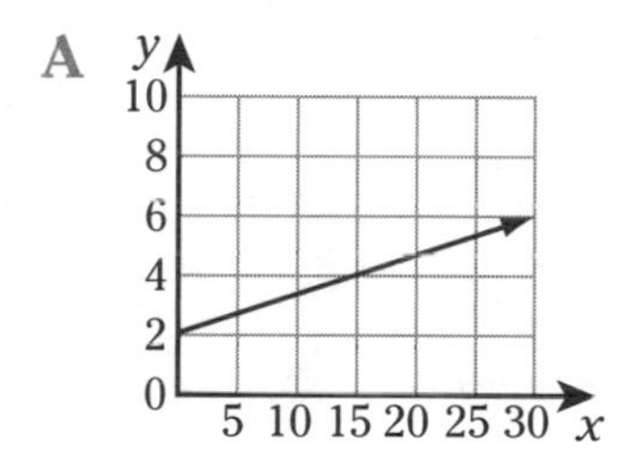

B

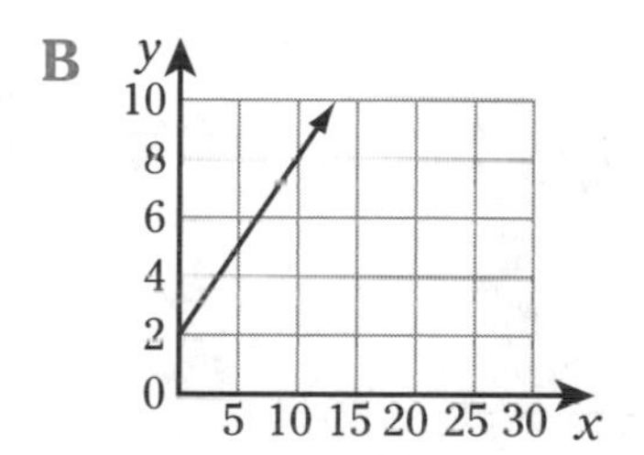

C

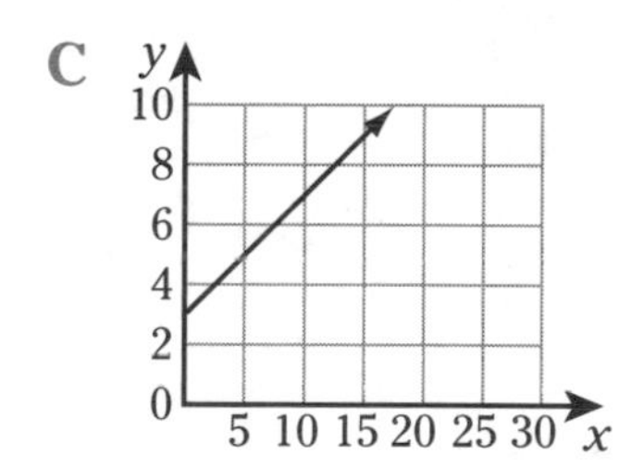

D

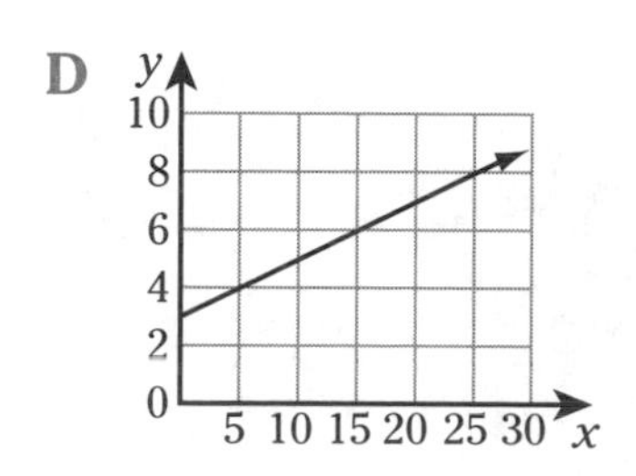

Read each problem. Circle the letter of the best answer.

5. Gordon earns $10 an hour mowing lawns and $15 an hour tutoring. He plans to earn at least $300 a week doing these jobs in the summer. The inequality below can be used to find the number of hours he could do these jobs and reach his goal.

$$10x + 15y \geq 300$$

Which of these graphs shows the solution to this inequality?

A
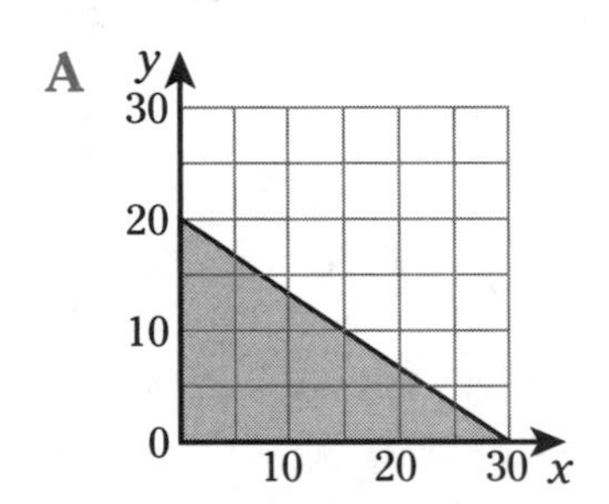

B
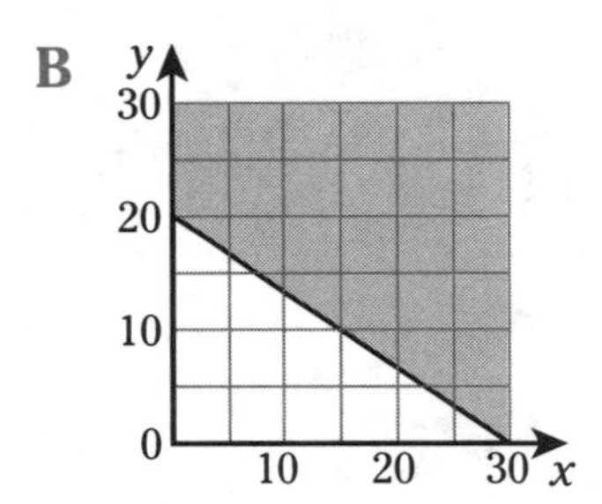

C
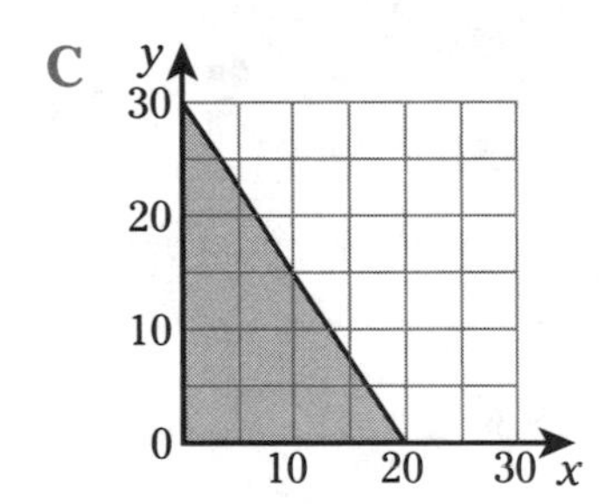

D
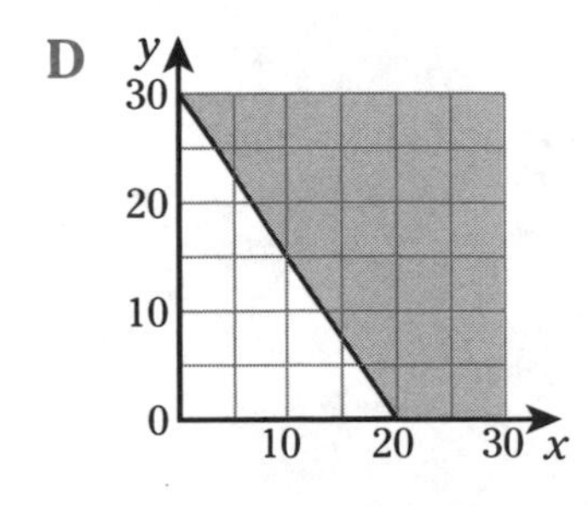

6. Which equation is graphed on the coordinate plane below?

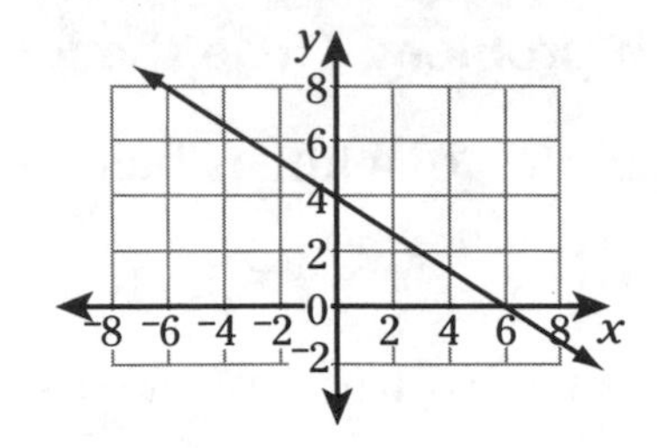

A $y = -\frac{2}{3}(x - 6)$

B $y = -\frac{3}{2}(x - 4)$

C $y = \frac{3}{2}(x + 4)$

D $y = \frac{2}{3}(x + 6)$

7. Solve for x:

$$2(x - 1) + 4(x - 3) = 9$$

A $x = -\frac{21}{2}$

B $x = -\frac{13}{2}$

C $x = \frac{13}{6}$

D $x = \frac{23}{6}$

8. Which equation represents a line perpendicular to $2x - y = 5$ with a y-intercept of 3?

A $2x + y = 3$

B $x + 2y = 3$

C $2x + y = 6$

D $x + 2y = 6$

Read each problem. Circle the letter of the best answer.

9. A line contains the point (2, 4) and has a slope of -3. Which equation represents this line?

   A $-3x + y = 10$

   B $-3x - y = 10$

   C $3x + y = 10$

   D $3x - y = 10$

10. What is the solution to the equation $3y - 6 = 18$?

   A $y = 4$ C $y = 8$

   B $y = 6$ D $y = 12$

11. What is the x-intercept of the line $y = 3x + 4$?

   A $(-\frac{4}{3}, 0)$ C $(-4, 0)$

   B $(\frac{4}{3}, 0)$ D $(4, 0)$

12. Which of the following is the equation of the line shown graphed below?

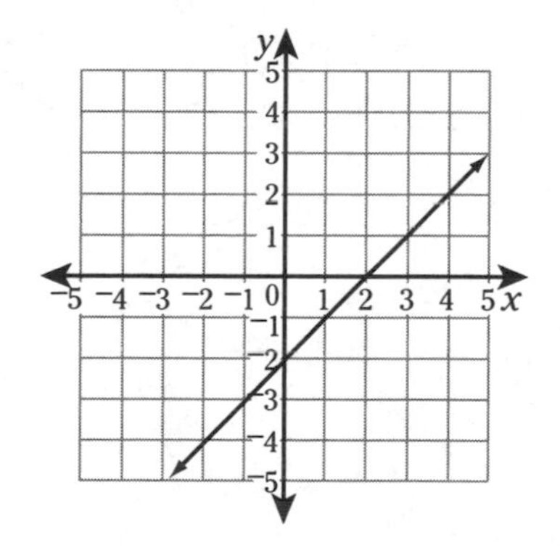

   A $y = x - 2$ C $y = -x - 2$

   B $y = x + 2$ D $y = -x + 2$

13. Which of the following is the graph of $2x + y = 1$?

A

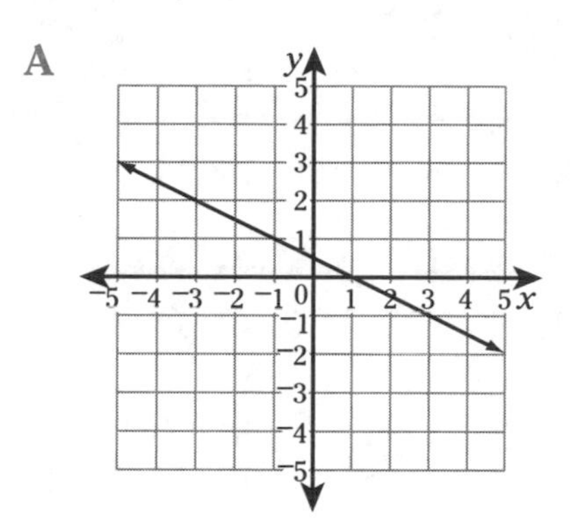

B

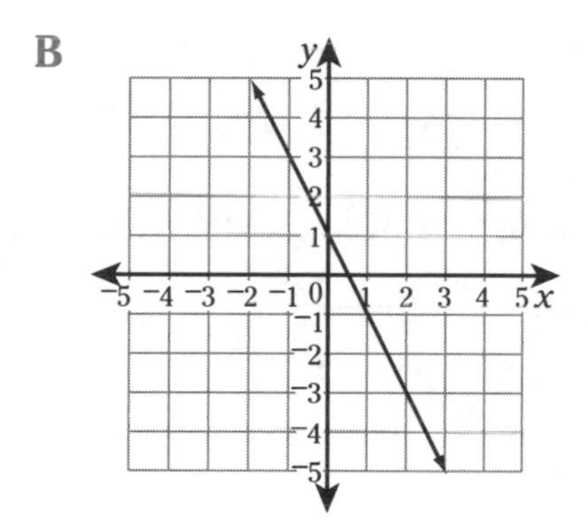

C

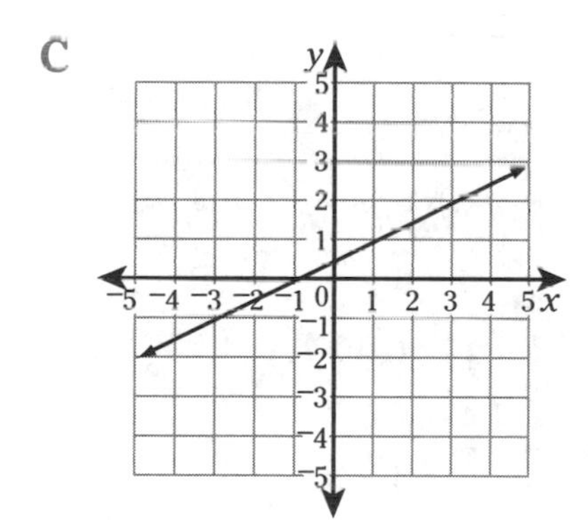

D

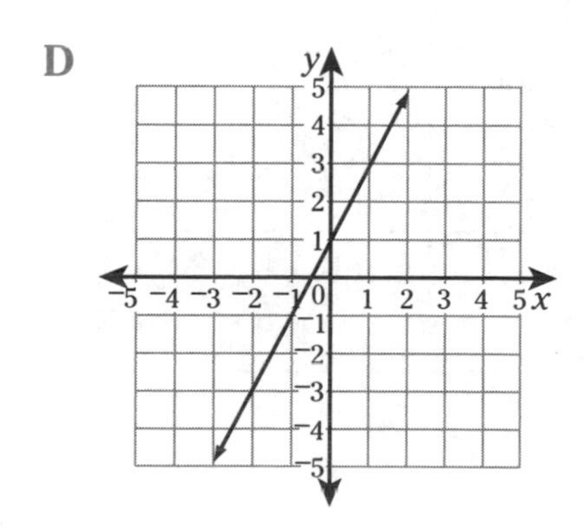

Read the problem. Circle the letter of the best answer.

14. In the inequality $\$10h + \$50 \geq \$130$, h represents the number of hours Leonard worked. Which graph shows the solution set to this inequality?

A 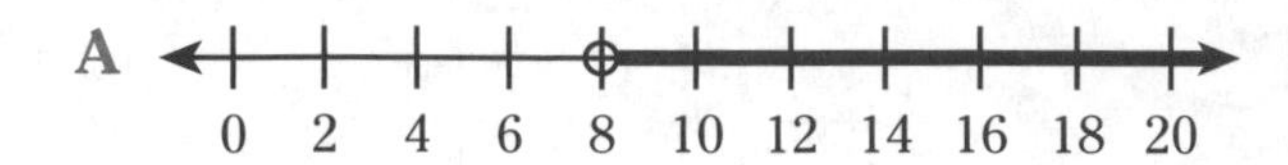

B

0 2 4 6 8 10 12 14 16 18 20

C

0 2 4 6 8 10 12 14 16 18 20

D

0 2 4 6 8 10 12 14 16 18 20

Read each problem. Fill in your answer on the response grid.

15. Two points on a line are (5, 0) and (8, -6). What is the slope of the line?

16. What is the value of n in the equation $5n + 10 = 45$?

Read each problem. Write your answers.

17. An equation of a line is below.

$$y + 6 = 2(x + 4)$$

What is the y-intercept of this line?

Answer: ____________

18. The line of an equation is shown on the coordinate plane below.

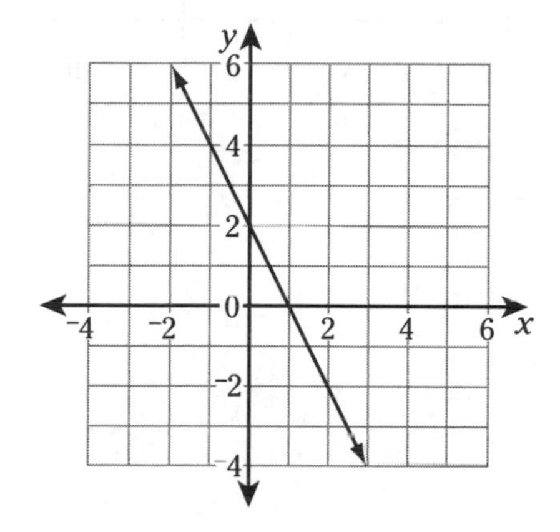

Write an equation, in slope-intercept form, for a line parallel to this line that passes through the point (4, 4).

Answer: ________________________

Write an equation, in slope-intercept form, for a line perpendicular to this line that passes through the point (2, -2).

Answer: ________________________

Read each problem. Write your answers.

19. Look at the inequality below.

$$2(t + 10) \leq 60$$

Solve the inequality for t.

Answer: ______________________

Graph the solution to the inequality on the number line.

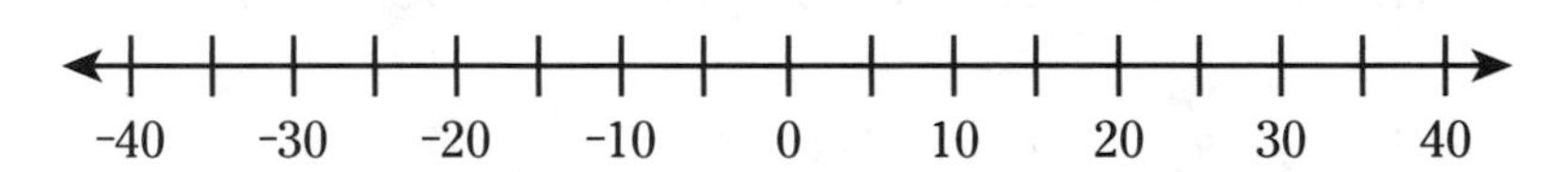

20. A line contains points (6, 7) and (2, 5).

What is the equation of this line?

Answer: ________________

What is the slope of the line containing points (6, 7) and (2, 5)?

Answer: ___________

21. What is the solution to the equation $6(y + 2) + 2(y - 1) = 6$?

Answer: ___________

Read each problem. Write your answers.

22. The graph shows the relationship between the number of hamburgers purchased and the total cost of the hamburgers.

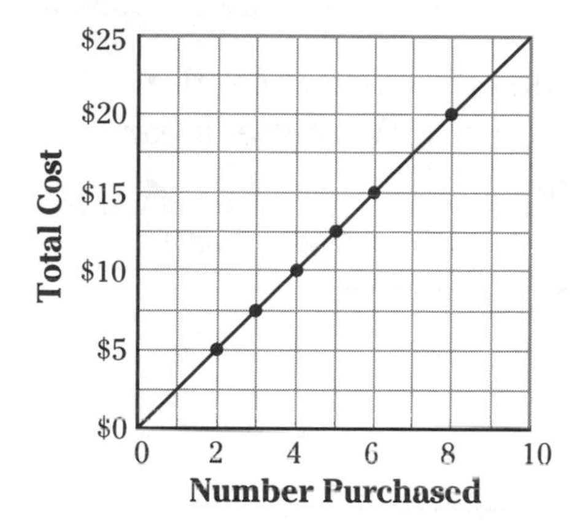

What is the meaning of the slope of the line on the graph?

____

____

____

____

23. Look at the inequality below.

$$3x + 4y < 20$$

Graph the solution to this inequality on the coordinate plane below.

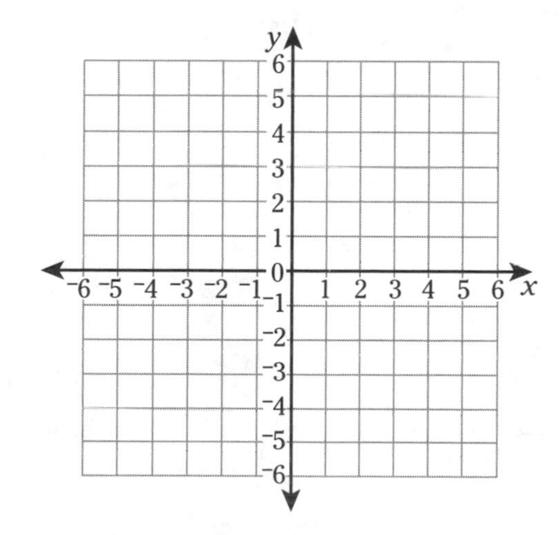

Read the problem. Write your answers.

24. Linda purchased some office equipment for $24,000. Her accountant told her that the equipment would decrease in value by $2,000 each year until it had no value.

    Create a table of values to show the relationship between t, the time in years, and V, the value of the equipment. Write the linear equation that represents the relationship.

EQUIPMENT VALUE

t	V

Answer: ____________________

Graph the value of the office equipment over time.

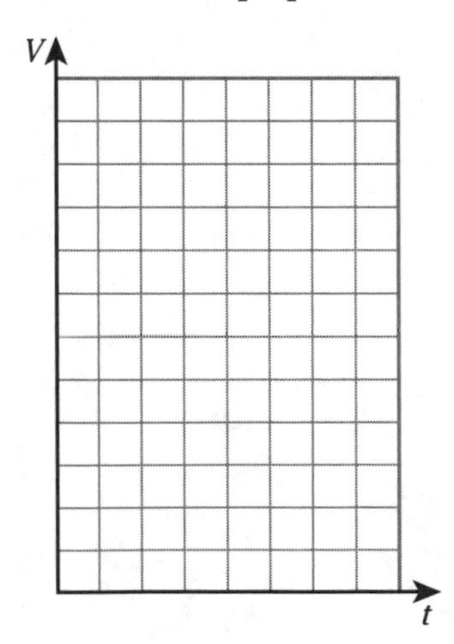

Unit 3
Pairs of Linear Equations and Inequalities

Systems of linear equations and inequalities consist of pairs of connected equations or inequalities. They can be used in real-life situations, such as finding which on-line company can provide you with a better deal for a large order of books. In solving pairs of linear equations or inequalities, you determine the point or region that makes both equations or both inequalities true. There are a variety of solution methods to use.

There are two lessons in this unit:

1. **Solving Pairs of Linear Equations** reviews writing and solving systems of equations using graphing, substitution, elimination, and multiplication.
2. **Solving Pairs of Linear Inequalities** reviews writing and solving systems of inequalities, as well as graphing the solution.

LESSON 1

Solving Pairs of Linear Equations

Standards A1.3.1, 3

Many real-world situations are described by linear equations, whose graphs are straight lines. In many problem-solving situations, it is important to determine where, if at all, two straight lines intersect. The point of intersection usually has special significance in the context of the problem.

Solving Systems of Equations by Graphing

Graphing is one way the point of intersection can be found for a system involving two equations of straight lines.

A **system of equations** is a set of two or more equations that must be solved at the same time.

Consider the system of equations below.

$$\begin{cases} y = x + 4 \\ y = 2x \end{cases}$$

Each equation, by itself, has an infinite number of solutions. For example, the points (0, 4), (1, 5), and (2, 6) are just a few of the solutions to the first equation. However, when solving a system of two equations, you are looking for points that satisfy both equations at the same time.

To solve this system, graph both equations on the same coordinate plane.

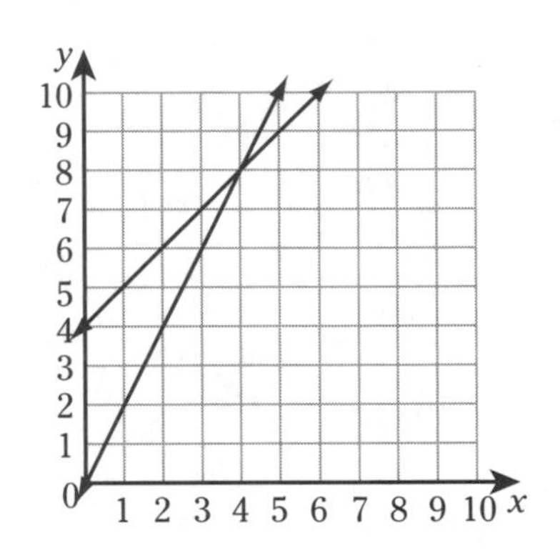

It is easy to see from the graph that the lines intersect at the point (4, 8). You can check that this is correct by substituting $x = 4$ and $y = 8$ into each equation to show that both equations are true.

$y = x + 4$ $\qquad$ $y = 2x$

$8 = 4 + 4$ ✓ $\qquad$ $8 = 2(4)$ ✓

Now try this question.

S-1 Marnie needs to print posters for a community event. Stellar Printers will charge Marnie a \$300 set-up fee plus \$1 per poster. Artemis Printers will charge Marnie a \$200 set-up fee plus \$1.50 per poster.

Write and solve a system of equations that relates the total cost at each company to the number of posters printed. Use the graphing method.

What does the solution to your system of equations represent in the context of the problem?

For the first part, the printing costs for the two companies can be modeled by this system of equations, where y is the cost in dollars and x is the number of posters.

$$\begin{cases} y = 300 + 1.00x \text{ (Stellar Printers)} \\ y = 200 + 1.50x \text{ (Artemis Printers)} \end{cases}$$

You can graph both of these equations to find where they intersect. A graph is shown below.

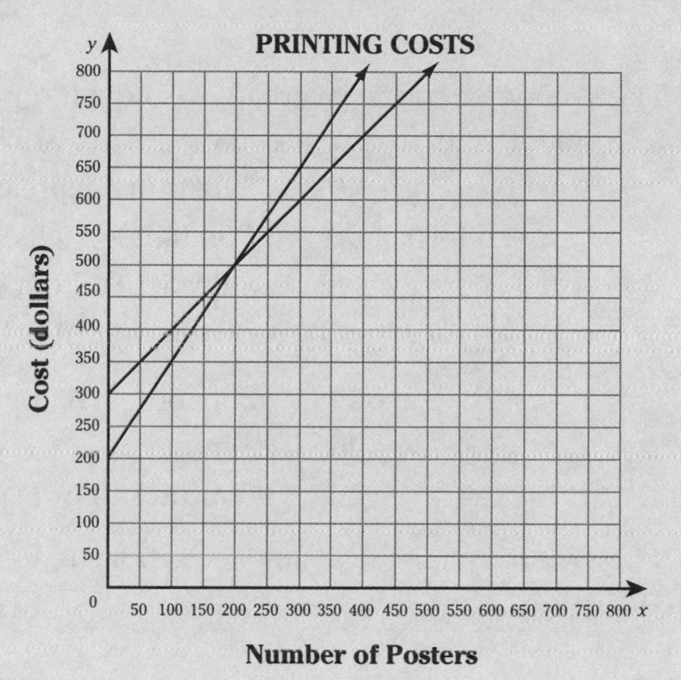

Use the graph to see that the two lines intersect at (200, 500). This point is the solution to the system of equations.

For the second part, it means that both companies will charge Marnie the same amount of money, $500, to print 200 posters.

Solving Systems of Equations Using Substitution

Using algebra techniques, such as **substitution,** is another way systems of equations can be solved. Use these steps when solving systems of equations using substitution:

1. Solve at least one equation for either x or y.
2. Substitute the resulting expression for the variable it equals in the other equation.
3. Solve the equation.
4. Substitute the value of the variable found in step 3 into either original equation to find the value of the other variable.

The sample below uses substitution to find the solution to a system of equations.

S-2 What is the solution to the system of equations below?

$$\begin{cases} -x + y = 40 \\ y = 5x + 80 \end{cases}$$

A $(10, 50)$

B $(-10, 30)$

C $(30, 10)$

D $(30, 70)$

The second equation is already set equal to y. Substitute the expression $5x + 80$ for y into the first equation. Then solve the resulting equation for x.

$-x + (5x + 80) = 40$	Substitute expression for y.
$4x + 80 = 40$	Combine variable terms.
$4x = -40$	Subtract 80 from each side.
$x = -10$	Divide each side by 4.
$-(-10) + y = 40$	Substitute -10 for x into the first equation.
$10 + y = 40$	Simplify.
$y = 30$	Subtract 10 from each side.

The solution to the system of equations is $x = -10$ and $y = 30$. Choice B is correct.

Solving Systems of Equations Using Elimination

A second method used for solving systems of equations algebraically is known as the **elimination method.** With the elimination method, equations are added or subtracted to eliminate one of the variables making it possible to solve for the remaining variable.

To solve the system below, you can simply add the two equations. The y-terms cancel out, and then you can solve for x:

$$\begin{aligned} x + y &= 3 \\ \underline{2x - y} &\underline{= 3} \\ 3x \quad &= 6 \\ x &= 2 \end{aligned}$$

(Notice that $+ y$ added to $- y$ equals 0.)

Then find y by substituting $x = 2$ in either one of the original equations:

$$\begin{aligned} x + y &= 3 \\ 2 + y &= 3 \\ y &= 1 \end{aligned}$$

So the solution is $x = 2$ and $y = 1$, or simply $(2, 1)$.

In the following sample question, adding the equations causes the x-terms to cancel out.

S-3 What is the solution to the system of equations shown below?

$$\begin{cases} 4x - y = 7 \\ -4x - 2y = 2 \end{cases}$$

A (-1, 3) **C** (2, -3)

B (1, -3) **D** (3, 5)

Adding the equations gives the equation $-3y = 9$, which means $y = -3$. Substituting $y = -3$ in the first equation, and solving for x, you get: $4x - (-3) = 7 \rightarrow 4x = 4 \rightarrow x = 1$. So the solution is (1, -3). Choice B is correct.

Solving Systems of Equations Using Multiplication

To solve a system of equations, sometimes you must multiply one or both equations by an appropriate number before you add the two equations. Look at this example:

$$\begin{cases} x + 2y = 5 \\ 3x + 3y = 6 \end{cases}$$

Simply adding these equations will not cause either the x-terms or the y-terms to cancel out. But if you multiply both sides of the first equation by -3, then add the equations, the x-terms will cancel out:

$$\begin{array}{r} (-3)(x + 2y) = (5)(-3) \\ 3x + 3y = 6 \\ \hline \end{array} \quad \rightarrow \quad \begin{array}{r} -3x - 6y = -15 \\ 3x + 3y = 6 \\ \hline -3y = -9 \\ y = 3 \end{array}$$

Substitute $y = 3$ in one of the original two equations and solve for x:

$$\begin{aligned} x + 2y &= 5 \\ x + 2(3) &= 5 \\ x + 6 &= 5 \\ x &= -1 \end{aligned}$$

So the solution is (-1, 3). In other words, the lines $x + 2y = 5$ and $3x + 3y = 6$ both contain the point (-1, 3). To do the following sample problem, multiply the first equation by a certain number that will make the x-terms cancel when the equations are added.

S-4 What is the solution to the system of equations shown below?

$$\begin{cases} x - 4y = 9 \\ 2x + 3y = -4 \end{cases}$$

A (1, -4) **C** (5, -1)

B (1, -2) **D** (7, -6)

Multiply the first equation by -2, and then add to get rid of the x-terms. Solving for y, you should get $y = -2$. Then substitute $y = -2$ into one of the original equations to get $x = 1$. So the solution is $(1, -2)$. Choice B is correct.

When two lines are graphed on the same coordinate system, there are three possibilities:

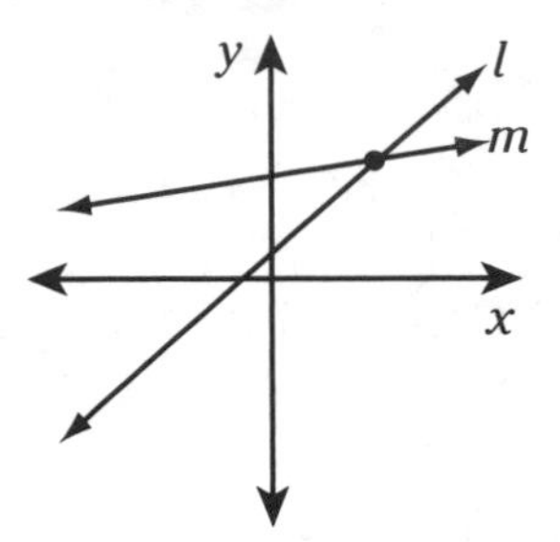

Two lines that intersect in 1 point — One solution to the system of equations

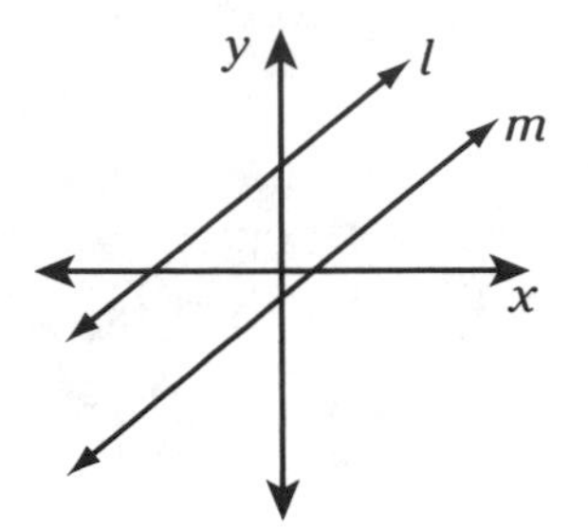

Two lines that do not intersect (parallel lines) — No solution to the system of equations

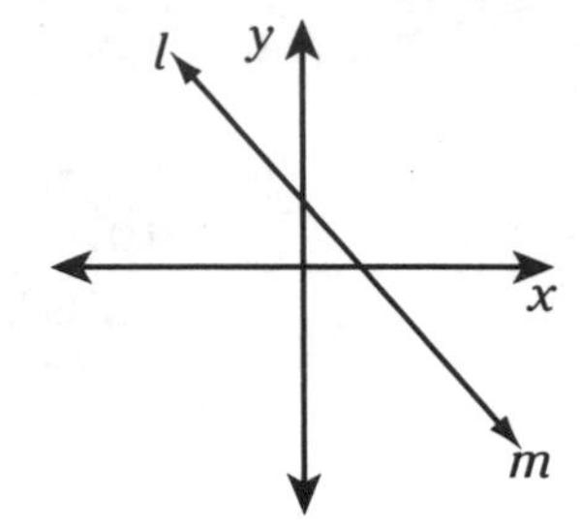

Two identical lines — Infinite number of solutions to the system of equations

The following examples show a system with no solution and a system with an infinite number of solutions.

$$\begin{cases} x - 2y = 4 \\ -x + 2y = 7 \end{cases} \qquad \begin{array}{r} x - 2y = 4 \\ \underline{-x + 2y = 7} \\ 0 = 7 \end{array}$$

Since $0 = 7$ is never true, this system has no solution. The lines described by the equations $x - 2y = 4$ and $-x + 2y = 7$ are parallel.

$$\begin{cases} -4x - 6y = -10 \\ 4x + 6y = 10 \end{cases} \qquad \begin{array}{r} -4x - 6y = -10 \\ \underline{4x - 6y = \ \ 10} \\ 0 = \ \ 0 \end{array}$$

Since $0 = 0$ is always true, this system has an infinite number of solutions. The equations $-4x - 6y = -10$ and $4x + 6y = 10$ describe the same line.

IT'S YOUR TURN

Read each problem. Circle the letter of the best answer.

1. What is the solution to the system of equations graphed below?

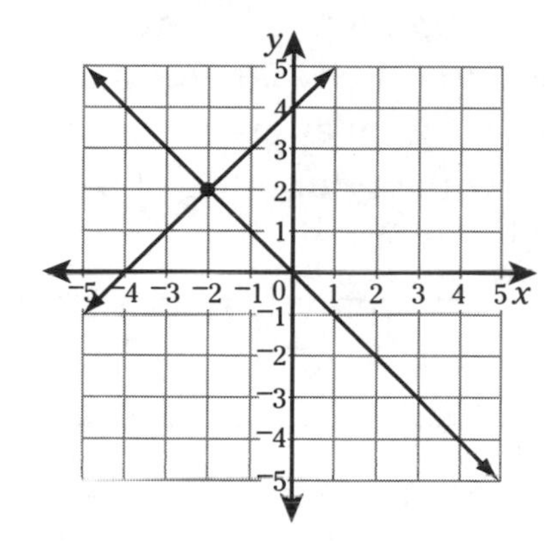

A (-4, 0)

B (-2, 2)

C (0, 0)

D (0, 4)

2. What is the solution to the system of equations shown below?

$$\begin{cases} 2x + 2y = 12 \\ 6x - 2y = 20 \end{cases}$$

A (0, 6)

B (2, 2)

C (3, 3)

D (4, 2)

3. Study the system of equations below.

$$\begin{cases} x + y = -4 \\ x - y = 10 \end{cases}$$

What is the solution to the system of equations?

A (-4, 10)

B (10, 4)

C (3, -7)

D (7, -3)

Read each problem. Fill in your answer on the response grid.

4. What is the y-value of the solution to the system of equations shown below?

$$\begin{cases} 5x + 4y = 12 \\ -5x - 2y = -16 \end{cases}$$

5. Danielle bought a total of 8 pounds of peanuts and cashews. Peanuts cost $2 per pound and cashews cost $5 per pound. The total amount Danielle spent on the peanuts and cashews was $25. How many pounds of peanuts did Danielle buy?

Read the problem. Circle the letter of the best answer.

6. Look at the system of equations below.

$$\begin{cases} y = x + 2 \\ y = 2x - 3 \end{cases}$$

Which coordinate plane shows the solution to this system of equations?

A

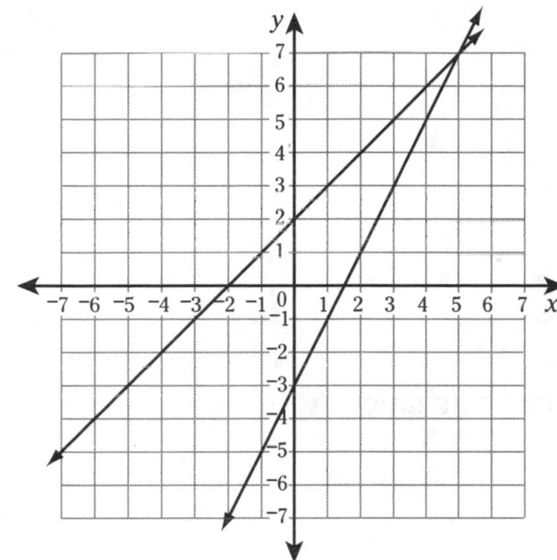

C

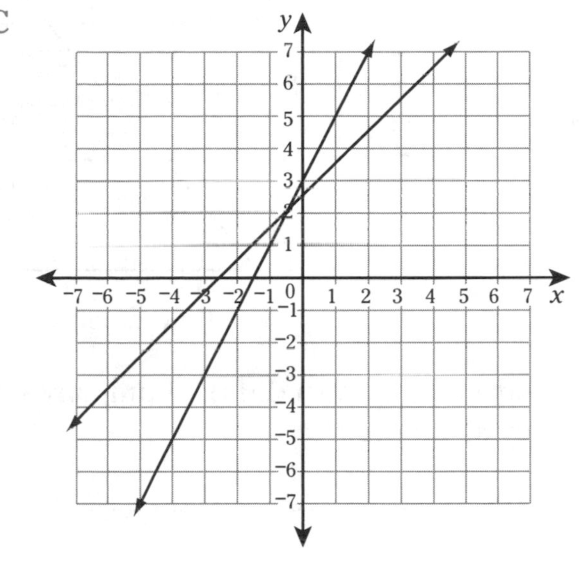

B

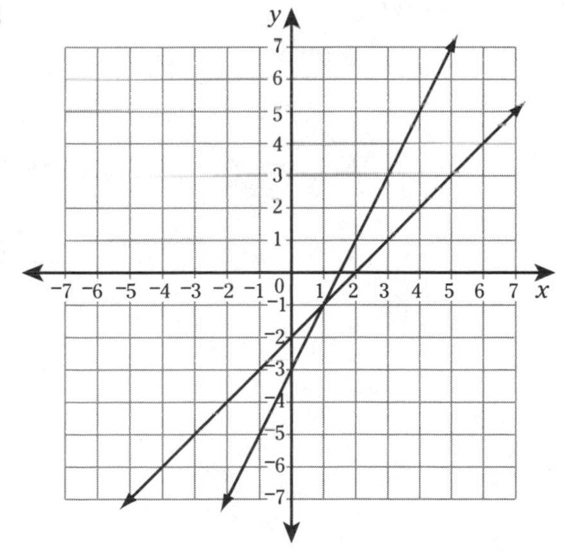

D

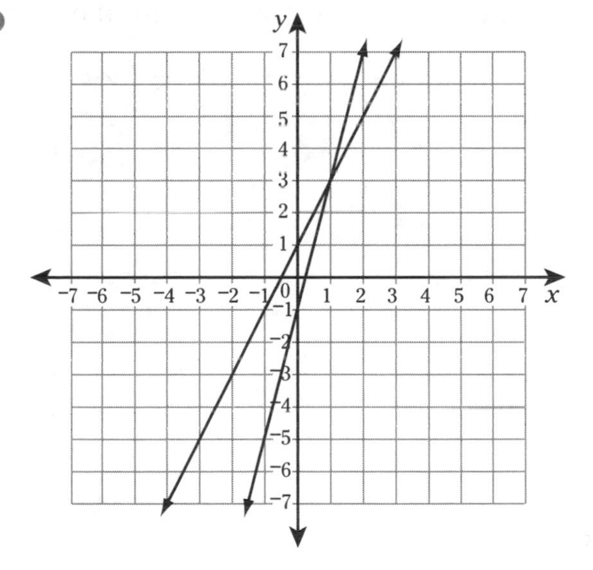

Read each problem. Write your answers.

7. A new company's expenses and income are graphed below.

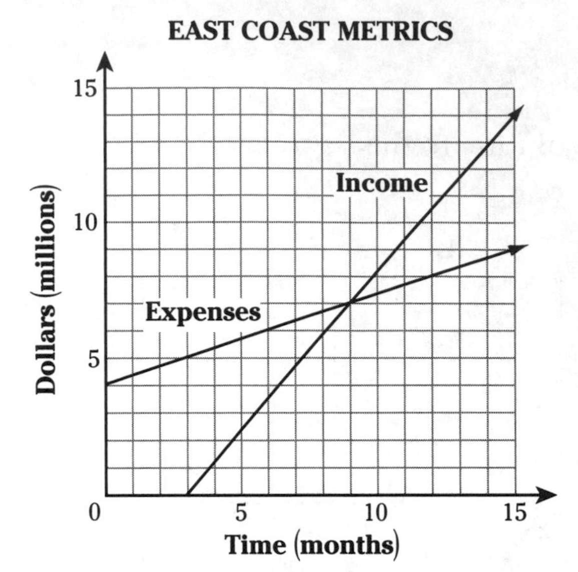

During which month did the company start to make as much money as it spent?

Answer: ______________________

8. Find the solution to the system of equations shown below.

$$\begin{cases} 3x - 5y = 16 \\ 4x + 2y = 4 \end{cases}$$

Answer: ___________

Read the problem. Write your answers.

9. At Corner Store Video, Nina can pay $6 to sign up and then rent DVDs for $2 each. At Pricebuster Video, there is no charge for signing up but it costs $4 each to rent DVDs.

   Write a system of linear equations that relates the total cost at each video store to the number of DVDs rented.

   Answer: ______________________

   Graph the system of equations you wrote above. Label the axes and each equation on your graph.

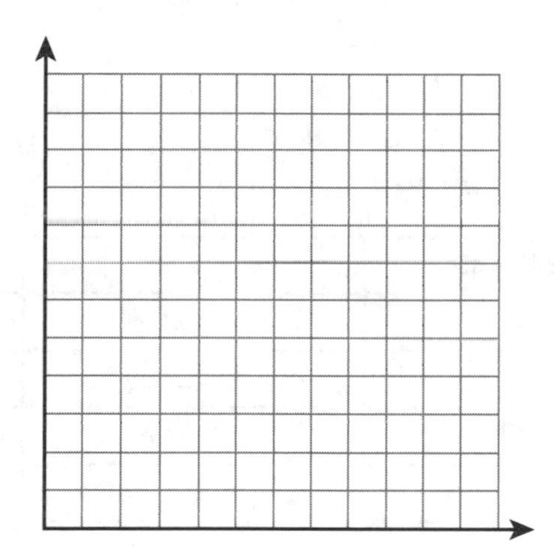

   What does the point of intersection of these two equations represent in the context of the problem?

   ____

   ____

LESSON 2

Solving Pairs of Linear Inequalities

Standard A1.3.2

Systems of Linear Inequalities

Like linear equations, the graphs of two linear inequalities can be graphed on the same coordinate system. To solve a system of linear inequalities, graph the two lines and then shade the appropriate region. The solution to this type of system is the area where their shaded regions overlap.

For example, sketch the graph of the solution to the system of inequalities below.

$$\begin{cases} x + y \geq 2 \\ x - 2y < -2 \end{cases}$$

> Graphs of inequalities with $\geq$ or $\leq$ include the line.
> Graphs of inequalities with $>$ or $<$ do ***not*** include the line.

First graph the lines $x + y = 2$ and $x - 2y = -2$. Use a solid line for $x + y = 2$ (because of the $\geq$ sign) and a dotted or dashed line for $x - 2y = -2$ (because of the $<$ sign).

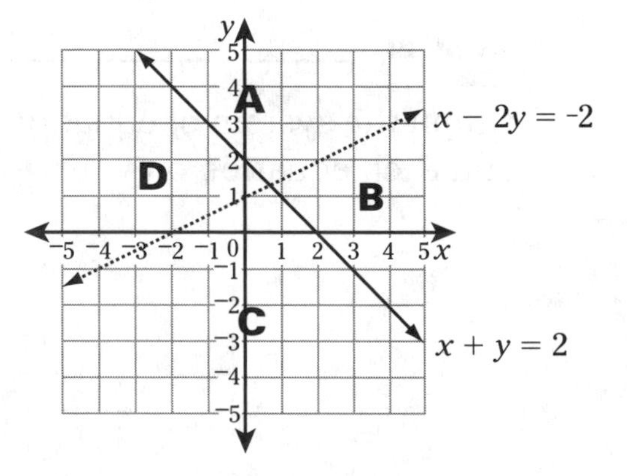

The two lines divide the coordinate plane into four regions, labeled A, B, C, and D as shown here. Now try a test point in each region to find out which region to shade. Find the region where the x- and y-values of the test point satisfy ***both*** inequalities:

Region	Test Point	$x + y \geq 2$	$x - 2y < -2$
A	(2, 3)	$2 + 3 \geq 2$: True	$2 - 6 < -2$: True
B	(4, 1)	$4 + 1 \geq 2$: True	$4 - 2 < -2$: False
C	(1, 0)	$1 + 0 \geq 2$: False	$1 - 0 < -2$: False
D	(-2, 2)	$-2 + 2 \geq 2$: False	$-2 - 4 < -2$: True

The test point in region A is the only one that satisfies both inequalities. So region A should be shaded, and the solution looks like this:

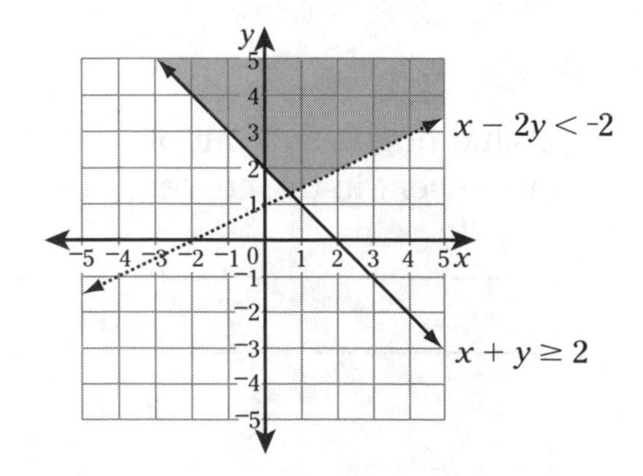

The sample questions that follow show how to graph the solution to a system of inequalities and how to write a system of linear inequalities.

S-1 Which graph represents the solution to the system of inequalities shown below?

$$\begin{cases} y \geq 2x - 3 \\ x + y < 4 \end{cases}$$

A

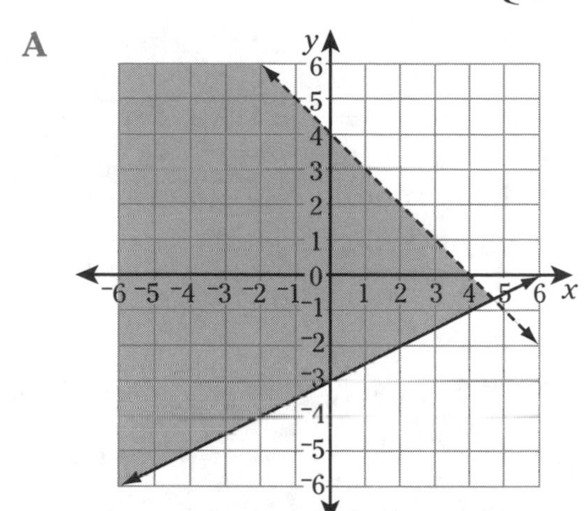

C

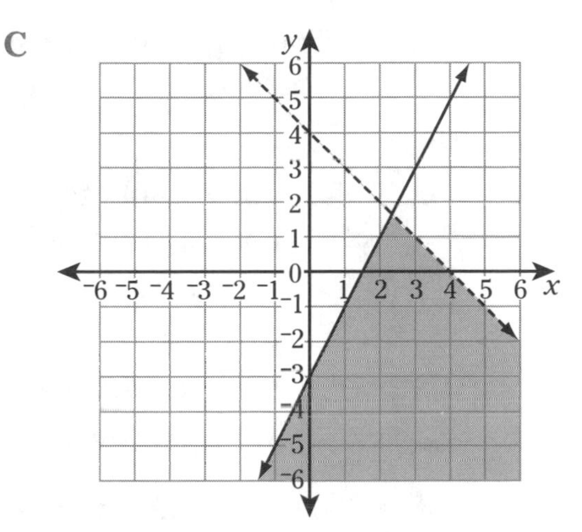

B

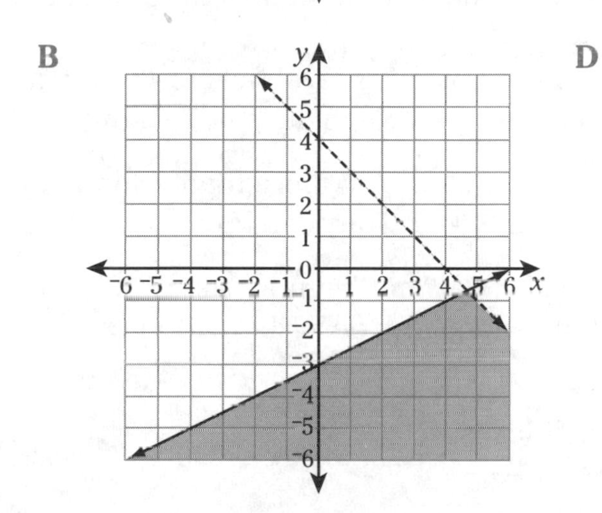

D

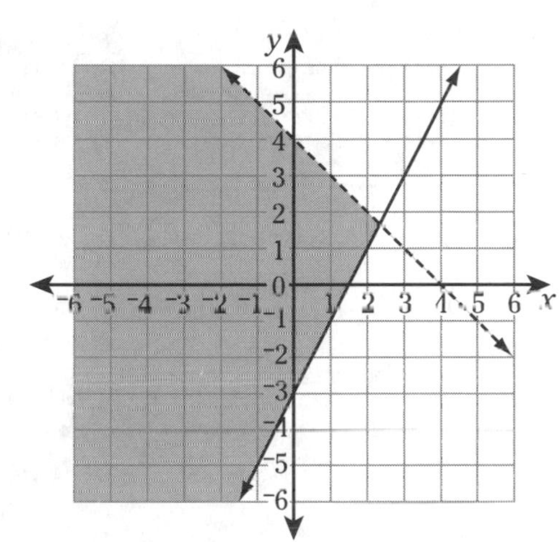

To graph the inequality $y \geq 2x - 3$, first graph $y = 2x - 3$. Test the point (0, 0) to see if this point is included in the solution:

$y \geq 2x - 3 \rightarrow 0 \geq 2(0) - 3$

Since $0 \geq -3$, this point is included in the solution. The area to the left of this inequality containing the point (0, 0) should be shaded.

Rewrite the second inequality by solving for *y*. This will make it easier to graph.

$x + y < 4$ becomes $y < -x + 4$

To graph $y < -x + 4$, first graph $y = -x + 4$. The line will be dashed since the inequality does not include the line itself. Test the point (0, 0) to see if this point is included in the solution:

$$y < -x + 4 \rightarrow 0 < 0 + 4$$

Since $0 < 4$, this point is included in the solution. The area below this inequality containing the point (0, 0) should be shaded.

The solution is the area where both shaded regions overlap. Choice D is correct.

S-2 Tony wants to use \$200 he earned to buy some concert tickets for himself and some friends.

- He wants to buy no more than 8 concert tickets.
- Lower level tickets cost \$35 each.
- Upper level tickets cost \$20 each.

The symbol $\leq$ means "at most" or "no more than." The symbol $\geq$ means "at least" or "no fewer than."

Write a system of inequalities that models this situation.

Let x represent the number of lower level tickets Tony can buy. Let y represent the number of upper level tickets he can buy.

The inequality $\leq$ is used to show "no more than." So the inequality describing the number of tickets Tony can buy is $x + y \leq 8$.

The total cost of the tickets cannot be more than \$200 since this is all the money Tony has. So the inequality describing total cost of the tickets is $35x + 20y \leq 200$.

The system of inequalities is: $\begin{cases} x + y \leq 8 \\ 35x + 20y \leq 200 \end{cases}$

IT'S YOUR TURN

Read each problem. Circle the letter of the best answer.

1. Which of the following graphs represents the solution to the system of inequalities given below?

$$\begin{cases} y < x - 3 \\ y \geq -\frac{1}{2}x \end{cases}$$

A

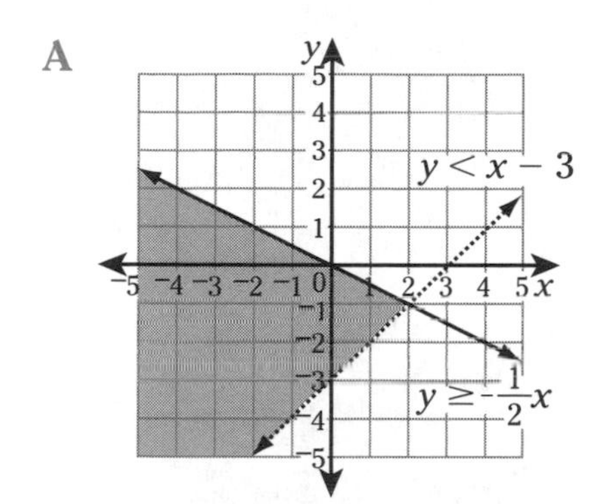

B

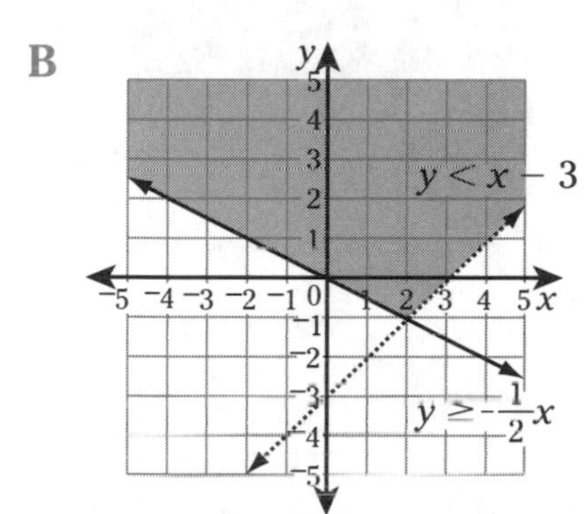

C

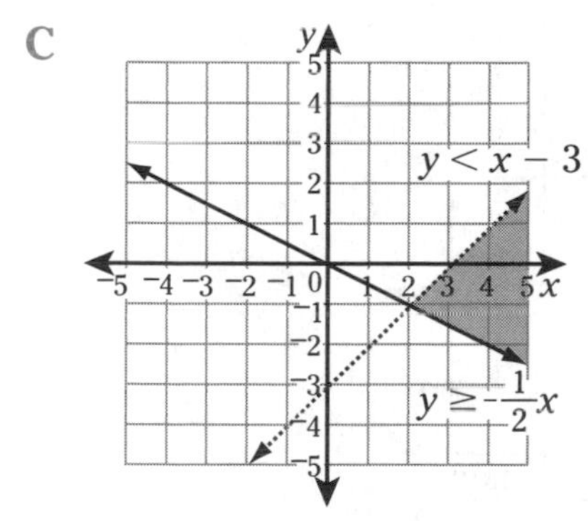

D

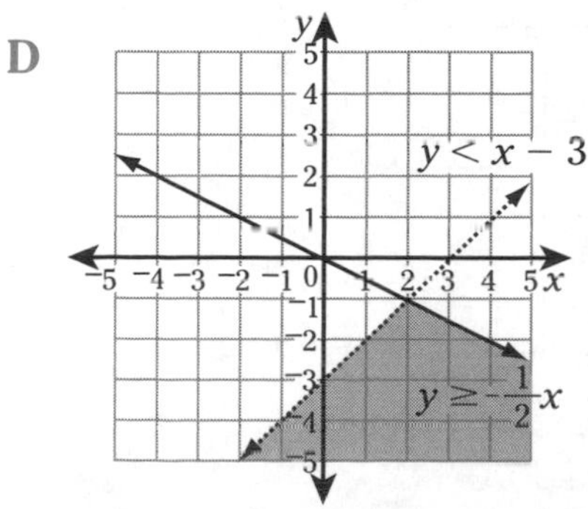

2. Which system of inequalities is shown below?

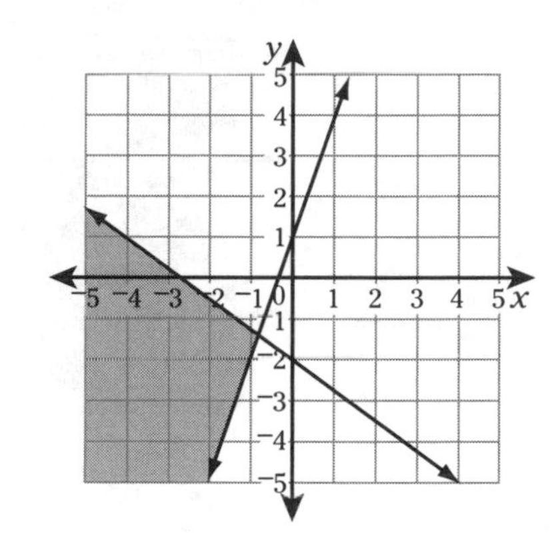

A $\begin{cases} 3x - y \leq -1 \\ 3x + 4y \leq -8 \end{cases}$

B $\begin{cases} 3x - y \leq -1 \\ 3x + 4y \geq -8 \end{cases}$

C $\begin{cases} 3x - y \geq -1 \\ 3x + 4y \leq -8 \end{cases}$

D $\begin{cases} 3x - y \geq -1 \\ 3x + 4y \geq -8 \end{cases}$

3. Nobu will put a fence around a rectangular playing field. He wants the perimeter to be at most 320 yards. He also wants the length to be at least twice the width. Which system of inequalities can be used to model this situation?

A $\begin{cases} 2l + 2w \leq 320 \\ w \geq 2l \end{cases}$

B $\begin{cases} 2l + 2w \leq 320 \\ l \geq 2w \end{cases}$

C $\begin{cases} 2l + 2w \geq 320 \\ l \leq 2w \end{cases}$

D $\begin{cases} 2l + 2w \geq 320 \\ w \geq 2l \end{cases}$

Read the problem. Circle the letter of the best answer.

4. Which system of inequalities is modeled by the graph below?

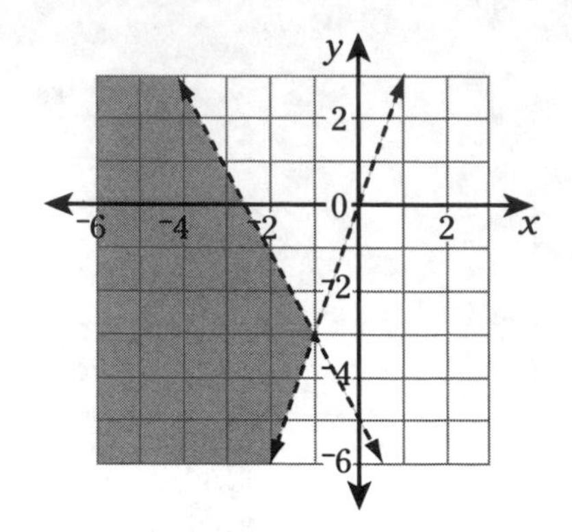

A $\begin{cases} y > 3x \\ y < -2x - 5 \end{cases}$

B $\begin{cases} y < 3x \\ y < -2x - 5 \end{cases}$

C $\begin{cases} y > 3x \\ y > -2x - 5 \end{cases}$

D $\begin{cases} y < 3x \\ y > -2x - 5 \end{cases}$

Read the problem. Write your answer.

5. Graph the solution to this system of inequalities.

$$\begin{cases} y \leq 2x + 1 \\ 2x + y \leq 12 \end{cases}$$

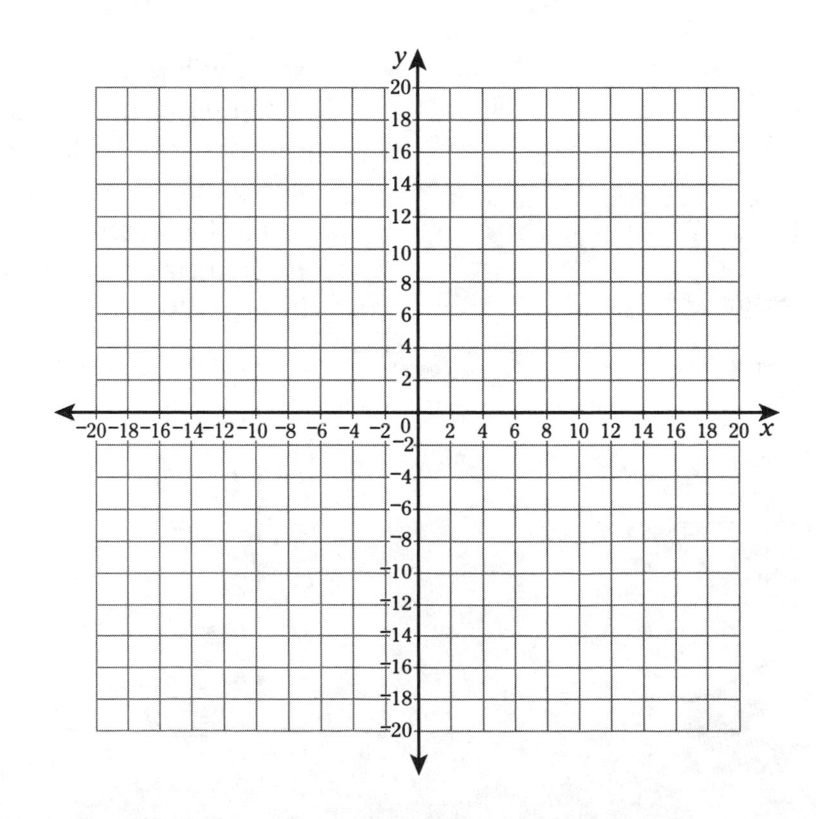

Pairs of Linear Equations and Inequalities Review

Read each problem. Circle the letter of the best answer.

1. What is the solution to the system of equations shown below?

$$\begin{cases} 3x + 4y = 13 \\ 2x - 2y = 4 \end{cases}$$

A $(3, 1)$

B $(3, 4)$

C $(7, -2)$

D $(8, 6)$

2. How many solutions are there to the system of equations graphed below?

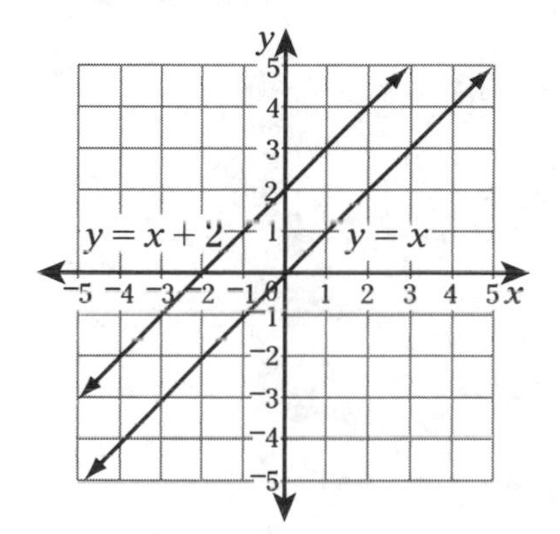

A 0

B 1

C 2

D infinitely many

3. Olivia buys 2 pounds of cheese and 3.5 pounds of meat at a deli for \$27.00. Marcella buys 3 pounds of cheese and 1.5 pounds of meat at the deli for \$18.00. What is the total cost for 1 pound of cheese and 1 pound of meat?

A \$4.50

B \$6.00

C \$7.50

D \$9.00

4. What is the solution to the system of equations shown below?

$$\begin{cases} y = 2x + 5 \\ y + 3x = 0 \end{cases}$$

A $(-1, 3)$

B $(1, -3)$

C $(-3, 1)$

D $(3, -1)$

5. What is the solution to the system of equations shown below?

$$\begin{cases} x - 3y = 6 \\ 2x - 6y = 12 \end{cases}$$

A $(0, -2)$

B $(6, 0)$

C no solution

D infinitely many solutions

Read the problem. Circle the letter of the best answer.

6. Which graph shows the solution to the system of inequalities shown below?

$$\begin{cases} y < x + 4 \\ y \geq 2x \end{cases}$$

A
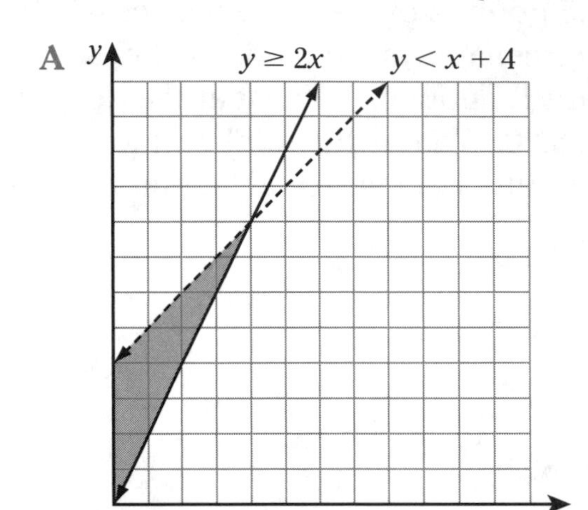

C
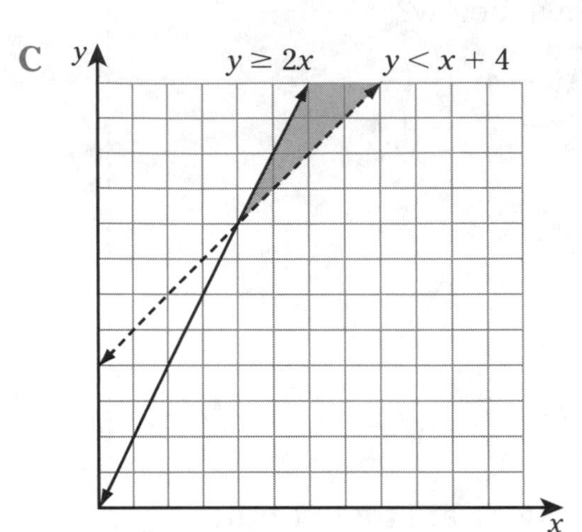

B
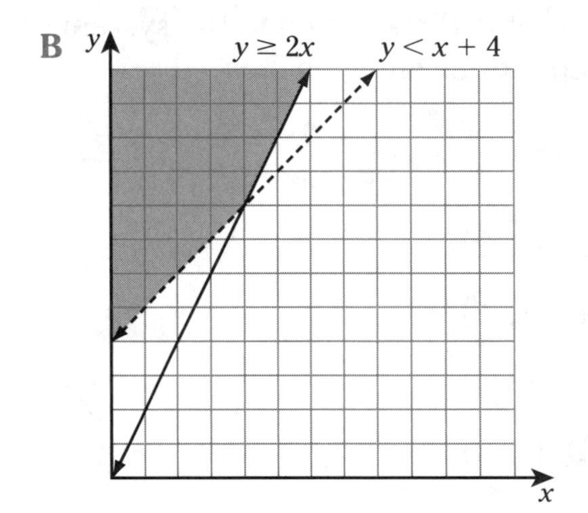

D
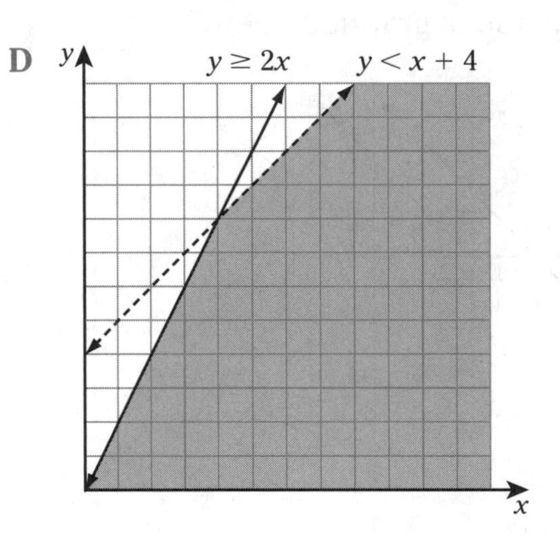

Read each problem. Fill in your answer on the response grid.

7. What is the y-value of the solution to the system of equations shown below?

$$\begin{cases} y = -6x + 1 \\ y = 6x + 9 \end{cases}$$

8. Vic trains for a race by jogging and riding his bike every week.

   - Last week, he covered a total distance of 60 miles jogging and biking.
   - He jogs at an average rate of 6 miles per hour.
   - He rides his bike at an average rate of 10 miles per hour.

   If Vic trained a total of 7 hours last week, how many hours did he ride his bike?

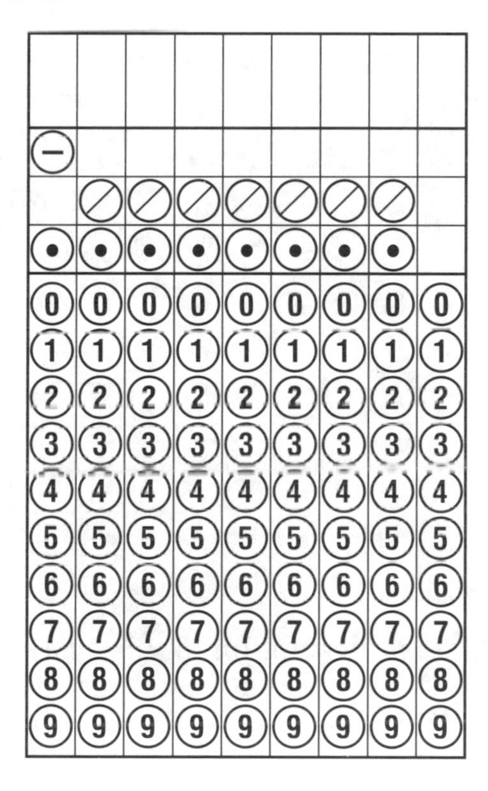

Read the problem. Write your answers.

9. Look at the system of equations below.

$$\begin{cases} y = 2x + 5 \\ y + 3x = 0 \end{cases}$$

Graph the solution to the system of equations on the coordinate plane. Label each line.

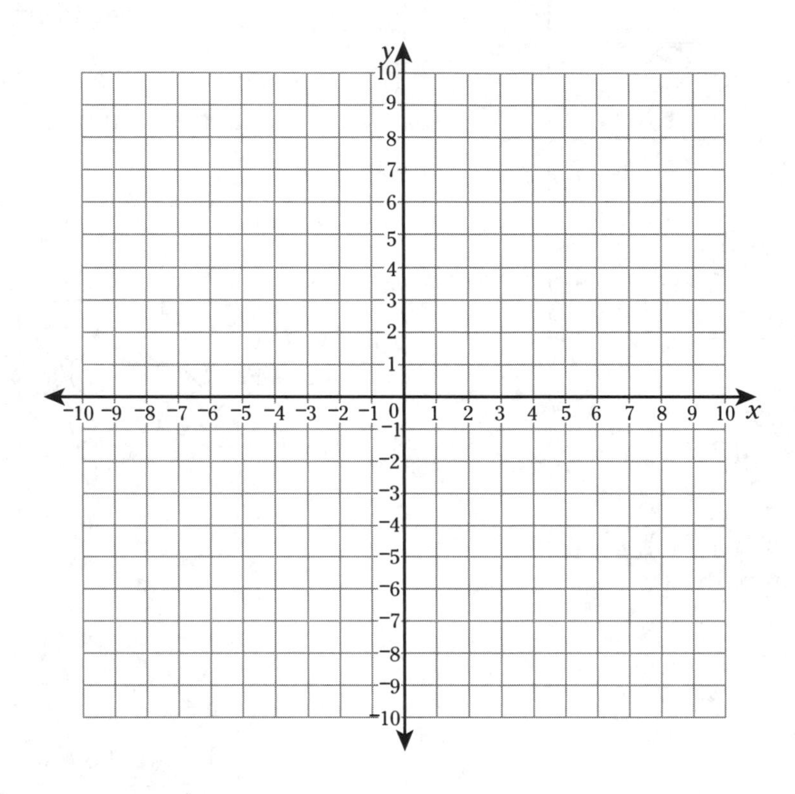

What is the solution to this system of equations?

Answer: ____________

Read each problem. Write your answers.

10. Look at the system of inequalities below.

$$\begin{cases} y < 2x - 3 \\ y \leq -\frac{1}{3}x + 3 \end{cases}$$

Graph the solution to this system of inequalities on the coordinate plane below.

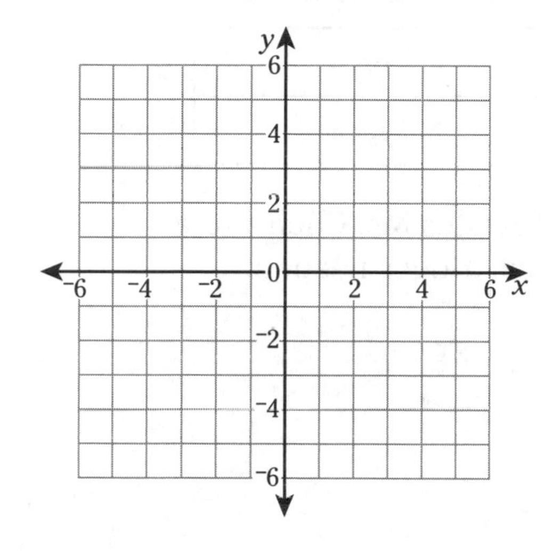

11. What is the solution to the system of equations shown below?

$$\begin{cases} x \quad 2y = 4 \\ 3x + 4y = 12 \end{cases}$$

Answer: ____________

Read the problem. Write your answers.

12. Ms. Chen is buying a printer for her computer. She needs to choose between two different brands, the Voltroxx printer and the Inkwest printer. For whichever printer she buys, she will also need to buy ink cartridges. Information about the two printers is shown in the table below.

PRINTER COMPARISON

Brand of Printer	Cost of Printer	Cost of Ink Cartridges
Voltroxx	$50	$30 each
Inkwest	$80	$27 each

Write a system of linear equations that relates Ms. Chen's total cost for each printer to the number of cartridges needed.

Answer: ______________________

What is the solution to this system of equations?

Answer: ___________

Explain what the solution to this system of equations represents in the context of the problem.

____

____

____

____

Read the problem. Write your answers.

13. Mateo collected at least 200 pennies and dimes. The total value of these coins is at most $10.00.

Write a system of inequalities representing this data.

Answer: ______________________

Graph the system of inequalities you wrote above.

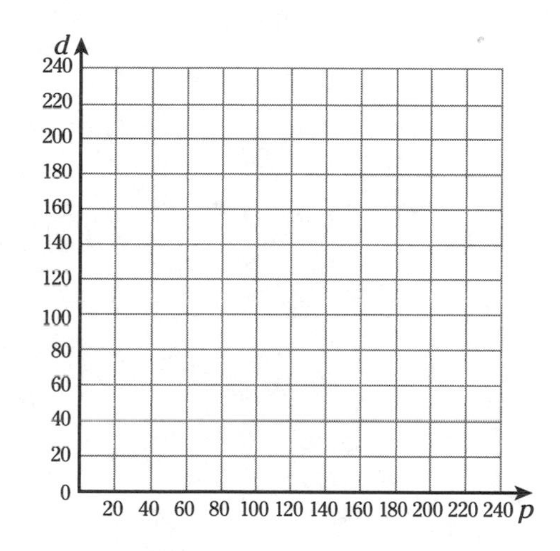

Unit 4
Polynomials

Polynomials are a common type of algebraic expression. In algebra, you must be able to work fluently with different kinds of polynomials. It is important to be able to perform operations with polynomials and to factor them. These skills will help you as you pursue higher mathematics.

There are five lessons in this unit:

1. **Adding and Subtracting Polynomials** reviews adding and subtracting polynomials.
2. **Operations with Monomials** reviews multiplying and dividing monomials, as well as raising a monomial to a power and finding the root of a monomial.
3. **Multiplying and Dividing Polynomials** reviews multiplying and dividing polynomials by monomials.
4. **Factoring Algebraic Expressions** reviews factoring polynomials, including finding the greatest common factor and finding the difference of two squares.
5. **Factoring Trinomials** reviews factoring trinomials in different forms.

LESSON 1

Adding and Subtracting Polynomials

Standard A1.4.2

A **polynomial** is an algebraic expression of one or more terms. A **monomial** is a polynomial with only one term, like 8, $8y$, or $8y^2$. A **binomial** is a polynomial with two terms, like $6x - 7$.

A **polynomial expression** is a monomial or the sum or difference of more than one monomial expression.

Adding and Subtracting Polynomials

To add polynomials, simply combine like terms. See how it works in this example:

$$(x^2 - 9x + 3) + (2x^2 + x - 4) = 3x^2 - 8x - 1$$

To subtract polynomials, change the sign of each term in the second polynomial and then add. For example:

$$(2x^3 + 4x^2 - 6x) - (4x^3 - 3x^2 + 5x)$$

is written as: $(2x^3 + 4x^2 - 6x) + (-4x^3 + 3x^2 - 5x)$

which equals: $-2x^3 + 7x^2 - 11x$

> Subtracting is adding the opposite:
> $a - b = a + (-b)$.

Try these sample questions.

S-1 $(4x^2 - 6) - (x^2 + 2) =$

A $3x^2 - 8$

B $3x^2 - 4$

C $5x^2 - 8$

D $5x^2 - 4$

Changing the signs of each term in the second polynomial gives the addition problem $(4x^2 - 6) + (-x^2 - 2)$, which simplifies to $3x^2 - 8$. Choice A is correct.

S-2 What is the simplified form of the expression below?

$$(6x^2 + 4y^2) + (5x^2 - 3y^2)$$

A $x^2 + y^2$

B $x^2 + 7y^2$

C $11x^2 + y^2$

D $11x^2 + 7y^2$

To add these binomials, simply combine like terms: $6x^2 + 5x^2 = 11x^2$ and $4y^2 - 3y^2 = y^2$. So the simplified form is $11x^2 + y^2$. Choice C is correct.

IT'S YOUR TURN

Read each problem. Circle the letter of the best answer.

1. What is the simplified form of the expression below?

   $(2w^3 + 4w^2 + 5) + (3w^3 + w^2 + 4w)$

   A $5w^3 + 5w^2 + 9$

   B $5w^3 + 5w^2 + 9w$

   C $5w^3 + 5w^2 + 4w + 5$

   D $5w^3 + 4w^2 + 5w + 4$

2. What is the simplified form of the difference shown below?

   $(3a^2 - 6a - 1) - (5a^2 - 2a + 3)$

   A $-2a^2 - 4a - 4$

   B $-2a^2 - 8a + 2$

   C $2a^2 - 4a + 2$

   D $2a^2 - 8a - 4$

3. Which expression represents the perimeter of the rectangle shown below?

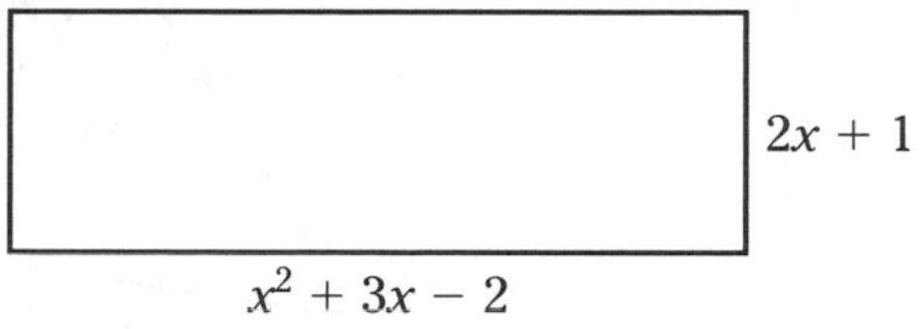

   A $x^2 + x - 3$

   B $x^2 + 5x - 1$

   C $2x^2 + 2x - 6$

   D $2x^2 + 10x - 2$

4. Subtract:

   $(9y^2 - 4y + 3) - (5y^2 + 2y - 7) =$

   A $4y^2 - 6y - 4$

   B $4y^2 - 6y + 10$

   C $4y^2 - 2y - 4$

   D $4y^2 - 2y + 10$

Read each problem. Write your answers.

5. The perimeter of the triangle shown below is $19z - 7$.

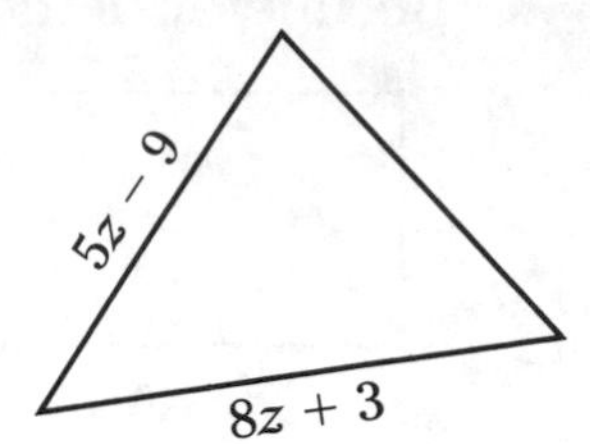

Write an expression in simplest terms to represent the length of the remaining side.

Answer: ______________________

6. Simplify:

$$(4b^2 + 4b - 5) + (2b^2 + 3b - 1)$$

Answer: ______________________

LESSON 2 

Operations with Monomials

Standard A1.4.1

A **monomial** consists of a constant or a number multiplied by one or more variables, which may have exponents. If the number is 1, it's usually not written. For example, the monomial $1x^2$ is usually written simply as x^2. Examples of other monomials are 6, $4x$, $-7y^3$, and a^4b^5c.

When working with monomials, you may also need to use the properties of exponents.

Multiplying Exponents

The product of powers with the same base can be written using one exponent. For example, $h^4 \cdot h^3 = (h \cdot h \cdot h \cdot h) \cdot (h \cdot h \cdot h) = h^7$. The sum of the exponents of the expression $h^4 \cdot h^3$ equals the exponent of h^7.

> For any base $x \neq 0$ and integers m and n, $x^m \cdot x^n = x^{m+n}$.

Try this sample question.

S-1 How can the expression $z^8 \cdot z^2$ be written using one exponent?

A z^4

B z^6

C z^{10}

D z^{16}

Since both bases are the same, $z^8 \cdot z^2$ can be rewritten using one exponent by adding the exponents together: $z^8 \cdot z^2 = z^{8+2} = z^{10}$. Choice C is correct.

Dividing Exponents

Quotients of powers with the same base, like products of powers, can be written using one exponent. To divide powers, exponents are subtracted. For example, $\frac{b^7}{b^3} = \frac{b \cdot b \cdot b \cdot b \cdot b \cdot b \cdot b}{b \cdot b \cdot b} = b \cdot b \cdot b \cdot b = b^4$. The difference between the exponents in the numerator and the denominator of the expression $\frac{b^7}{b^3}$ equals the exponent of b^4.

> For any base $x \neq 0$ and integers m and n, $\frac{x^m}{x^n} = x^{m-n}$.

Try this sample constructed-response question.

S-2 Look at the expression below.

$$\frac{a^{12}}{a^4}$$

Write an equivalent expression with base a using only one exponent.

Since both bases are the same, the expression $\frac{a^{12}}{a^4}$ can be rewritten using one exponent by subtracting the exponents. So, $\frac{a^{12}}{a^4} = a^{12-4} = a^8$.

Powers of Powers

Powers can be raised to powers by finding the product of the exponents. For example, $(k^5)^2 = k^{5 \cdot 2} = k^{10}$. This is true since $(k^5)^2 = (k^5) \cdot (k^5) = (k \cdot k \cdot k \cdot k \cdot k) \cdot (k \cdot k \cdot k \cdot k \cdot k) = k^{10}$.

For any base $x \neq 0$ and integers m and n, $(x^m)^n = x^{mn}$.

Try this sample question.

S-3 Which expression has the same value as $(w^3)^5$?

A w^8

B w^{15}

C w^{35}

D w^{243}

Multiply the exponents 3 and 5 to find the new exponent. The base stays the same: $(w^3)^5 = w^{3 \cdot 5} = w^{15}$. Choice B is correct.

Multiplying Monomials

To multiply monomials, first multiply any numbers, and then multiply the variables with the same bases. For example, to multiply $(3x^5y^3)(4x^2y)$, remember that $3 \cdot 4 = 12$, $x^5 \cdot x^2 = x^7$, and $y^3 \cdot y = y^4$. So $(3x^5y^3)(4x^2y) = 12x^7y^4$.

Remember these rules:

$$x^m \cdot x^n = x^{m+n}$$

$$\frac{x^m}{x^n} = x^{m-n}$$

$$x^1 = x \qquad x^0 = 1$$

Try this sample question.

S-4 Multiply:

$$(8ab^2)(5a^4b^3) =$$

A $40a^4b^5$

B $40a^5b^5$

C $40a^4b^6$

D $40a^5b^6$

First multiply the numbers, and then the variables: $8 \cdot 5 = 40$, $a \cdot a^4 = a^5$, and $b^2 \cdot b^3 = b^5$. In choices A and C, the variable a was treated like a^0 instead of a^1. In choices C and D, the exponents of the variable b were multiplied instead of added. Choice B is correct.

Dividing Monomials

To divide monomials, first divide any numbers, and then divide the variables. For example, to divide $\frac{24x^5y^4}{2xy^3}$, remember that $\frac{24}{2} = 12$, $\frac{x^5}{x} = x^4$, and $\frac{y^4}{y^3} = y$. So $\frac{24x^5y^4}{2xy^3} = 12x^4y$. This procedure applies whether the division is written as a fraction or with a division sign.

When an exponential expression is divided by itself, it equals 1:

$$\frac{x^5}{x^5} = 1$$

This lets you "cancel" any expression that appears in ***both*** the numerator and denominator of a fraction:

$$\frac{7y^3}{y^3} = 7 \qquad \frac{a^2}{8a^2} = \frac{1}{8}$$

Try this sample question.

S-5 Divide:

$$\frac{30y^2z^6}{5y^5z^2} =$$

A $6y^3z^3$

B $6y^3z^4$

C $\frac{6z^3}{y^3}$

D $\frac{6z^4}{y^3}$

A positive number, a, raised to a negative exponent, n, is not negative. It results in a fraction.

$$a^{-n} = \frac{1}{a^n}$$

Because $\frac{30}{5} = 6$, $\frac{y^2}{y^5} = \frac{1}{y^3}$, and $\frac{z^6}{z^2} = z^4$, the answer has $6z^4$ in the numerator and y^3 in the denominator. In choices A and B, the expression y^3 was placed in the numerator instead of the denominator. In choices A and C, the exponents of the variable z were divided instead of subtracted. Choice D is correct.

Raising a Monomial to a Power

To raise a monomial to a power, raise each part of it to the power. For example, $(3x^4y)^2 = 3^2 \cdot (x^4)^2 \cdot y^2 = 9x^8y^2$.

Remember these rules:

$$(x^m)^n = x^{mn}$$

$$\sqrt[n]{x^m} = x^{m \div n}$$

Try this sample question.

S-6 Evaluate $(2a^2b^5)^3$.

A $6a^5b^8$

B $6a^6b^{15}$

C $8a^5b^8$

D $8a^6b^{15}$

Cube each part: $2^3 = 8$, $(a^2)^3 = a^6$, and $(b^5)^3 = b^{15}$. In choices A and B, the number 2 was multiplied by 3 instead of raised to the 3rd power. In choices A and C, the exponents were added instead of multiplied. Choice D is correct.

Finding the Root of a Monomial

To take the square root of a monomial, take the square root of the number (if there is one), and divide any exponents by 2. For example, $\sqrt{9x^8} = 3x^4$.

> The square root of x is the number that must be squared to get x. For example, $\sqrt{25} = 5$ because $5^2 = 25$.

Try this sample question.

S-7 Evaluate $\sqrt{16x^6y^{10}}$.

A $4x^3y^5$

B $4x^4y^8$

C $8x^3y^5$

D $8x^4y^8$

Find the square root of each part: $\sqrt{16} = 4$, $\sqrt{x^6} = x^3$, and $\sqrt{y^{10}} = y^5$. You can check by squaring the answer and seeing that the result is the expression inside the square root: $(4x^3y^5)^2 = 16x^6y^{10}$. In choices C and D, the square root of 16 was found by dividing by 2, which is not correct. Instead, $\sqrt{16} = 4$ because $4^2 = 16$. In choices B and D, the exponents were decreased by 2, instead of divided by 2. Choice A is correct.

To find the nth root of a monomial, take the nth root of the number (if there is one), and then divide any exponents by n. For example, $\sqrt[3]{64a^{12}b^3} = 4a^4b$, because $\sqrt[3]{64} = 4$, $\sqrt[3]{a^{12}} = a^4$, and $\sqrt[3]{b^3} = b$.

> The nth root of x is the number that must be raised to the nth power to get x. For example, $\sqrt[3]{8} = 2$ because $2^3 = 2 \cdot 2 \cdot 2 = 8$.

Try this sample question.

S-8 Evaluate $\sqrt[4]{x^8y^{20}z^4}$.

A $x^2y^5z^0$

B x^2y^5z

C $x^4y^{16}z^0$

D $x^4y^{16}z$

Divide each exponent by 4 to find the answer. In choices A and C, the fourth root of z^4 was written as z^0 instead of z^1, or simply z. In choices C and D, the exponents were decreased by 4, instead of divided by 4. Choice B is correct.

IT'S YOUR TURN

Read each problem. Circle the letter of the best answer.

1. Evaluate $(10x^4y^3)(3x^2y)$.

   A $30x^6y^3$

   B $30x^6y^4$

   C $30x^8y^3$

   D $30x^8y^4$

2. Simplify:

   $$(x^3y^4)^2 =$$

   A x^5y^4

   B x^6y^8

   C x^6y^{16}

   D x^9y^{16}

3. Which expression is equivalent to $m^3 \cdot m^2 \cdot m^6$?

   A m^{11}

   B m^{22}

   C m^{30}

   D m^{36}

4. Simplify:

   $$\sqrt{4a^8b^2} =$$

   A $2a^4b$

   B $2a^4b^4$

   C $16a^4b$

   D $16a^4b^4$

5. Evaluate:

   $$32x^9 \div 8x^3 =$$

   A $4x^3$

   B $4x^6$

   C $4x^{12}$

   D $4x^{27}$

6. Which expression has the same value as $\left(\frac{n^4}{n^2}\right)^3$?

   A n^2

   B n^5

   C n^6

   D n^{10}

7. Which expression has the same value as the one below?

   $$(a^3 \cdot b^5)^6$$

   A ab^{14}

   B ab^{48}

   C $a^9 \cdot b^{11}$

   D $a^{18} \cdot b^{30}$

Read each problem. Write your answers.

8. Simplify:

$$(3ab^7)^4 =$$

Answer: ____________

9. What is the value of this expression? Do not use negative exponents in your answer.

$$\frac{q^2 \cdot q^4}{q^{10}}$$

Answer: ____________

10. Simplify:

$$\frac{(x^3y^6)(xy^2)}{x^4y^4} =$$

Answer: ____________

11. Simplify:

$$\sqrt[3]{216m^9n^{30}}$$

Answer: ____________

LESSON 3

Multiplying and Dividing Polynomials

Standard A1.4.2

Multiplying Polynomials

To multiply polynomial expressions, multiply each term in the first polynomial by each term in the second polynomial. Then combine like terms, if needed, to simplify the resulting polynomial expression. For example:

$$\begin{aligned}(4x + 3)(x - 2) &= 4x(x - 2) + 3(x - 2)\\ &= 4x^2 - 8x + 3x - 6\\ &= 4x^2 - 5x - 6\end{aligned}$$

Now try this sample question.

S-1 The length of a rectangle is $5x + 1$ units long. The width of the rectangle is $2x + 5$ units long. What is the area, in square units, of the rectangle?

A $7x^2 + 6$

B $10x^2 + 5$

C $10x^2 + 7x + 5$

D $10x^2 + 27x + 5$

The area of a rectangle is length × width. So, the area of this rectangle is $(5x + 1)(2x + 5)$. To find the area, multiply each term in $5x + 1$ by each term in $2x + 5$.

$$\begin{aligned}(5x + 1)(2x + 5) &= 5x(2x + 5) + 1(2x + 5)\\ &= 10x^2 + 25x + 2x + 5\end{aligned}$$

Combine like terms. This gives $10x^2 + 27x + 5$. Choice D is correct.

Dividing Polynomials

Sometimes you may be asked to divide a polynomial expression by a monomial expression. Each term of the polynomial expression must be divided by the monomial.

In the example below, the monomial $4p$ divides each term of the polynomial, creating separate fractions. Then common terms are canceled within each fraction to simplify the expression.

$$\begin{aligned}\frac{16p^5 - 4p^3 - 12p^2}{4p} &= \frac{16p^5}{4p} - \frac{4p^3}{4p} - \frac{12p^2}{4p}\\ &= 4p^4 - p^2 - 3p\end{aligned}$$

When multiplying variable terms with like bases, add the exponents.

$$x^5 \cdot x^2 = x^{5+2} = x^7$$

When dividing variable terms with like bases, subtract the exponents.

$$x^5 \div x^2 = x^{5-2} = x^3$$

Try the sample question below.

S-2 What is the simplified form of the expression below?

$$(9x^4 + 6x^3 - 15x^2) \div 3x^2$$

A $3x^2 + 2x - 5$

B $6x^2 + 3x - 12$

C $3x^2 + 6x^3 - 15x^2$

D $6x^2 + 6x^3 - 15x^2$

This item can be rewritten as the sum and difference of separate fractions:

$$\frac{9x^4}{3x^2} + \frac{6x^3}{3x^2} - \frac{15x^2}{3x^2}$$

Simplifying each fraction gives $3x^2 + 2x - 5$. Choice A is correct.

IT'S YOUR TURN

Read each problem. Circle the letter of the best answer.

1. Which expression represents the product of $2xy$ and $3xy + 5y - xy^2$?

   A $5xy + 5y - xy^2$

   B $6xy + 10y - 2xy^2$

   C $5xy^2 + 7xy - 2xy^3$

   D $6x^2y^2 + 10xy^2 - 2x^2y^3$

2. The area of a triangle equals $\frac{1}{2} \cdot$ base $\cdot$ height. A triangle has an area of $8m^2 + 12m$ square units. The height of the triangle is $2m$ units. Which expression represents the base of the triangle?

   A $2m + 3$

   B $8m + 12$

   C $4m^2 + 6m$

   D $16m^3 + 24m^2$

3. $5y^2(8y^3 - 2y^2 + 7y) =$

   A $13y^5 + 3y^4 + 12y^3$

   B $13y^6 + 3y^4 + 12y^2$

   C $40y^5 - 10y^4 + 35y^3$

   D $40y^6 - 10y^4 + 35y^2$

4. $\frac{20x^8 + 16x^7 - 4x^6}{4x^6} =$

   A $5x^2 + 4x - 1$

   B $5x^2 + 16x - 4$

   C $16x^2 + 12x - 1$

   D $16x^2 + 16x - 4$

5. $(5x + 3)(x^2 - x - 4) =$

   A $5x^3 - 3x - 4$

   B $5x^3 - 3x - 12$

   C $5x^3 - 2x^2 - 23x - 12$

   D $5x^3 + 3x^2 - 20x - 12$

Read each problem. Write your answers.

6. $\dfrac{15y^7 + 12y^6 - 9y^5}{3y^3} =$

Answer: ______________________

7. Write an expression in simplest form that represents the area of the square shown below.

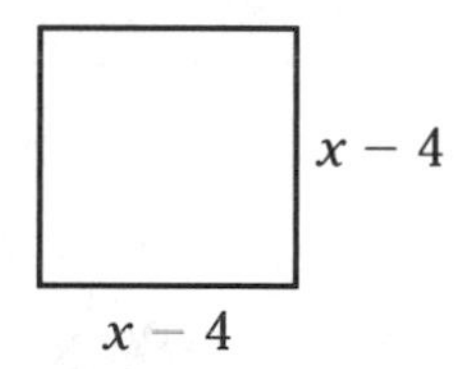

Answer: ______________________

LESSON 4 Factoring Algebraic Expressions

Standard A1.4.3

Using GCF to Factor

The **greatest common factor** (GCF) can be used when factoring an expression with variables, or unknown values. The GCF is the greatest factor that evenly divides into a set of numbers or terms.

For example, to find the GCF of the expression $6x^3 - 12x^2$, first list all prime factors of each term. This includes breaking down variables into prime factors. For a variable raised to a power, n, just like with whole numbers raised to a power, the prime factors are the product of the variable by itself n times.

$$6x^3 = \mathbf{2} \cdot \mathbf{3} \cdot \boldsymbol{x} \cdot \boldsymbol{x} \cdot x$$
$$12x^2 = \mathbf{2} \cdot 2 \cdot \mathbf{3} \cdot \boldsymbol{x} \cdot \boldsymbol{x}$$

Look for common factors between the two terms. Both $6x^3$ and $12x^2$ have these factors in common: **2, 3, *x*,** and ***x***. The GCF is the product of these factors: $2 \cdot 3 \cdot x \cdot x$, or $6x^2$.

The GCF for a set of variable terms is each variable raised to its smallest exponent. For example, the GFC of m^2n^5 and m^3n is m^2n.

Try this sample question.

S-1 What is the GCF of the expression $9p^5q + 6p^4q^2 - 15p^2q^4$?

A $3p^2q$

B $6p^2q^2$

C $30p^5q^2$

D $90p^5q^4$

There are three terms in this expression, and the prime factors of each term are:

$$9p^5q = \mathbf{3} \cdot 3 \cdot \boldsymbol{p} \cdot \boldsymbol{p} \cdot p \cdot p \cdot p \cdot \boldsymbol{q}$$
$$6p^4q^2 = 2 \cdot \mathbf{3} \cdot \boldsymbol{p} \cdot \boldsymbol{p} \cdot p \cdot p \cdot \boldsymbol{q} \cdot q$$
$$15p^2q^4 = \mathbf{3} \cdot 5 \cdot \boldsymbol{p} \cdot \boldsymbol{p} \cdot \boldsymbol{q} \cdot q \cdot q \cdot q$$

The common factors in all three terms are $\mathbf{3} \cdot \boldsymbol{p} \cdot \boldsymbol{p} \cdot \boldsymbol{q}$, or $3p^2q$. Choice A is correct.

The GCF can be used when factoring algebraic expressions. The GCF divides each term. The product of that result and the GCF is the fully factored form.

To check that an expression is factored correctly, multiply the factored form. The result should be the original expression.

For example, in $ab^2 + ab$, the GCF of each term is ab. When ab divides each term, the result is $\frac{ab^2}{ab} + \frac{ab}{ab} = b + 1$. The factored form, then, is $ab(b + 1)$.

Now try this question.

S-2 What is the factored form of the expression below?

$$40x^4y^3 - 25x^2y^2 - 50x^3y^2$$

A $5x^2y^2(8x^2y - 5 - 10x)$

B $5x^2y^2(8x^2y - 5xy - 10x)$

C $5xy(8x^2y - 25xy - 50x^2y)$

D $5xy(8x^4y^3 - 5x^2y^2 - 10x^3y^2)$

First find the GCF of each term. Start by listing the prime factors of 40, 25, and 50:

$40 = 2 \cdot 2 \cdot 2 \cdot \mathbf{5}$

$25 = \mathbf{5} \cdot 5$

$50 = 2 \cdot \mathbf{5} \cdot 5$ The common factor in all three numbers is 5.

To find the GCF of each variable part, look for the variables with the smallest exponents. In $40x^4y^3 - 25x^2y^2 - 50x^3y^2$, the x variable with the smallest exponent is x^2. The y variable with the smallest exponent is y^2. So the GCF of the expression is $5x^2y^2$.

Divide the GCF into each term:

$$\frac{40x^4y^3}{5x^2y^2} - \frac{25x^2y^2}{5x^2y^2} - \frac{50x^3y^2}{5x^2y^2} = 8x^2y - 5 - 10x$$

The factored form is $5x^2y^2(8x^2y - 5 - 10x)$. Choice A is correct.

Factoring by Grouping

Some algebraic expressions having four or more terms can be factored by **grouping** terms together. For example, consider the expression $6k^2 - 4k + 3k - 2$. This can be factored by grouping the first two terms and the last two terms together:

$(6k^2 - 4k) + (3k - 2) = 2k(3k - 2) + 1(3k - 2)$ Factor each grouping.

$= (3k - 2)(2k + 1)$ Factor $3k - 2$ from each resulting term.

Try the sample question below.

S-3 What is the factored form of the expression below?

$$12z^3 + 10z^2 - 30z - 25$$

A $(6z - 5)(2z^2 + 5)$

B $(6z + 5)(2z^2 - 5)$

C $(6z^2 + 5)(2z - 5)$

D $(6z^2 - 5)(2z + 5)$

Group the first two terms and the last two terms together. Then factor each set of terms:

$$(12z^3 + 10z^2) + (-30z - 25) = 2z^2(6z + 5) - 5(6z + 5)$$

Now factor $6z + 5$ from the resulting expression:

$$2z^2(6z + 5) - 5(6z + 5) = (6z + 5)(2z^2 - 5)$$

Choice B is correct.

Difference of Two Squares

Look at what happens when $x + 3$ multiplies $x - 3$.

$$(x + 3)(x - 3) = x^2 - 3x + 3x - 9 = x^2 - 9$$

The result is a **difference of two squares,** since x^2 and 9 are both perfect squares. To factor a polynomial that is the difference of two squares, follow this rule:

- For any real numbers a and b, $a^2 - b^2 = (a + b)(a - b)$.

For example, $25h^2 - 4k^2 = (5h + 2k)(5h - 2k)$.

Polynomials of the form $a^2 + b^2$ cannot be factored the same way as polynomials of the form $a^2 - b^2$.

Try this sample question.

S-4 Which shows the factored form of the expression below?

$$2y^2 - 50$$

A $2(y + 5)(y - 5)$

B $2(y + 25)(y - 25)$

C $(2y + 5)(2y - 5)$

D $(2y + 25)(2y - 25)$

First factor out the common factor 2. This results in $2(y^2 - 25)$. Next factor the difference of two squares and include the 2 that was factored out first. This results in $2(y + 5)(y - 5)$. Choice A is correct.

IT'S YOUR TURN

Read each problem. Circle the letter of the best answer.

1. Which expression shows the factored form of $a^2b^5 + a^3b^3$?

   A $a^2b^3(b^2 + a)$

   B $a^2b^3(1 + ab^2)$

   C $a^3b^3(b^2 + 1)$

   D $a^2b^5(1 + ab^2)$

2. Which expression is equivalent to $80hj + 64h^2j^2 + 36h^2j$?

   A $4hj(20 + 16hj + 9j)$

   B $4hj(20 + 16hj + 9h)$

   C $8hj(10 + 8hj + 4h)$

   D $8hj(10hj + 8h^2j^2 + 4h)$

3. Which shows the simplified form of the expression below?

   $$90y^4 - 120y - 360y^3 + 30y^2$$

   A $30y(y + 4)(y^2 - 3)$

   B $30y(y + 4)(3y^2 - 1)$

   C $30y(y - 4)(y^2 + 3)$

   D $30y(y - 4)(3y^2 + 1)$

4. A square has an area equal to $4s^2 - 1$ square units. Which expression represents the product of each side of the square?

   A $(s + 1)(4s - 1)$

   B $(2s + 1)(2s - 1)$

   C $(4s + 1)(s - 1)$

   D $(4s + 1)(4s - 1)$

5. Which shows the factored form of the expression below?

   $$100 - p^{16}$$

   A $(10 + p^4)(10 - p^4)$

   B $(100 + p^4)(100 - p^4)$

   C $(10 + p^8)(10 - p^8)$

   D $(10 + p^{16})(10 - p^{16})$

Read the problem. Write your answer.

6. What is the factored form of the expression below?

   $$20w - 5 - w^2 + 4w^3$$

Answer: ____________________

LESSON 5

Factoring Trinomials

Standard A1.4.3

Factoring Trinomials of the Form $x^2 + bx + c$

A **trinomial** is a polynomial with exactly three terms. The general form of a trinomial is $ax^2 + bx + c$, where a, b, and c are real numbers. You can factor trinomials by combining factors of the first and last terms that add to equal the middle term.

Consider the trinomial $x^2 + 6x + 8$. Here, $a = 1$, $b = 6$, and $c = 8$. To factor trinomials where $a = 1$, follow these steps.

Find factors of c that add to equal b. In $x^2 + 6x + 8$, find factors of 8 that add to 6.

Factors	Sum of Factors
1 and 8	$1 + 8 = 9$
2 and 4	$2 + 4 = 6$ ✓

The factors 2 and 4 add to 6.

Then write the factors of the trinomial using parentheses.

$$x^2 + 6x + 8 = (x + 2)(x + 4)$$

Notice that the first factors inside each set of parentheses, x, multiply to equal the first term, x^2. You can check that the entire trinomial is factored correctly by multiplying the two factors together. The result should be the original trinomial. Check:

$$(x + 2)(x + 4) = x^2 + 4x + 2x + 8 = x^2 + 6x + 8$$

Try this sample question.

S-1 Which shows the factored form of $x^2 - 5x - 24$?

A $(x - 3)(x + 8)$

B $(x + 3)(x - 8)$

C $(x - 12)(x + 2)$

D $(x + 12)(x - 2)$

In this trinomial, $a = 1$, $b = -5$, and $c = -24$. Since $a = 1$, find factors of -24 that add to equal -5.

Factors	Sum of Factors	Factors	Sum of Factors
1 and -24	$1 + (-24) = -23$	-1 and 24	$-1 + 24 = 23$
2 and -12	$2 + (-12) = -10$	-2 and 12	$-2 + 12 = 10$
3 and -8	$3 + (-8) = -5$ ✓	-3 and 8	$-3 + 8 = 5$
4 and -6	$4 + (-6) = -2$	-4 and 6	$-4 + 6 = 2$

The factors 3 and -8 multiply to equal -24 and add to equal -5. The factored form, then, of $x^2 - 5x - 24$ is $(x + 3)(x - 8)$. Choice B is correct.

Factors of trinomials can be found using area models shaped like rectangles. The dimensions of the rectangle represent the factors of the trinomial. An example of how to find the factors of a trinomial presented as a rectangular area model follows.

S-2 The area of the rectangle shown below is $x^2 + 6x + 3x + 18$.

	l	
w	x^2	$6x$
	$3x$	18

What are the dimensions, l and w, of this rectangle?

A $l = x + 3$ and $w = x + 9$

B $l = x + 6$ and $w - x + 3$

C $l = x + 6$ and $w = x + 18$

D $l = x + 9$ and $w = x + 18$

Combine like terms in the expression for the area:

$$x^2 + 6x + 3x + 18 = x^2 + 9x + 18$$

Then find factors of 18 that add to equal 9.

Factors	Sum of Factors
6 and 3	$6 + 3 = 9$

The factors 6 and 3 multiply to equal 18 and add to equal 9. The factored form of the area of the rectangle, then, is $(x + 6)(x + 3)$. The length is $x + 6$ and the width is $x + 3$. Choice B is correct.

You can check that these dimensions are correct by recreating the area model of the rectangle. Start with the possible dimensions written outside the large rectangle. Then multiply the factors and fill in the corresponding smaller rectangles inside the large rectangle.

	x	$+6$
x		
$+3$		

means

	x	$+6$
x	x^2	$+6x$
$+3$	$+3x$	$+18$

This area inside this rectangle matches the given rectangle, so the factors are correct.

Factoring Trinomials of the Form $ax^2 + bx + c$

Not all trinomials will have a first term with $a = 1$. Consider the trinomial $5x^2 + 13x + 6$. To factor such a trinomial, factors of both a and c must be combined to add to b. In this trinomial, $a = 5$ and $c = 6$. Look for factors of 5 and 6 that combine to equal 13.

Factors of 5	Factors of 6	Combinations of Factors
1 and 5	1 and 6	$1 \cdot 1 + 5 \cdot 6 = 1 + 30 = 31$
	6 and 1	$1 \cdot 6 + 5 \cdot 1 = 6 + 5 = 11$
	2 and 3	$1 \cdot 2 + 5 \cdot 3 = 2 + 15 = 17$
	3 and 2	$1 \cdot 3 + 5 \cdot 2 = 3 + 10 = 13$ ✓

The only factors of 5 are 1 and 5. Place these in the first term of each set of parentheses:

$(1x + \quad)(5x + \quad)$

The factors of 6 that combine with the factors of 5 are 3 and 2. Since 1 multiplies 3, 3 is placed in the parentheses ***not*** containing $1x$. Since 5 multiplies 2, 2 is placed in the parentheses ***not*** containing $5x$. So, $5x^2 + 13x + 6 = (1x + 2)(5x + 3) = (x + 2)(5x + 3)$.

Now try this sample question.

S-3 Which shows the factored form of $2x^2 + x - 28$?

A $(x - 2)(2x + 14)$

B $(x + 2)(2x - 14)$

C $(x - 4)(2x + 7)$

D $(x + 4)(2x - 7)$

In this trinomial, $a = 2$, $b = 1$, and $c = -28$. Since $a \neq 1$, find factors of both 2 and -28 that add to equal +1.

Factors	Combinations of Factors	
1 and 2; 1 and -28	$1 \cdot 1 + 2 \cdot -28 = -55$	$1 \cdot -28 + 2 \cdot 1 = -26$
-1 and 28	$1 \cdot -1 + 2 \cdot 28 = 55$	$1 \cdot 28 + 2 \cdot -1 = 26$
1 and 2; 2 and -14	$1 \cdot 2 + 2 \cdot -14 = -26$	$1 \cdot -14 + 2 \cdot 2 = -10$
-2 and 14	$1 \cdot -2 + 2 \cdot 14 = 26$	$1 \cdot 14 + 2 \cdot -2 = 10$
1 and 2; 4 and -7	$1 \cdot 4 + 2 \cdot -7 = -10$	$1 \cdot -7 + 2 \cdot 4 = 1$ ✓
-4 and 7	$1 \cdot -4 + 2 \cdot 7 = 10$	$1 \cdot 7 + 2 \cdot -4 = -1$

The factors 1 and 2 from 2 and 4 and -7 from -28 combine to equal 1. So $2x^2 + x - 28$ factors to $(x + 4)(2x - 7)$. Choice D is correct.

IT'S YOUR TURN

Read each problem. Circle the letter of the best answer.

1. Which expression represents the factored form of $x^2 - 13x + 36$?

   A $(x - 4)(x - 9)$ C $(x + 9)(x - 4)$

   B $(x - 3)(x - 12)$ D $(x + 12)(x - 3)$

2. Which expression represents the factored form of $12x^2 + x - 6$?

   A $(2x + 3)(6x - 2)$

   B $(2x + 6)(6x - 1)$

   C $(3x + 2)(4x - 3)$

   D $(4x + 3)(3x - 2)$

3. What value of b makes the equation below true?

   $$9x^2 + bx - 10 = (3x - 5)(3x + 2)$$

   A -9 C 6

   B -6 D 9

4. Which expression shows the factored form of the area model shown below?

$3x^2$	$8x$
$15x$	40

   A $(x + 5)(3x + 8)$

   B $(x + 8)(3x + 5)$

   C $(x + 8)(3x + 15)$

   D $(x + 15)(3x + 8)$

5. What is the factored form of $a^2 - 12a + 20$?

   A $(a - 20)(a - 1)$

   B $(a - 10)(a - 2)$

   C $(a - 8)(a - 4)$

   D $(a - 5)(a - 4)$

Read the problem. Write your answer.

6. What is the value of b that makes the equation below true?

   $$x^2 + bx - 35 = (x + 5)(x - 7)$$

Answer: ____________

Polynomials Review

Read each problem. Circle the letter of the best answer.

1. What is the simplified form of the expression below?

$$5k^3 - 2k^2 + 7k - (3k^3 - k^2 + 4k)$$

A $2k^3 - k^2 + 3k$

B $2k^3 - 3k^2 + 3k$

C $2k^3 + k^2 + 11k$

D $2k^3 - 3k^2 + 11k$

2. Simplify:

$$\frac{24a^5b^3}{6a^7b} =$$

A $4a^2b^2$

B $4a^2b^3$

C $\frac{4b^2}{a^2}$

D $\frac{4b^3}{a^2}$

3. Simplify:

$$\sqrt[3]{27x^{12}} =$$

A $3x^4$

B $3x^9$

C $9x^4$

D $9x^9$

4. A square has a side length equal to $5x - 3y$ inches. What is the area of this square?

A $20x - 12y$ sq in.

B $25x^2 - 9y^2$ sq in.

C $25x^2 - 15xy - 9y^2$ sq in.

D $25x^2 - 30xy + 9y^2$ sq in.

5. The volume, in cubic centimeters, of a rectangular prism is $10x^6 - 15x^4 + 35x^2$. The height of the prism is $5x^2$ centimeters. Which expression represents the area, in square centimeters, of the base of this prism?

A $2x^3 - 3x^2 + 7$

B $2x^4 - 3x^2 + 7$

C $5x^3 - 10x^2 + 30$

D $5x^4 - 10x^2 + 30$

6. What is the greatest common factor of the expression below?

$$8x^2y^4 - 6x^3y^2 + 12x^2y^2$$

A $2x^2y^2$

B $2x^3y^4$

C $24x^2y^2$

D $24x^3y^4$

7. Which of these shows the factored form of the expression below?

$$45b^2 - 20$$

A $5(3b - 2)(3b + 2)$

B $5(3b - 2)(3b - 2)$

C $5(9b - 4)(9b + 4)$

D $5(9b - 4)(9b - 4)$

Read each problem. Circle the letter of the best answer.

8. An area model is shown below.

$6x^2$	$8x$
$3x$	4

m

Which expression represents the length of the side labeled m?

A $2x + 1$

B $2x + 4$

C $8x + 4$

D $6x^2 + 3x$

9. Simplify $(5a^2b^3)^4$.

A $20a^6b^7$

B $20a^8b^{12}$

C $625a^6b^7$

D $625a^8b^{12}$

10. Which expression is equivalent to the one shown below?

$$\frac{56h^4k^2}{12hk^3}$$

A $\frac{9h^3}{4k}$

B $\frac{9h^4}{4k}$

C $\frac{14h^3}{3k}$

D $\frac{14h^4}{3k}$

11. Which expression is equivalent to $a^5 \cdot a^4 \cdot a^3$?

A a^{12}

B a^{23}

C a^{27}

D a^{60}

Read each problem. Write your answers.

12. Factor $3x^2 - 11x + 6$ completely.

Answer: ____________________

13. Find the square root of $\sqrt{36x^{10}y^2}$.

Answer: ____________________

Read each problem. Write your answers.

14. Solve this expression.

$$\frac{(4m^2n^4)(7m^8n^2)}{m^5n^7}$$

Answer: ______________________

15. The outline of a rectangular blanket is shown below.

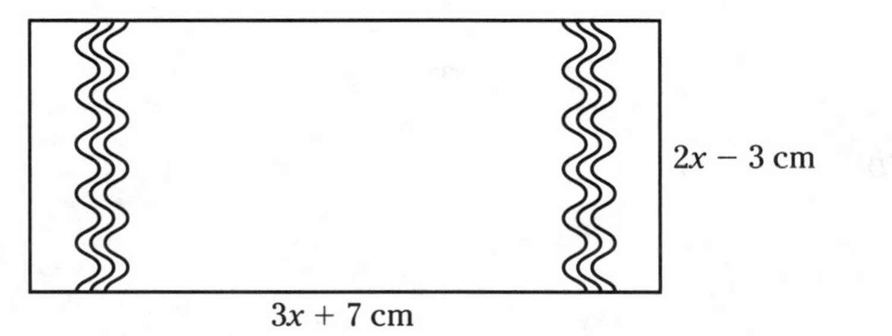

What is the perimeter, in centimeters, of the blanket?

Answer: ____________

What is the area, in square centimeters, of the blanket?

Answer: ______________________

Unit 5
Quadratic Equations and Functions

Not all algebraic equations are linear, which means not every equation's graph results in a straight line. Quadratic equations are a unique type of algebraic equation. You use many of the same skills you use to understand linear equations when solving quadratic equations. However, you must also use and understand new algebraic concepts, such as the quadratic formula. The graphs of quadratic equations are a different shape than you may be used to creating. When graphing a quadratic equation, you will learn to recognize its shape as a parabola.

There are six lessons in this unit:

1. **Solving Quadratic Equations** reviews solving quadratic equations by factoring.
2. **More Solving Quadratic Equations** reviews solving quadratic equations by completing the square.
3. **The Quadratic Formula** reviews the quadratic formula and how to use it to solve quadratic equations.
4. **Graphing Quadratic Equations** reviews identifying and creating graphs for quadratic equations.
5. **Zeros of a Quadratic Function** reviews the connections between the solutions of an equation, the zeros of a function, the x-intercepts of a graph, and the factors of a quadratic expression.
6. **Linear and Non-linear Graphs** reviews drawing and interpreting linear and non-linear graphs that represent given situations.

LESSON 1

Solving Quadratic Equations

Standards A1.5.2, 3

Solving Equations by Factoring

A **quadratic equation** results when a quadratic expression is set equal to a certain value. An example of a quadratic equation is $x^2 + 6x + 5 = 0$. You can solve this equation by factoring the quadratic expression and applying the zero product property.

> Remember to set quadratic equations equal to 0 before solving.

- **Zero Product Property:** For real numbers a and b, if $a \cdot b = 0$, then either $a = 0$ or $b = 0$.

For example, factoring $x^2 + 6x + 5 = 0$ gives $(x + 1)(x + 5) = 0$. According to the zero product property, either $x + 1 = 0$ or $x + 5 = 0$. So, $x = -1$ or $x = -5$.

Try this sample question.

S-1 What is the solution to the equation $3z^2 - 2 = 5z$?

A $z = \frac{1}{3}$ or $z = -2$

B $z = -\frac{1}{3}$ or $z = 2$

C $z = \frac{5}{3}$ or $z = -1$

D $z = -\frac{5}{3}$ or $z = 1$

Set the equation equal to 0 by subtracting $5z$ from each side.

$$3z^2 - 5z - 2 = 0$$

Factor the quadratic expression by finding factors of 3 and -2 that combine to equal -5.

Factors	Combinations of Factors	
1 and 3; 1 and -2	$1 \cdot 1 + 3 \cdot -2 = -5$ ✓	$1 \cdot -2 + 3 \cdot 1 = 1$
-1 and 2	$1 \cdot -1 + 3 \cdot 2 = 5$	$1 \cdot 2 + 3 \cdot -1 = -1$

The factors of -2 that combine with the factors of 3 are 1 and -2. Since $1z$ multiplies 1, these terms are placed in opposite factors. Likewise, since 3 multiplies -2, $3z$ is placed in the opposite factor as -2. So, $3z^2 - 5z - 2 = (3z + 1)(1z - 2)$ or $(3z + 1)(z - 2)$.

$$(3z + 1)(z - 2) = 0$$

Apply the zero product property by setting each separate factor equal to 0. Then solve for the variable.

$$3z + 1 = 0 \quad \text{or} \quad z - 2 = 0$$

$$z = -\frac{1}{3} \quad \text{or} \quad z = 2$$

Choice B is correct.

IT'S YOUR TURN

Read each problem. Circle the letter of the best answer.

1. What are the solutions to the equation below?

$$2x^2 - 5x - 12 = 0$$

A $x = \frac{2}{3}$ or $x = -4$

B $x = \frac{3}{2}$ or $x = -3$

C $x = -\frac{2}{3}$ or $x = 3$

D $x = -\frac{3}{2}$ or $x = 4$

2. What values of y represent the solution to the equation below?

$$2y^2 + 5y = 3y^2 - 2y - 18$$

A $y = -2$ or $y = 9$

B $y = -3$ or $y = 6$

C $y = -6$ or $y = 3$

D $y = -9$ or $y = 2$

Read the problem. Write your answers.

3. The area of the triangular sail shown below is 110 square feet.

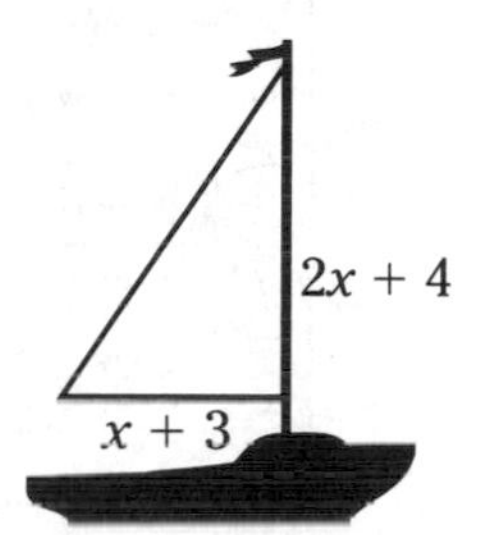

Write an equation for the area of the sail and solve for x.

Answer: ____________________

Explain how you know which value of x to use to find the area of the sail.

____

____

____

____

Read each problem. Fill in your answer on the response grid.

4. What value of n makes the equation below true? (Hint: There are two possible answers.)

$$(n + 1)(n + 3) = 15$$

5. The bottom of a rectangular swimming pool has an area of 216 square feet. The length of the swimming pool is 6 feet longer than its width.

$(x + 6)$ ft

x ft

$A = 216\text{ ft}^2$

What is the length in feet of the swimming pool?

LESSON 2

More Solving Quadratic Equations

Standards A1.5.2, 3

Solving Equations by Completing the Square

Sometimes quadratic equations cannot be solved easily by factoring. In these cases, another method known as **completing the square** can be used.

To solve an equation by completing the square, first write the equation in the form $x^2 + bx = c$. Then add the value $\left(\frac{b}{2}\right)^2$ to both sides of the equation. This results in a perfect square trinomial on one side and a constant on the other. Take the square roots of each side and solve for the variable.

A **perfect square trinomial** is in the form $x^2 + 2k + k^2$ and factors to the form $(x + k)^2$.

Look at the example below:

$x^2 - 6x - 80 = 0$	
$x^2 - 6x = 80$	Write the equation in the form $x^2 + bx = c$.
$x^2 - 6x + 9 = 80 + 9$	Add $\left(\frac{6}{2}\right)^2$, or 9, to both sides of the equation.
$(x - 3)^2 = 89$	Rewrite $x^2 - 6x + 9$ as a perfect square trinomial.
$\sqrt{(x - 3)^2} = \sqrt{89}$	Take the square root of both sides.
$x - 3 \approx \pm 9.4$	Simplify.
$x \approx 9.4 + 3$ or $x \approx -9.4 + 3$	Add 3 to both sides.
$x \approx 12.4$ or $x \approx -6.4$	Simplify.

Try these sample questions.

S-1 What value of k makes the expression below a perfect square trinomial?

$$x^2 - 16x + k$$

A 4

B 8

C 16

D 64

For $x^2 - 16x + k$ to be a perfect square trinomial, the value of $k = \left(\frac{-16}{2}\right)^2 = (-8)^2 = 64$. Choice D is correct.

S-2 Bridget solves the equation $2m^2 + 24m + 18 = 0$ by completing the square. Which equation can she use to solve this equation?

A $(m + 3)^2 = 21$

B $(m + 6)^2 = 27$

C $(m + 6)^2 = 45$

D $(m + 12)^2 = 135$

First divide each part by 2 to get an equivalent equation with a beginning coefficient of 1:

$$\frac{2m^2}{2} + \frac{24m}{2} + \frac{18}{2} = m^2 + 12m + 9$$

Write the left side of this equation as a perfect square trinomial:

$m^2 + 12m = -9$	Write the equation in $x^2 + bx = c$ form.
$m^2 + 12m + 36 = -9 + 36$	Add $\left(\frac{12}{2}\right)^2$, or 36, to both sides of the equation.
$(m + 6)^2 = 27$	Write $m^2 + 12m + 36$ as a perfect square trinomial.

Choice B is correct.

IT'S YOUR TURN

Read each problem. Circle the letter of the best answer.

1. What values of b make the expression $x^2 + bx + 81$ a perfect square trinomial?

A 9 and -9

B 18 and -18

C 81 and -81

D 162 and -162

2. What are the solutions to the equation below?

$$x^2 - 4x - 9 = 0$$

A $x \approx -0.2$ or $x \approx 4.2$

B $x \approx -4.2$ or $x \approx 0.2$

C $x \approx -5.6$ or $x \approx 1.6$

D $x \approx -1.6$ or $x \approx 5.6$

3. What are the solutions to $(x + 5)^2 = 121$?

A $x = 7$ or $x = -17$

B $x = 6$ or $x = -16$

C $x = -6$ or $x = 16$

D $x = -7$ or $x = 17$

4. Solve the equation below by completing the square.

$$x^2 - 14x - 95 = 0$$

A $x = 5$ or $x = -19$

B $x = -5$ or $x = 19$

C $x = 0.22$ or $x = 13.8$

D $x = -0.22$ or $x = -13.8$

Read each problem. Write your answers.

5. Solve this equation by completing the square.

$$3x^2 + 30x - 12 = 0$$

Answer: ______________________

6. A square has sides measuring $x + 3$. The area of the square is 49 square units.

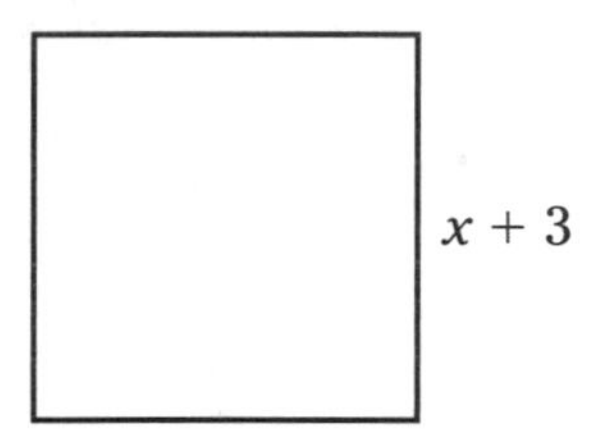

What is the value of x in this situation?

Answer: ___________

Explain how you know your answer is correct.

____

____

____

____

LESSON 3 

The Quadratic Formula

Standards A1.5.2, 3

Solving Equations by Using the Quadratic Formula

All quadratic equations can be solved by the **quadratic formula.** The quadratic formula is derived from the steps you take each time you solve a quadratic equation by completing the square.

- **The Quadratic Formula:** For any quadratic equation $ax^2 + bx + c = 0$ where $a \neq 0$, $x = \frac{-b \pm \sqrt{b^2 - 4ac}}{2a}$.

Consider the equation $3x^2 + x - 2 = 0$. In this equation, $a = 3$, $b = 1$, and $c = -2$. Use the quadratic formula to solve for x:

> Equations must be set equal to 0 before applying the quadratic formula.

$$x = \frac{-1 \pm \sqrt{1^2 - 4(3)(-2)}}{2(3)}$$

$$= \frac{-1 \pm \sqrt{1 - (-24)}}{6}$$

$$= \frac{-1 \pm \sqrt{25}}{6}$$

$$= \frac{-1 \pm 5}{6}$$

$$x = \frac{-1 + 5}{6} = \frac{2}{3} \text{ or } x = \frac{-1 - 5}{6} = -1$$

Try this sample question.

S-1 What are the solutions to the equation $6x^2 - 3x = 5$? Round to the nearest tenth.

Set the equation equal to 0 by subtracting 5 from each side:

$$6x^2 - 3x - 5 = 0$$

The equation cannot be easily factored, so use the quadratic formula to solve for x. Identify the values of a, b, and c:

$$a = 6, b = -3, c = -5$$

Substitute these values into the quadratic formula and solve for x. You can use a calculator to help compute the steps in the quadratic formula.

$$x = \frac{-(-3) \pm \sqrt{(-3)^2 - 4(6)(-5)}}{2(6)}$$

$$= \frac{3 \pm \sqrt{9 - (-120)}}{12}$$

$$= \frac{3 \pm \sqrt{129}}{12}$$

$$\approx \frac{3 \pm 11.358}{12}$$

$$x \approx \frac{3 + 11.358}{12} \approx 1.2 \text{ or } x \approx \frac{3 - 11.358}{12} \approx -0.7$$

The solutions to the equation are $x \approx 1.2$ or $x \approx -0.7$.

IT'S YOUR TURN

Read each problem. Circle the letter of the best answer.

1. Which values of x make the equation $x^2 + 10x + 7 = 12$ true?

   A $x = -5 \pm \sqrt{30}$

   B $x = 5 \pm \sqrt{30}$

   C $x = -5 \pm \sqrt{105}$

   D $x = 5 \pm \sqrt{105}$

2. The area of a rectangle is 75 square inches.

   - The length of the rectangle is $2x$ inches.
   - The width of the rectangle is $x + 6$ inches.

   Which of these equations can be used to solve for x?

   A $x = \frac{-2 \pm \sqrt{456}}{4}$

   B $x - \frac{-2 \pm \sqrt{744}}{2}$

   C $x = \frac{-12 \pm \sqrt{456}}{2}$

   D $x = \frac{-12 \pm \sqrt{744}}{4}$

3. A football is kicked into the air. The height of the football after t seconds is modeled by the equation below.

   $$h = -16t^2 + 50t + 5$$

   About how many seconds is the ball in the air before it touches the ground?

   A 1.67

   B 2.33

   C 3.22

   D 5.00

4. Solve for x:

   $$2x^2 + 7x = 4$$

   A $x = -4$ or $x = \frac{1}{2}$

   B $x = 4$ or $x = -\frac{1}{2}$

   C $x = \frac{-7 \pm \sqrt{17}}{4}$

   D $x = \frac{7 \pm \sqrt{17}}{4}$

Read each problem. Write your answers.

5. Use the quadratic formula to solve for x:

$$5x^2 = -4x + 2$$

Answer: ______________________

6. Solve this equation using the quadratic formula.

$$15x^2 + 7x = 4$$

Answer: ______________________

Read the problem. Write your answer.

7. Look at this quadratic equation.

$$5x^2 + 8x + 3 = 0$$

Solve the equation using the quadratic formula.

Answer: ______________________

Graphing Quadratic Equations

Standard A1.5.1

In the real world, not all graphs are straight lines. Many graphs of real-world phenomena are curves or combinations of lines and curves. These are known as **non-linear equations.** You can match the graph of a non-linear equation to a table by comparing points that lie on the graph with those in the table. Likewise, given a non-linear equation, you can make a table of values to compare against points found on its graph.

Graphing Quadratic Equations

The graph of a **quadratic equation** has a symmetric curved shape called a **parabola.**

To graph a quadratic equation, make a table of values by substituting values for x into the equation and solving for y. Then plot those points on a coordinate plane and draw the graph. For example, to graph $y = x^2$, you could make a table of values as shown below. Notice that the points in the table also lie on the graph of the equation.

$y = x^2$

x	y
0	0
1	1
−1	1
2	4
−2	4
3	9
−3	9

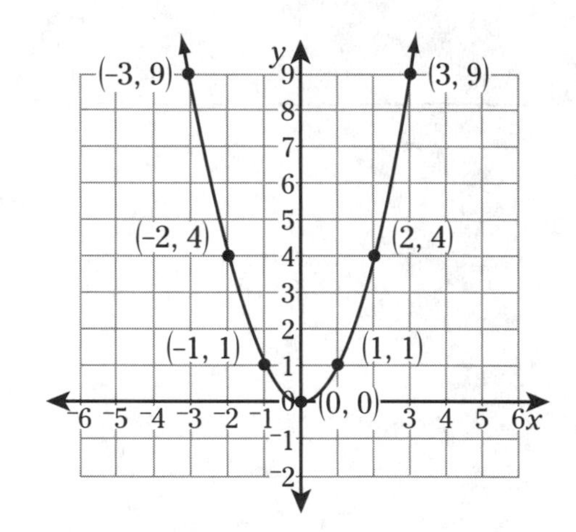

Try this sample question.

S-1 A company markets a new cell phone accessory. The equation $P = -50d^2 + 1{,}500d$ is used to predict the total monthly profit, P, of the accessory priced at d dollars. Which graph best models this equation?

A

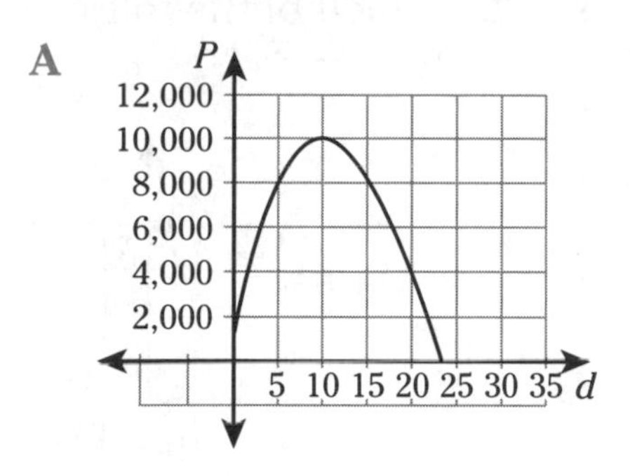

C

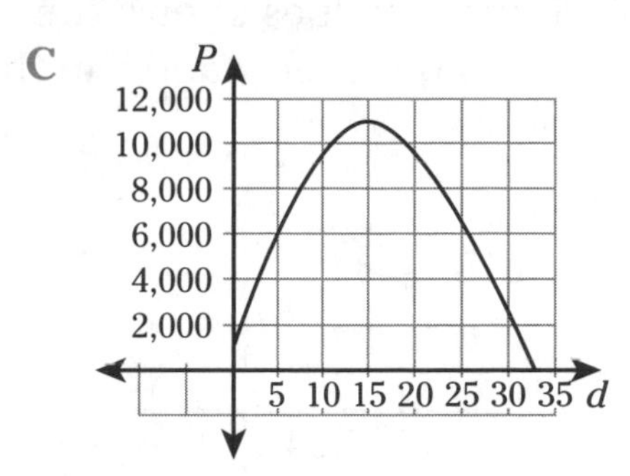

B

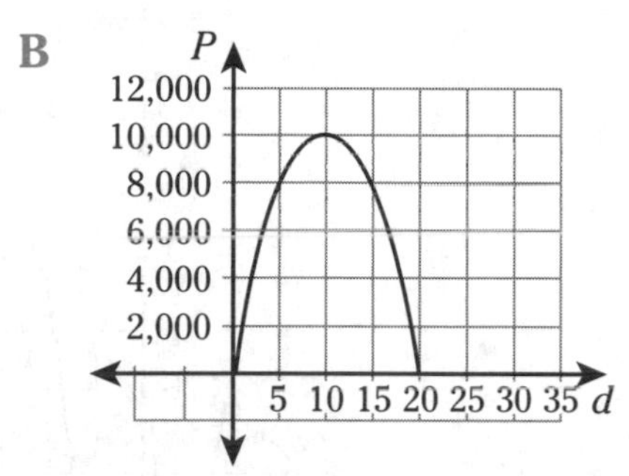

D

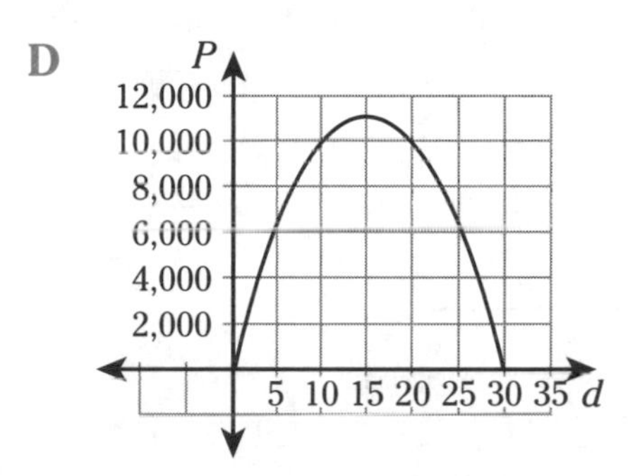

First make a table by choosing some values for d and plugging them into the given equation.

d	0	5	10	15	20
P	0	6,250	10,000	11,250	10,000

Find the graph that contains the same points from the table. The graph in choice D contains these points. Choice D is correct.

IT'S YOUR TURN

Read each problem. Circle the letter of the best answer.

1. Which table of values shows the relationship between x and y in the graph below?

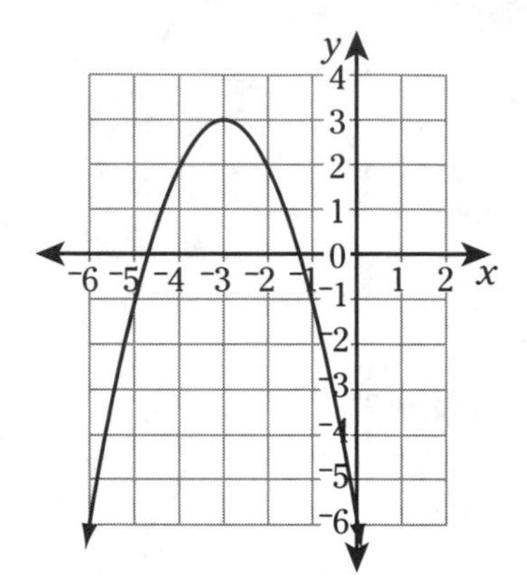

A

x	y
-4	-6
-3	-1
-2	2
-1	3

B

x	y
-4	2
-3	3
-2	2
-1	-1

C

x	y
-6	-4
-1	-3
2	-2
3	-1

D

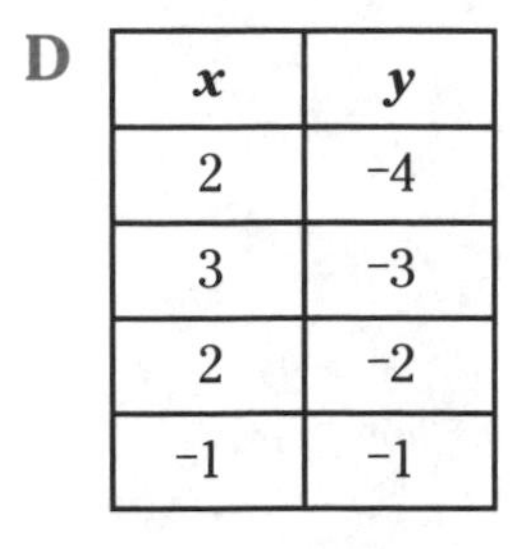

x	y
2	-4
3	-3
2	-2
-1	-1

2. Which of the following shows the graph for $y = 4x^2$?

A

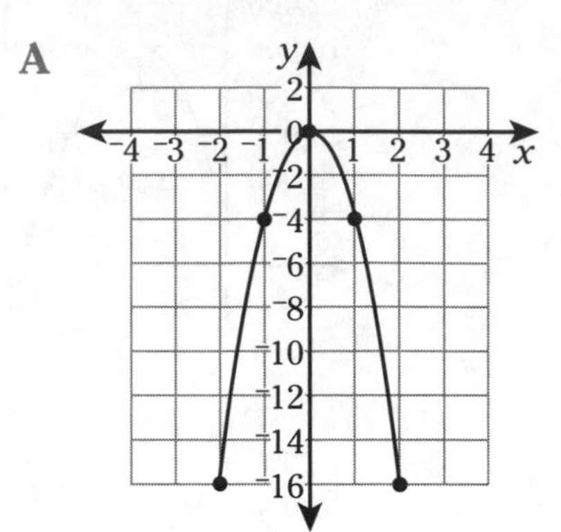

B

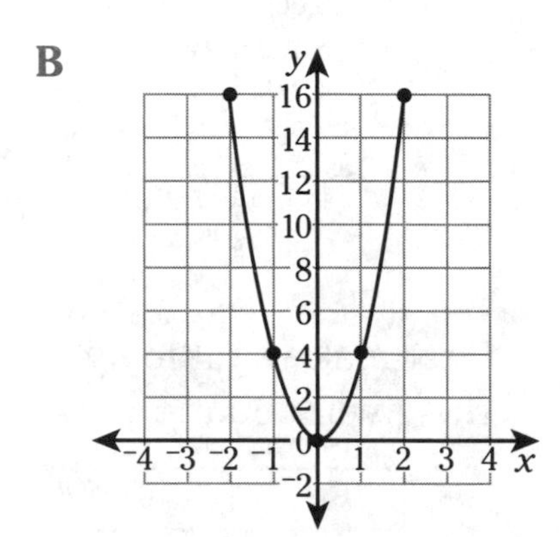

C

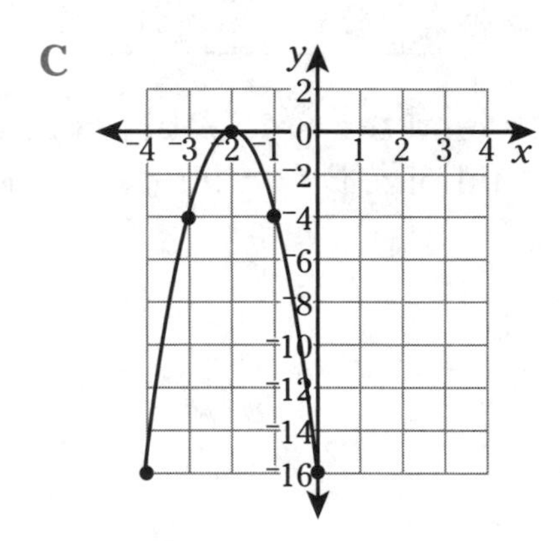

D

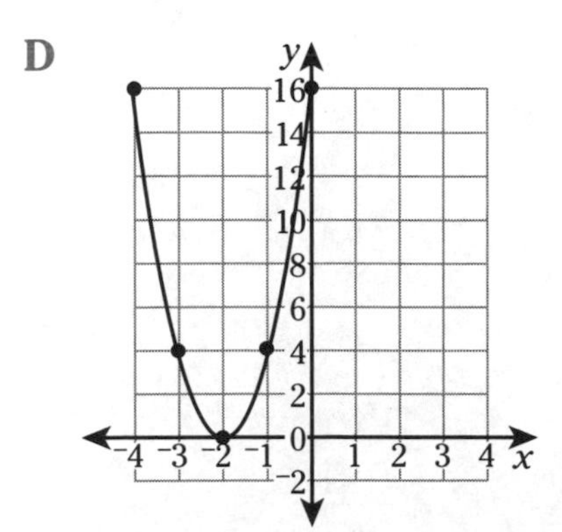

Read the problem. Write your answers.

3. Look at the quadratic equation below.

$$y = x^2 - 2x - 3$$

Complete the table of values for this quadratic equation.

x	3	2	1	0			
y							

Using your table of values, graph the quadratic equation on the coordinate plane below.

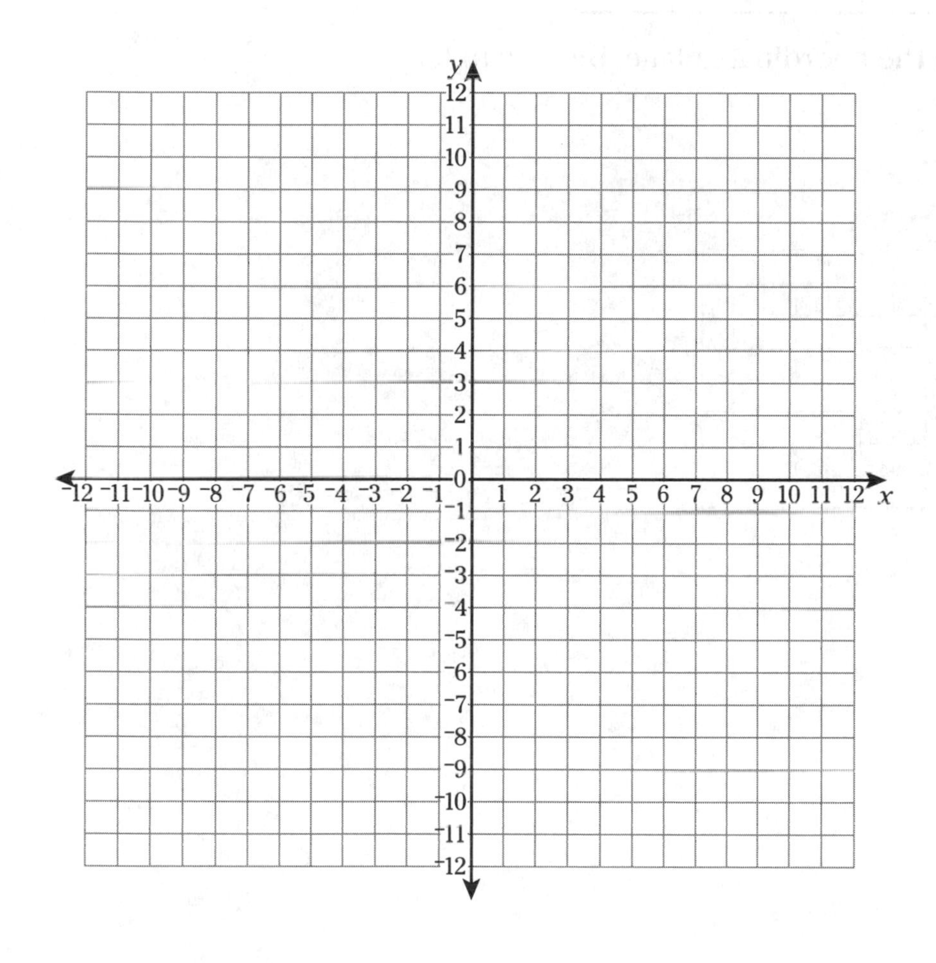

Read the problem. Write your answers.

4. Marty jumps from a diving board 15 feet from the surface of the water in a pool. His height, t seconds before he reaches the water, is modeled by the equation below.

$$h = -0.5t^2 + 0.5t + 15$$

Make a table of values to show Marty's height in feet 0, 1, 2, and 3 seconds after jumping from the diving board.

t				
h				

Graph this equation on the coordinate plane. Be sure to label each axis appropriately.

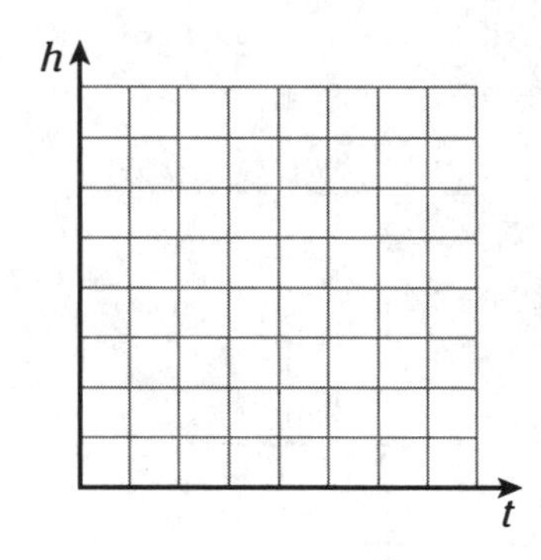

LESSON 5

Zeros of a Quadratic Function

Standard A1.5.4

Zeros of a Function

A **zero** of a function $f(x)$ is a value of x for which $f(x) = 0$. A zero of a function is also called a **root.** A quadratic function has either no zeros or two zeros.

Any solution of the equation $f(x) = 0$ is a zero (or root) of the function $f(x)$. This means you can find the zeros of a function by setting it equal to 0 and solving for the variable. For example, to find the zeros of $f(x) = x^2 + 4x - 12$, solve the equation $x^2 + 4x - 12 = 0$. Factoring this quadratic equation gives you $(x + 6)(x - 2) = 0$, so the solutions are $x = -6$ and $x = 2$. In other words, -6 and 2 are the zeros of the function $f(x) = x^2 + 4x - 12$.

Try this sample question.

S-1 What are the zeros of the function $g(x) = x^2 + 4x - 5$?

To find the zeros of $g(x) = x^2 + 4x - 5$, set the function equal to zero.

$$x^2 + 4x - 5 = 0$$

Factor the quadratic expression.

$$x^2 + 4x - 5 = (x - 4)(x - 1)$$

Set each factor equal to 0 and solve for x.

$$x - 4 = 0 \qquad x - 1 = 0$$
$$x = 4 \qquad x = 1$$

So this function is true when $x = 1$ and when $x = 4$. This function has two zeros: 1 and 4.

Zeros as x-intercepts

The zeros of a function are the x-intercepts of its graph. For example, the graph of the function $g(x) = x^2 + 4x - 5$ is a parabola that crosses the x-axis at the points (1, 0) and (4, 0). If you graph a function, you can find its zeros by finding its x-intercepts.

Suppose you use a graphing calculator to graph the function $f(x) = 2x^2 - 3x - 6$, as shown below.

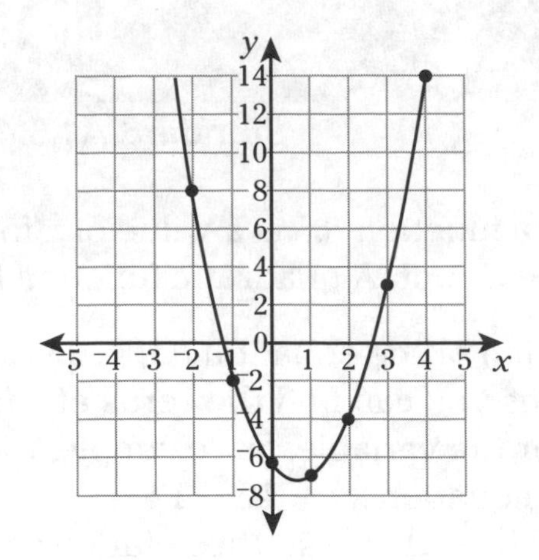

The x-intercepts of this function are the points where the graph crosses the x-axis: approximately (-1.14, 0) and (2.64, 0). So the zeros of $f(x)$ are -1.14 and 2.64.

Try this sample question.

S-2 Look at this function: $h(x) = -x^2 + 2x$.

Graph the equation on a coordinate plane.

What are the zeros of $h(x)$? Explain how you know.

First replace $h(x)$ with y, and write the equation as $y = -x^2 + 2x$. Use this equation to make a table of values, and sketch the graph on a coordinate plane.

x	y
-2	-8
-1	-3
0	0
1	1
2	0
3	-3
4	-8

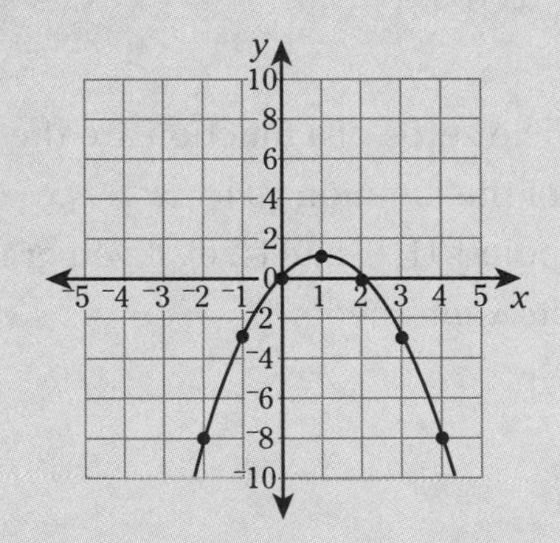

Next, look at the graph you made, and find the x-intercepts. They are (0, 0) and (2, 0). This means the zeros of $h(x)$ are 0 and 2. In other words, the value of $h(x)$ is 0 when $x = 0$ and when $x = 2$.

Zeros as Factors

If a function is a polynomial that can be factored, the zeros can be found using the factored form. For example, to find the zeros of the function $f(x) = 4x^2 - 36$, start by setting the equation equal to zero: $4x^2 - 36 = 0$. Factor out the 4 to get $4(x^2 - 9) = 0$. Then factor the difference of squares: $4(x + 3)(x - 3) = 0$. This means that $x + 3 = 0$ or $x - 3 = 0$. Solving these equations gives the two solutions: $x = -3$ and $x = 3$. So the zeros of $f(x) = 4x^2 - 36$ are -3 and 3. The graph of $f(x)$ has two x-intercepts: (-3, 0) and (3, 0).

Try this sample question.

S-3 What are the zeros of the function $p(x) = 2x^2 - 4x - 30$?

A -5 and 3

B -3 and 5

C -3

D 5

To find the zeros of $p(x)$, set the quadratic expression equal to zero, and solve for x by factoring the polynomial: $2x^2 - 4x - 30 = 0 \rightarrow (2x + 6)(x - 5) = 0$. If the product of two factors is 0, then one of the factors must be zero, so either $2x + 6 = 0$, or $x - 5 = 0$. Solving these equations gives two solutions: $x = -3$, and $x = 5$. This quadratic function has two zeros: -3 and 5. Choice B is correct.

IT'S YOUR TURN

Read each problem. Circle the letter of the best answer.

1. What are the zeros of the function $f(x) = x^2 + x - 20$?

   A -10 and 2

   B -5 and 4

   C -4 and 5

   D -2 and 10

2. What are the x-intercepts of the graph of the function $g(x) = x^2 - 6x + 8$?

   A (2, 0) and (-4, 0)

   B (-2, 0) and (4, 0)

   C (-2, 0) and (-4, 0)

   D (2, 0) and (4, 0)

Read the problem. Write your answers.

3. Look at the function below.

$$f(x) = 2x^2 - 3x - 10$$

Graph the function on the coordinate plane below.

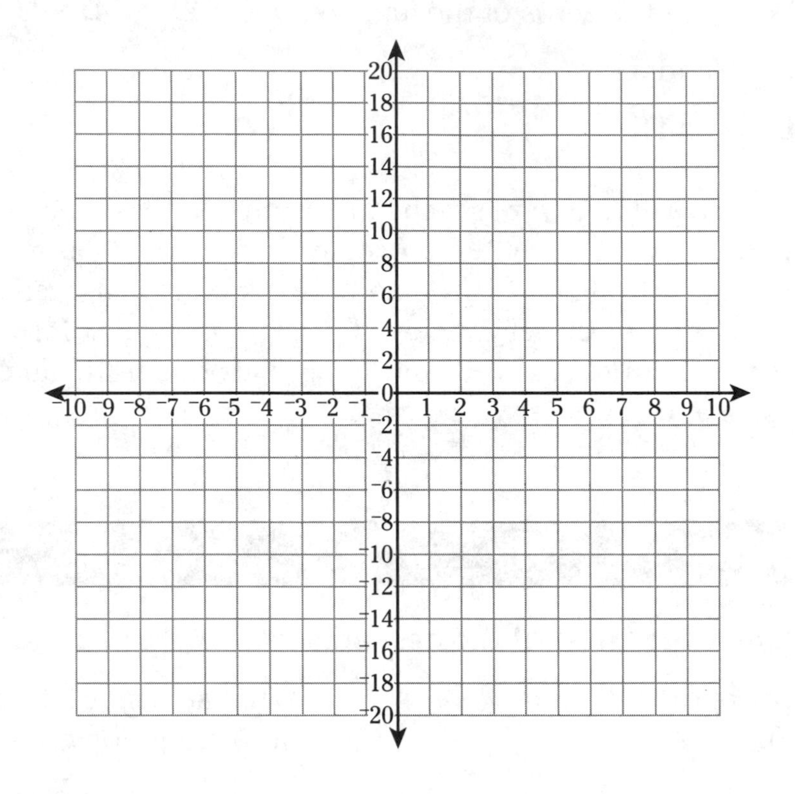

What are the approximate coordinates of the x-intercept(s) of the graph?

Answer: ______________________

What are the zero(s) of $f(x) = 2x^2 - 3x - 10$? Explain how you found your answer.

____

____

____

____

____

____

Read the problem. Write your answers.

4. Look at the function below.

$$g(x) = x^2 - 2x - 8$$

Use factoring to find the zeros of $g(x)$.

Answer: ____________

What are the x-intercepts of the graph of $g(x) = x^2 - 2x - 8$?

Answer: ________________________

LESSON 6

Linear and Non-linear Graphs

Standard A1.5.5

Understanding and using graphs that show quantitative relationships is an important real-life skill.

Representative Graphs

The relationship between two quantities can be represented on a graph. For example, suppose that hot dogs cost $2.00 each. The relationship between the number of hot dogs purchased and the total cost is shown by this graph:

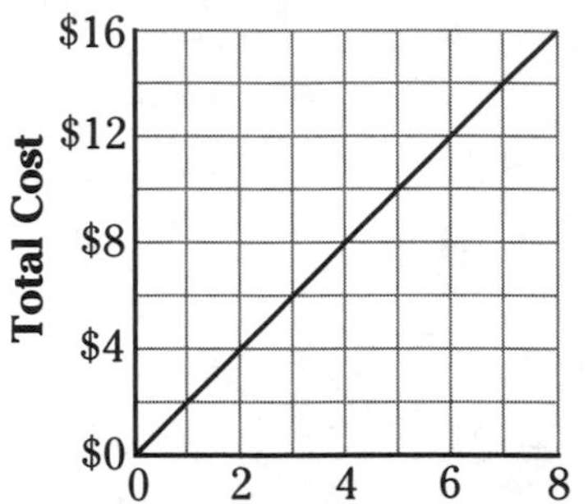

The number of hot dogs purchased is measured along the horizontal axis, and the total cost is measured along the vertical axis. The line sloping upward shows the relationship between the two quantities. For example, the line contains the point (5, $10) because 5 hot dogs would cost $10.

Try this sample question.

S-1 An airplane is traveling at 800 kilometers per hour. Which of the following graphs best shows the relationship between time and distance traveled for this airplane?

A 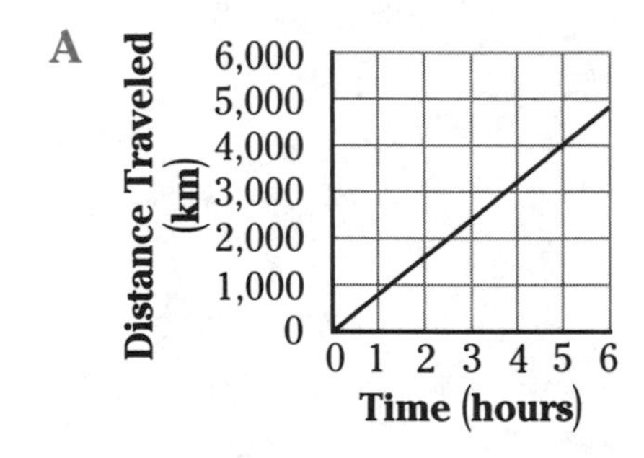

C 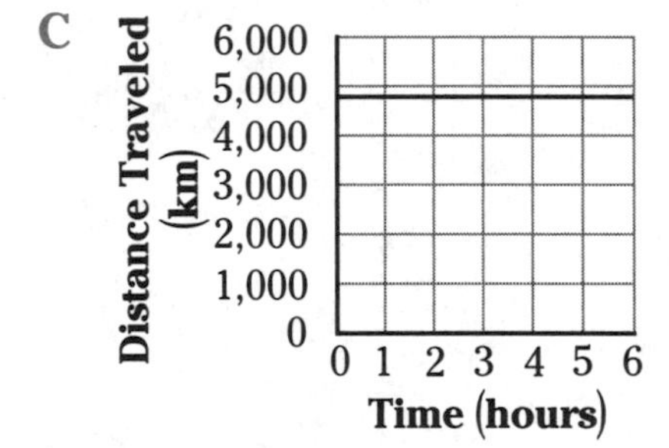

B 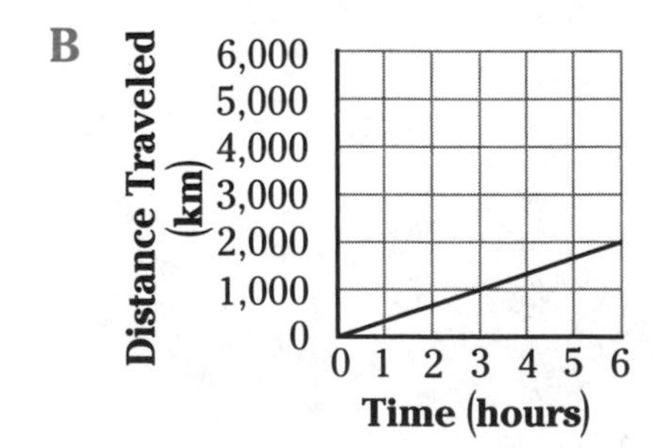

D 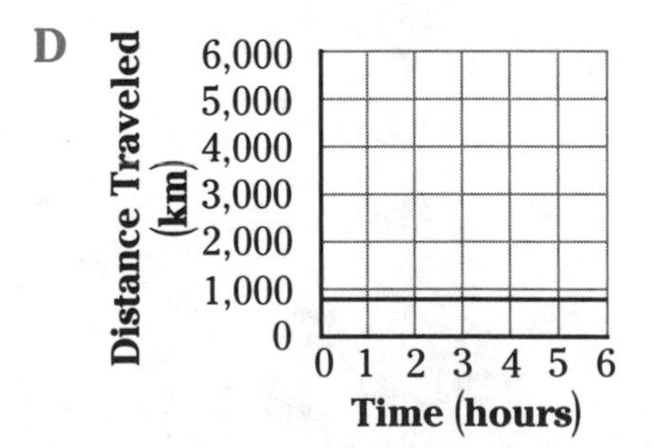

After 1 hour, the plane has traveled 800 km; after 2 hours, it has traveled 1,600 km; after 3 hours, it has traveled 2,400 km. The line in choice A contains each of these points. Choice A is correct.

A graph can also be used to show a relationship in very general terms. For example, suppose a mountain climber descended at a steady rate from a mountain peak. After an hour, she stopped to rest. Then she continued her descent. This situation is modeled by the graph below.

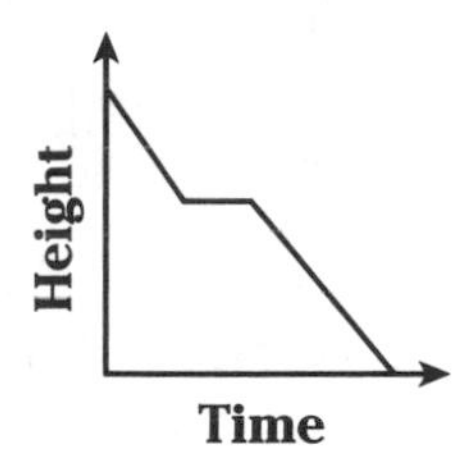

Interpreting Graphs

Sometimes you will need to be able to interpret the relationship on the graph. Then you need to understand what the graph shows.

Try these sample questions.

S-2 Mr. Bravo built a fire in his fireplace at 1:00 P.M. on a winter day. The graph shows how the temperature in his living room changed over time.

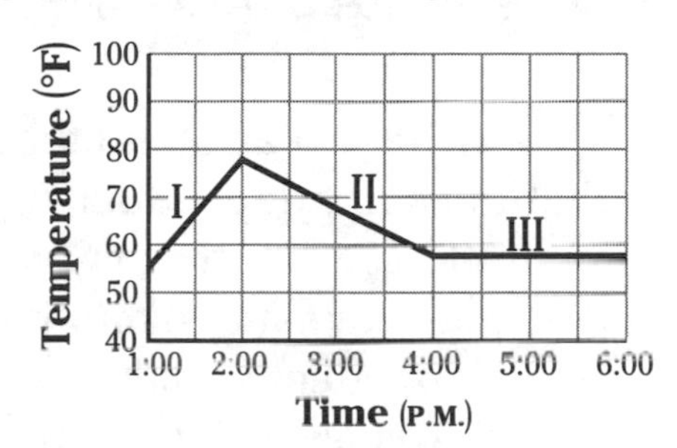

What does part III of the graph represent?

A the time before Mr. Bravo built the fire

B the time during which the room was warming up

C the time during which the room was cooling down

D the time after the fire was out

The graph shows the room temperature increasing from 1:00 P.M. to 2:00 P.M., decreasing from 2:00 P.M. to 4:00 P.M., and then remaining the same after 4:00 P.M. Choice D gives the only answer that makes sense.

S-3 Kelly hit a baseball. The height of the baseball is graphed below.

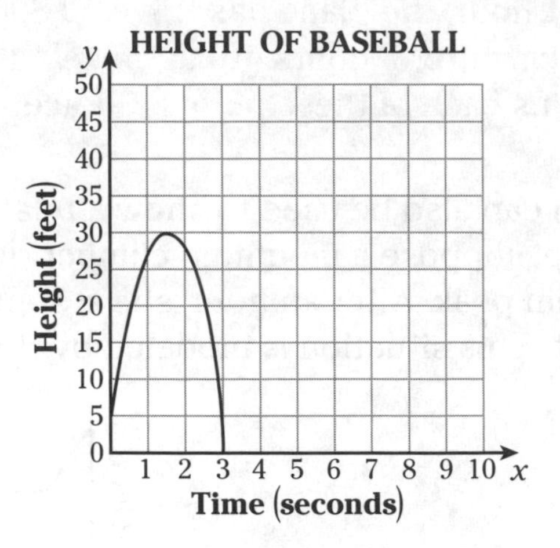

For how long was the ball more than 20 feet in the air?

A 0.5 second

B 1 second

C 1.5 seconds

D 2 seconds

At 0.5 second, the ball reached a height of 20 feet on its way up. At 2.5 seconds, the ball reached a height of 20 feet again, this time on its way down. The amount of time it was more than 20 feet in the air is given by the difference: 2.5 seconds − 0.5 second = 2 seconds. Choice D is correct.

Independent and Dependent Variables

In an equation, a variable can stand for any number. An **independent variable** has a value that does not depend on any other variable in the equation. Its value is not restricted by another variable. A **dependent variable,** in contrast, has a value that does depend on another variable. Its value is found only after a value for the independent variable is chosen. In equations such as $y = 3x + 2$ or $y = x^2 + 2x - 6$, y is always the dependent variable and x is the independent variable. In other words, the value of y is dependent on the value of x.

In some relationships, the variables are not given in terms of x and y; instead, they might be elements such as time and cost.

In this graph, the independent variable is time and the dependent variable is weight.

The puppy's weight increases as time passes. The increase is dependent on time passing. The passage of time is ***not*** dependent on the weight of the puppy increasing.

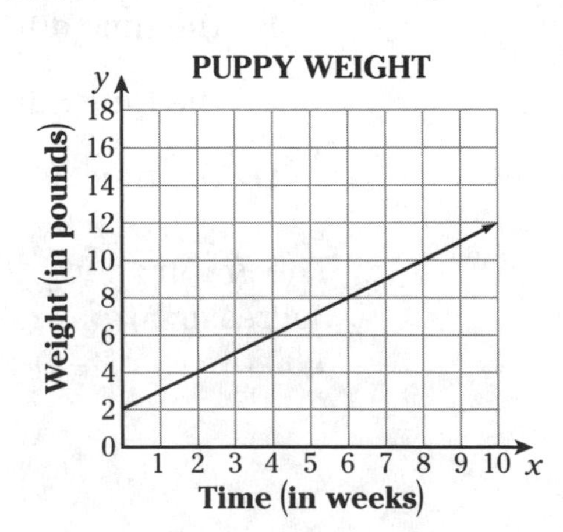

Try this sample question.

S-4 The formula for the perimeter of a square is $P = 4s$, where s = the length of one side. The graph below shows this relationship.

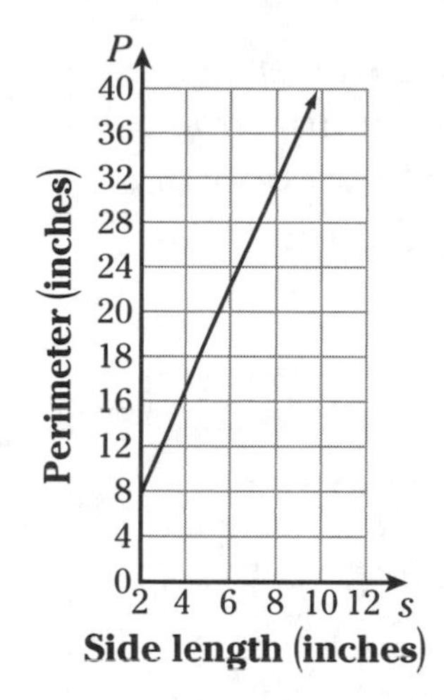

Describe the independent and dependent variables in this relationship.

The independent variable is *s*, the length of one side of a square. The value of *s* can be any positive number. The dependent variable is *P*, the perimeter of the square. The length of the perimeter is dependent on the length of the side of the square.

IT'S YOUR TURN

Read the problem. Circle the letter of the best answer.

1. An airplane took off from an airport and climbed to an altitude of 7,000 feet. It flew at 7,000 feet for 1 hour, before descending gradually and landing back at the airport. Which of the following graphs best represents this information?

A 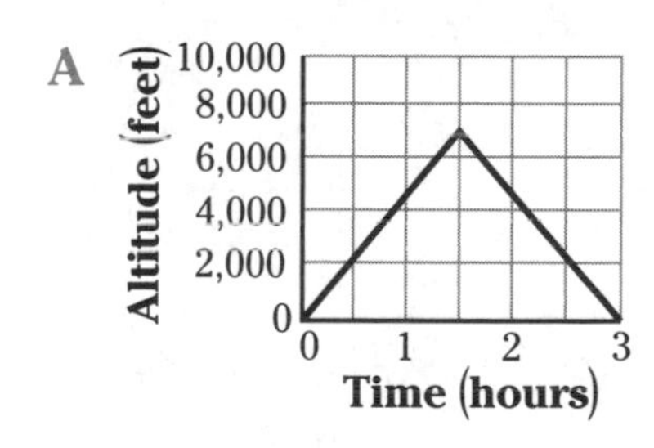

C 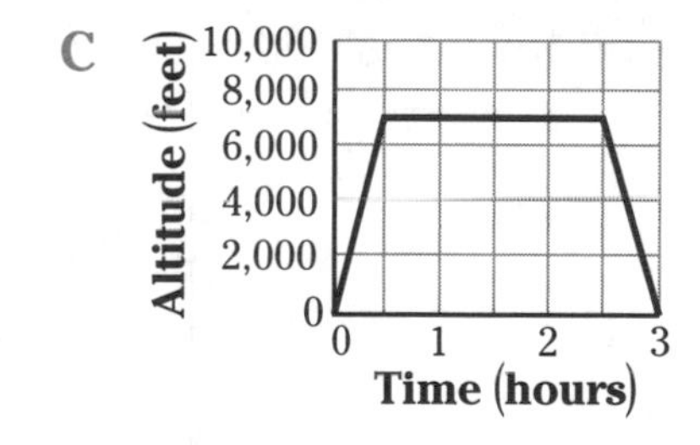

B 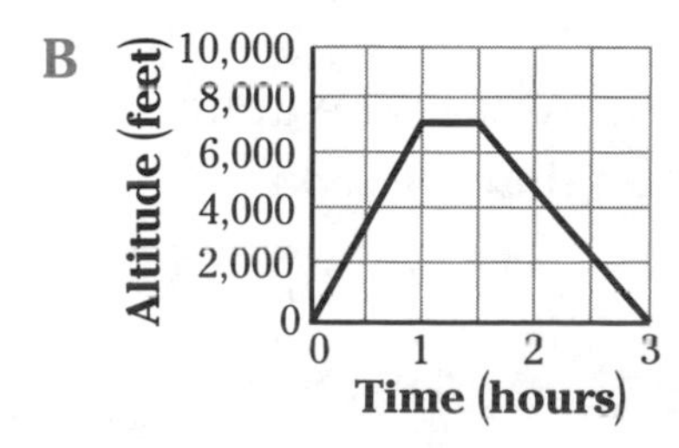

D 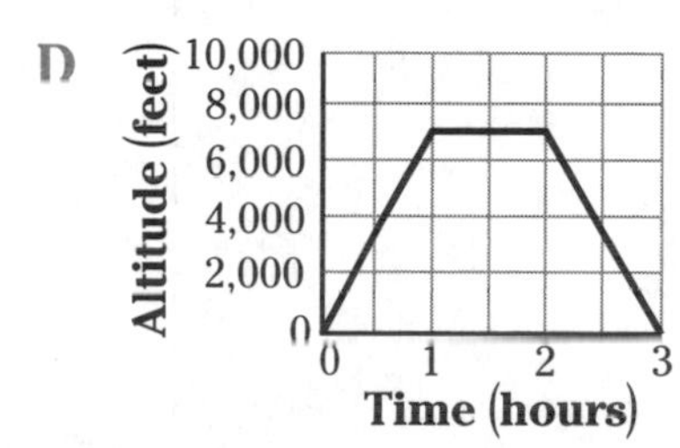

Read each problem. Circle the letter of the best answer.

2. Naomi left her apartment and went for a bicycle ride, returning to her apartment after 2 hours. The graph shows how her distance from home varied during that time.

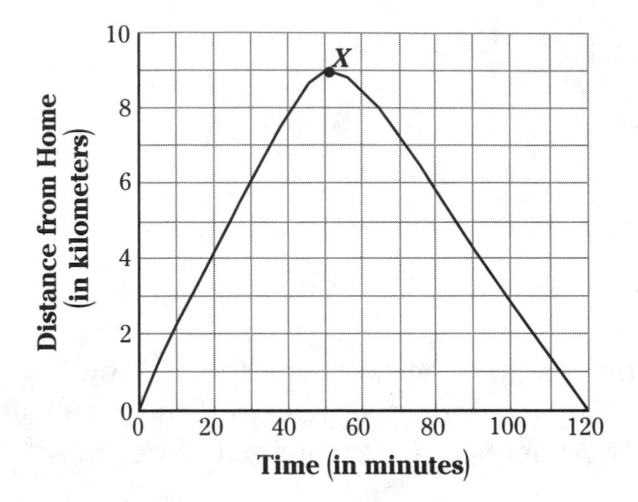

Which of the following best describes the meaning of the point marked X on the graph?

A the greatest distance from home that Naomi reached

B the moment when Naomi returned home

C the fastest speed that Naomi reached

D the time Naomi stopped for a rest

3. From a stopped position, a car sped up gradually until it reached a constant speed. Then the car stopped suddenly. Which of these graphs represents this situation?

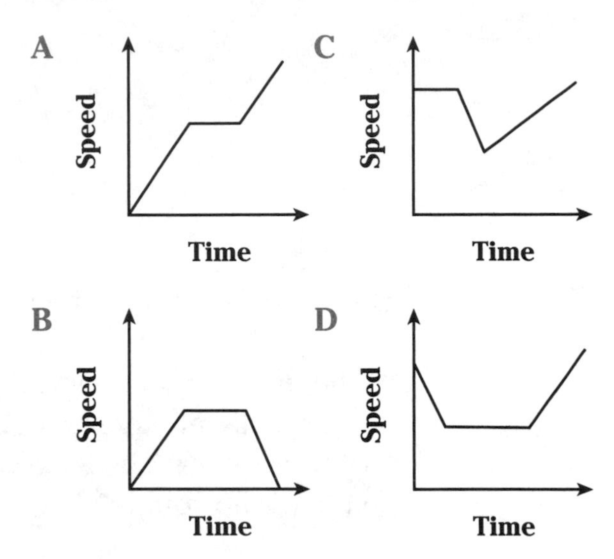

4. The graph below shows the value of a collectible action figure over time.

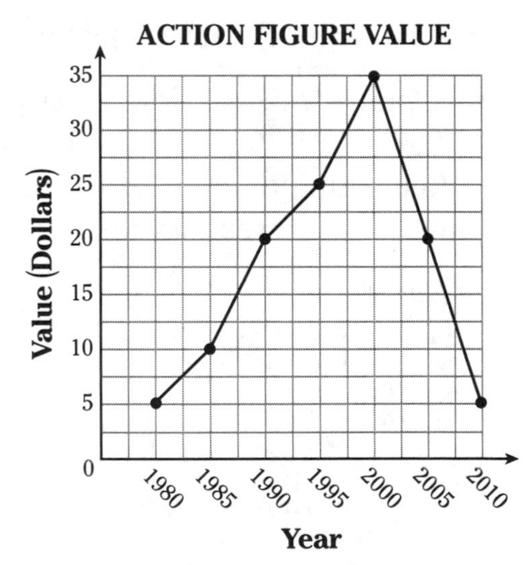

How much more was the action figure worth in 2005 than in 1985?

A \$2 **C** \$10

B \$5 **D** \$20

Read each problem. Write your answers.

5. The depth of a submarine is graphed below.

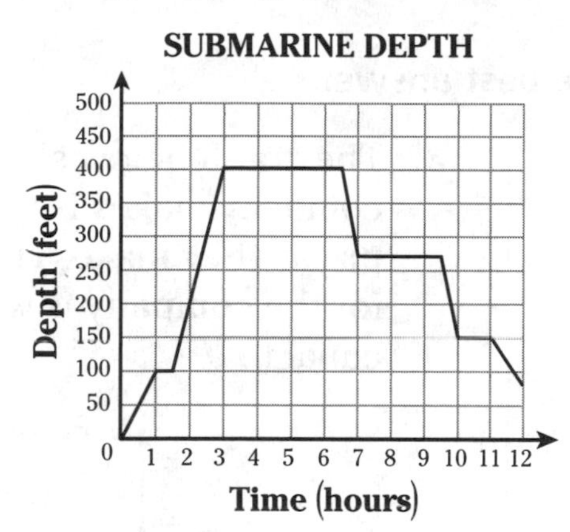

What is a reasonable statement you can make regarding the submarine's depth?

____

____

Make a prediction about the submarine's depth from hour 12 to hour 13.

____

____

6. In a cereal factory, there is a linear relationship between the number of boxes of cereal packaged and the number of hours that have passed. In this relationship, which is the independent variable? Which is the dependent variable?

Independent variable: ____________________

Dependent variable: ____________________

Quadratic Equations and Functions Review

Read each problem. Circle the letter of the best answer.

1. What is the solution to the quadratic equation below?

$$5x^2 = -4 - 12x$$

A $x = -\frac{1}{5}$ and $x = -4$

B $x = \frac{1}{5}$ and $x = 4$

C $x = -\frac{2}{5}$ and $x = -2$

D $x = \frac{2}{5}$ and $x = 2$

2. The graph of $g(x)$ is shown below.

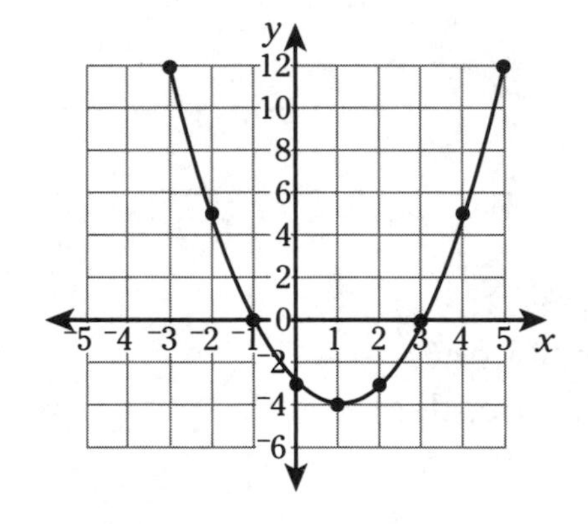

What are the zeros of $g(x)$?

A -3 and -1

B -1 and 3

C -3, -1, and 3

D 0, -1, and 3

3. The graph below shows how the profit a company makes is related to how many pizzas they make. The *break-even point* for the company is when the profit is equal to 0.

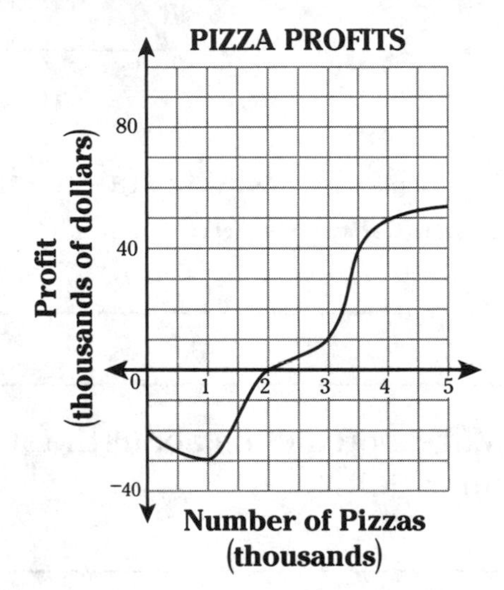

How many pizzas does the company make at the break-even point?

A 0

B 1,000

C 2,000

D 3,000

4. Which expression best represents the solution to the equation below?

$$x^2 + 4x - 3 = 0$$

A $x = 2 \pm \sqrt{7}$

B $x = -2 \pm \sqrt{7}$

C $x = 4 \pm 2\sqrt{7}$

D $x = -4 \pm 2\sqrt{7}$

Read each problem. Circle the letter of the best answer.

5. What is the solution to the quadratic equation below?

$$x^2 - 8x - 40 = 0$$

A $x \approx -5.38$ or $x \approx 13.38$

B $x \approx -3.48$ or $x \approx 11.48$

C $x \approx 3.48$ or $x \approx -11.48$

D $x \approx 5.38$ or $x \approx -13.38$

6. Each side of a rectangle is increased by 3 inches, as shown in the diagram below.

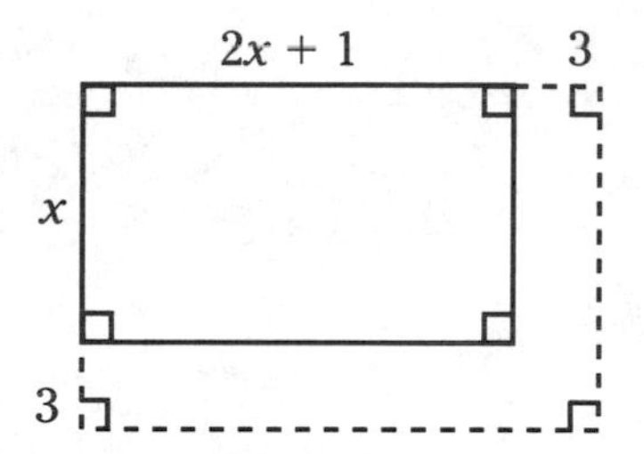

The area of the enlarged rectangle is 112 square inches. What is the area of the smaller rectangle?

A 103 square inches

B 90 square inches

C 78 square inches

D 55 square inches

7. What is the solution to this quadratic equation?

$$5x^2 - 20x = 60$$

A $x = -2$ or $x = 6$

B $x = 2$ or $x = -6$

C $x = -\frac{6}{5}$ or $x = 2$

D $x = \frac{6}{5}$ or $x = -2$

Read each problem. Write your answers.

8. Solve this equation:

$$(x - 9)^2 = 225$$

Answer: ______________________

9. Solve this quadratic equation.

$$2x^2 + 3x - 1 = 0$$

Answer: ______________________

10. What are the zeros of this quadratic function?

$$h(x) = 3x^2 + 10x - 8$$

Answer: ______________________

Read each problem. Write your answers.

11. Solve the equation below by using the quadratic formula.

$$2x(x + 9) = 2x - 8$$

Answer: ____________

12. Look at this quadratic equation.

$$y = -2x^2 + 5$$

Make a table of values for this equation.

x	-2	-1	0		
y					

Graph this equation on the coordinate plane below.

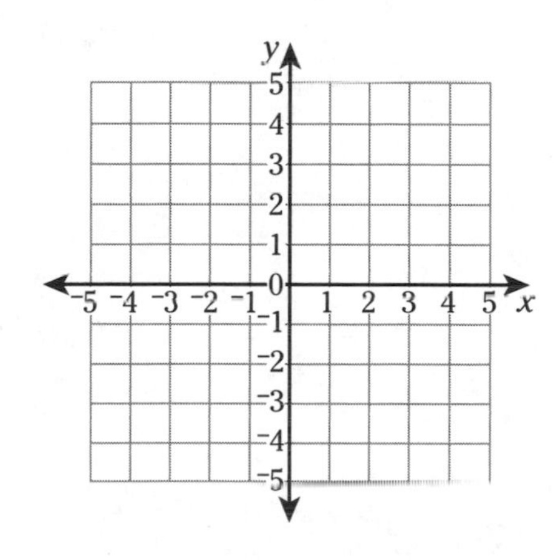

Read the problem. Write your answers.

13. Mr. and Mrs. Hileman are taking a trip. The graph below shows how their distance from home has changed over time.

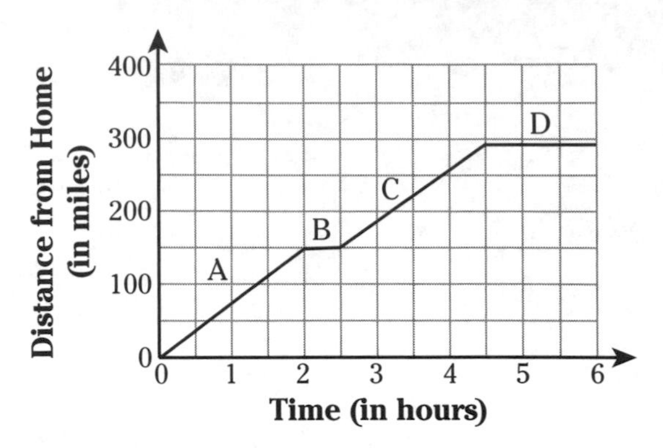

What does part A on the graph represent?

____

____

Explain what the independent and dependent variables are in this relationship.

____

____

____

____

Unit 6
Rational and Radical Expressions and Equations

Rational and radical expressions are two more types of algebraic expressions. You will use many of the skills you have already learned when you add, subtract, multiply, and divide rational expressions. You will use your knowledge of factoring and roots when you simplify rational and radical expressions. To solve rational or radical equations, you will expand on your ability to solve different types of equations.

There are four lessons in this unit:

1 **Rational Expressions** reviews how to add, subtract, multiply, and divide rational expressions. You will also simplify rational expressions.

2 **Solving Rational Equations** reviews how to find the value of a variable in rational equations.

3 **Radical Expressions** reviews how to simplify expressions that have a radical sign in them.

4 **Solving Radical Equations** reviews how to solve equations involving square roots, cube roots, and *n*th roots.

LESSON 1

Rational Expressions

Standard A1.6.1

Rational Expressions

A **rational expression** is the quotient of polynomials, where the polynomial in the denominator does not equal zero.

$$\frac{4}{9} \qquad \frac{x}{y} \qquad \frac{9}{x+6} \qquad \frac{x^2+2x-4}{x+2}$$

These are all rational expressions.

When a rational expression has no common factors other than 1 or -1 in its numerator and denominator, it is in simplified form. To simplify a rational expression, first factor each polynomial completely. Then divide both the numerator and denominator by the common factors.

For example, the rational expression $\frac{3b^3 + 6b}{18b}$ has $3b$ as a common factor in both its numerator and denominator. Factoring out the common factor results in $\frac{3b(b^2+2)}{3b(6)} = \frac{b^2+2}{6}$.

Try this sample question.

S-1 What is the simplified form of the expression $\frac{q^2+q-12}{q^2-16}$?

Factor both expressions in the numerator and denominator:

$$\frac{q^2+q-12}{q^2-16} = \frac{(q+4)(q-3)}{(q+4)(q-4)}$$

The common factor is $q + 4$. Canceling this common factor results in the simplified expression $\frac{q-3}{q-4}$.

Notice that q^2 is ***not*** a common factor of the ratio. For that reason, it cannot be canceled before factoring.

Adding and Subtracting Rational Expressions

When you add and subtract rational expressions, you use the same rules as when you add and subtract fractions. You need to find the least common denominator (LCD). Then change the expressions to equivalent expressions with common denominators. Add or subtract. Finally, simplify the expression to lowest terms.

For example, find the sum of $\frac{x+2}{x} + \frac{x-3}{x^2}$. To find the LCD, find the least common multiple (LCM) of x and x^2. Here the LCM is x^2. Multiply the numerator and the denominator of the first expression by x: $\frac{x(x+2)}{x(x)} = \frac{x^2+2x}{x^2}$. Add the equivalent expressions: $\frac{x^2+2x}{x^2} + \frac{x-3}{x^2} = \frac{x^2+2x+x-3}{x^2} = \frac{x^2+3x-3}{x^2}$. You cannot cancel out any common factors, so this expression is in lowest terms.

Try these sample questions.

S-2 What is the difference between these two rational expressions?

$$\frac{4x}{x^2+3x-10} - \frac{8}{x^2+3x-10}$$

The expressions already have a common denominator, so you just need to subtract the numerators. Since the denominator is a quadratic expression, make sure to factor it so you can check if you can cancel common factors: $\frac{4x}{x^2+3x-10} - \frac{8}{x^2+3x-10} = \frac{4x-8}{x^2+3x-10} = \frac{4(x-2)}{(x+5)(x-2)}$. Since $(x-2)$ is a factor in both the numerator and the denominator, you can cancel it. The simplified expression $\frac{4}{x-5}$ is the correct answer.

S-3 What is the sum of $\frac{2x}{x-3} + \frac{x}{x+5}$?

Since the denominators do not have any common factors, the common denominator will be $(x-3)(x+5)$. So multiply the numerator and denominator of the first expression by $(x+5)$: $\frac{2x(x+5)}{(x-3)(x+5)} = \frac{2x^2+10x}{(x-3)(x+5)}$. Multiply the numerator and denominator of the second expression by $(x-3)$: $\frac{x(x-3)}{(x-3)(x+5)} = \frac{x^2-3x}{(x-3)(x+5)}$. Add the numerators: $\frac{2x^2+10x}{(x-3)(x+5)} + \frac{x^2-3x}{(x-3)(x+5)} = \frac{2x^2+10x+x^2-3x}{(x-3)(x+5)} = \frac{3x^2+7x}{(x-3)(x+5)}$. Since the numerator cannot be factored, this expression is in simplest form.

It is not usual that you will be able to simplify a rational addition or subtraction problem. However, you should always check to be certain.

Multiplying Rational Expressions

When you multiply rational expressions, you multiply the numerators and the denominators. Factor where possible and simplify the product by canceling common factors.

For example, $\frac{2x}{x-3} \cdot \frac{x+6}{2x} = \frac{2x(x+6)}{(x-3)(2x)}$. You can cancel $2x$ from the numerator and the denominator. So the product is $\frac{x+6}{x-3}$.

Try this sample question:

S-4 What is the product of $\frac{x+2}{x-2} \cdot \frac{x^2-4}{x^2+5x+6}$?

A $\frac{x+2}{x+3}$

B $\frac{(x+2)(x-2)}{(x+3)}$

C $\frac{x-2}{x+3}$

D $\frac{x+2}{(x-2)(x+3)}$

Multiply the numerators and the denominators.

$$\frac{x+2}{x-2} \cdot \frac{x^2-4}{x^2+5x+6} = \frac{(x+2)(x^2-4)}{(x-2)(x^2+5x+6)}$$

Factor $x^2 - 4$ in the numerator and $x^2 + 5x + 6$ in the denominator.

$$\frac{(x+2)(x-2)(x+2)}{(x-2)(x+2)(x+3)}$$

You can cancel two sets of factors to simplify this expression:

$$\frac{\cancel{(x+2)}\cancel{(x-2)}(x+2)}{\cancel{(x-2)}\cancel{(x+2)}(x+3)}$$

The product of this expression is $\frac{(x+2)}{(x+3)}$. Choice A is correct.

Dividing Rational Expressions

To divide rational expressions, multiply the first term by the reciprocal of the second term.

For example, to divide $\frac{x-4}{x+3} \div \frac{x+7}{x-1}$, multiply by the reciprocal: $\frac{x-4}{x+3} \cdot \frac{x-1}{x+7}$. So the product is $\frac{(x-4)(x-1)}{(x+3)(x+7)}$.

Try this sample question.

S-5 Find the quotient of $\frac{x^2-4}{x} \div \frac{x-2}{x+4}$.

The reciprocal is the multiplicative inverse. To find the reciprocal of a rational expression, interchange the numerator and the denominator.

The reciprocal of $\frac{x-4}{x+5}$ is $\frac{x+5}{x-4}$.

First find the reciprocal of $\frac{x-2}{x+4}$: $\frac{x+4}{x-2}$. Set up a multiplication problem and multiply the numerators and the denominators: $\frac{x^2-4}{x} \cdot \frac{x+4}{x-2} = \frac{(x^2-4)(x+4)}{x(x-2)}$. Factor where possible, and then cancel common factors: $\frac{(x^2-4)(x+4)}{x(x-2)} = \frac{(x-2)(x+2)(x+4)}{x(x-2)}$. The answer is $\frac{(x+2)(x+4)}{x}$.

IT'S YOUR TURN

Read each problem. Circle the letter of the best answer.

1. What is the sum of $\frac{5x+10}{10x} + \frac{x+3}{5}$?

A $\frac{2x^2+5x+13}{10x}$

B $\frac{2x^2+11x+10}{10x}$

C $\frac{6x+13}{10x+5}$

D $\frac{5x^2+30}{50x}$

2. What is the simplified form of the expression below?

$$\frac{6y}{4y^2+10y}$$

A $\frac{1}{2y+5}$

B $\frac{3}{2y+5}$

C $\frac{3}{2(2y+5)}$

D $\frac{1}{4y^2+4y}$

3. Simplify this rational expression.

$$\frac{x^2-16}{x^2+5x+4}$$

A $\frac{-4}{5x}$

B $\frac{-16}{5x+4}$

C $\frac{x-4}{x+1}$

D $\frac{x+4}{x-1}$

Read each problem. Circle the letter of the best answer.

4. Find the product:

$$\frac{x^2 - 16}{x^2} \cdot \frac{x^2 - 9}{x^2 - x - 12}$$

A $\frac{(x + 4)(x - 3)}{x^2 - x - 12}$

B $\frac{2x^2 - 25}{x^2(x^2 - x - 12)}$

C $\frac{(x + 4)(x - 3)}{x^2}$

D $\frac{(x - 4)(x - 3)}{x^2}$

5. What is the simplified form of the rational expression $\frac{x^2 - 4x + 4}{3x^2 - x - 10}$?

A $\frac{x - 2}{3x - 5}$

B $\frac{x - 2}{3x + 5}$

C $\frac{(x - 2)^2}{3x + 5}$

D $\frac{(x - 2)^2}{(x + 2)(3x - 5)}$

Read each problem. Write your answers.

6. What is the simplified form of this rational expression?

$$\frac{6x^2 - 24}{x^2 + x - 2}$$

Answer: ____________

7. Find the difference:

$$\frac{2x^2 + 3}{x - 3} - \frac{x^2 + 8}{x - 3}$$

Answer: ____________

Read each problem. Write your answers.

8. What is the simplified form of the rational expression below?

$$\frac{-3x - 15}{5x^2 - 125}$$

Answer: ____________

9. Solve:

$$\frac{x^2 - 36}{x^2 - 8x + 16} \div \frac{2x - 12}{x^2 + x - 20}$$

Answer: ________________________

LESSON

2 

Solving Rational Equations

Standard A1.6.2

A **rational equation** is an equation that contains one or more rational expressions.

> To cross multiply, find the **cross products** and set them equal.
>
> $\frac{a}{b} \times \frac{c}{d} \rightarrow ad = bc$

Solving Algebraic Proportions

Some rational equations are **algebraic proportions,** meaning one rational expression is equal to another rational expression. To solve these rational equations, **cross multiply** and solve the resulting equation for the variable.

For example, to solve the proportion $\frac{x}{2} = \frac{8}{x}$, start by cross multiplying: $x^2 = 16$. Then find the square root of both sides of this equation to get the solution:

$\sqrt{x^2} = \sqrt{16}$, or $x = 4$.

After cross multiplying, you may need to move all the variables to one side of the equation before solving. Follow the same rule that applies to solving linear equations: Whatever operation you perform on one side of the equation, you must also perform on the other side.

For example, solve this rational equation for s: $\frac{5s}{7} = \frac{2s - 3}{4}$.

$20s = 14s - 21$	Cross multiply.
$20s - 14s = 14s - 21 - 14s$	Subtract $14s$ from both sides of the equation.
$6s = -21$	Simplify.
$6s \div 6 = -21 \div 6$	Divide both sides by 6.
$s = -\frac{21}{6}$ or $s = -\frac{7}{2}$	Simplify.

You could also write $s = -3\frac{1}{2}$.

Try this sample question.

S-1 What is the solution to this rational equation?

$$\frac{2y - 3}{4} = \frac{4y + 5}{-5}$$

A $y = \frac{5}{26}$

B $y = \frac{5}{6}$

C $y = -\frac{5}{6}$

D $y = -\frac{5}{26}$

Cross multiply, using the distributive property on each side of the equation: $4(4y + 5) = -5(2y - 3) \rightarrow 16y + 20 = -10y + 15$. Add $10y$ to both sides: $26y + 20 = 15$. Subtract 20 from both sides: $26y = -5$. Divide both sides by 26: $y = -\frac{5}{26}$. Choice D is correct.

Solving Rational Equations

Not all rational equations are proportions. You will need to solve rational equations that involve adding and subtracting on one side of the equals sign. There are two different methods you can use to solve these rational equations.

For example, solve this rational equation: $\frac{2}{x+2} + \frac{1}{x} = \frac{1}{4x}$.

Method 1:

Convert each term to an equivalent fraction with a common denominator. Once the terms have common denominators, you know that the two sides of the equation will be equal as long as the numerators are equal. So solve the numerators for the variable.

$$\frac{2}{x+2}\left(\frac{4x}{4x}\right) + \frac{1}{x}\left(\frac{4(x+2)}{4(x+2)}\right) = \frac{1}{4x}\left(\frac{x+2}{x+2}\right)$$

Change each term so the terms have a common denominator: $4x(x + 2)$.

$$\frac{8x}{4x(x+2)} + \frac{4(x+2)}{4x(x+2)} = \frac{x+2}{4x(x+2)}$$

$8x + 4(x + 2) = x + 2$	Solve the numerators.
$8x + 4x + 8 = x + 2$	Use the distributive property.
$12x + 8 - 8 = x + 2 - 8$	Subtract 8 from both sides.
$12x - x = x - 6 - x$	Subtract x from both sides.
$11x \div 11 = -6 \div 11$	Divide both sides by 11.
$x = -\frac{6}{11}$	

Method 2:

Find the common denominator. Multiply through both sides of the equation to eliminate the denominators. Then solve for the variable.

$$\frac{2}{x+2}\left(\frac{4x(x+2)}{1}\right) + \frac{1}{x}\left(\frac{4x(x+2)}{1}\right) = \frac{1}{4x}\left(\frac{4x(x+2)}{1}\right)$$

Multiply each term by the common denominator.

$$\frac{2}{\cancel{x+2}}\left(\frac{4x\cancel{(x+2)}}{1}\right) + \frac{1}{\cancel{x}}\left(\frac{4\cancel{x}(x+2)}{1}\right) = \frac{1}{\cancel{4x}}\left(\frac{\cancel{4x}(x+2)}{1}\right)$$

Factor out common factors.

$$\frac{2 \cdot 4x}{1} + \frac{4(x+2)}{1} = \frac{x+2}{1}$$

Solve the numerators.

$8x + 4x + 8 = x + 2$

$12x + 8 = x + 2$ Combine like terms.

$12x + 8 - 8 = x + 2 - 8$ Subtract 8 from both sides.

$12x - x = x - 6 - x$ Subtract x from both sides.

$11x \div 11 = -6 \div 11$ Divide both sides by 11.

$x = -\frac{6}{11}$

For both methods, always check your answer in the original equation to make sure the value for the variable does not cause any of the denominators to equal zero. You cannot divide by zero, so this value for the variable would be invalid. In these cases, there is no solution to the equation.

Try this sample question.

S-2 What is the solution to $\frac{x}{x+2} - \frac{1}{x+4} = \frac{2}{x^2+6x+8}$?

First factor the quadratic expression so you can find the factors in the common denominator: $x^2 + 6x + 8 = (x + 2)(x + 4)$. Since the factors of the quadratic are the same as the other denominators, the common denominator will be $(x + 2)(x + 4)$.

Multiply through on both sides using the common denominator:

$$\frac{x}{\cancel{x+2}}\left(\frac{\cancel{(x+2)}(x+4)}{1}\right) - \frac{1}{\cancel{x+4}}\left(\frac{(x+2)\cancel{(x+4)}}{1}\right) = \frac{2}{\cancel{(x+2)(x+4)}}\left(\frac{\cancel{(x+2)(x+4)}}{1}\right)$$

Solve the equation:

$x(x + 4) - (x + 2) = 2$

$x^2 + 4x - x - 2 = 2$ Use the distributive property to eliminate the parentheses. Don't forget to distribute the negative sign.

$x^2 + 3x - 2 = 2$ Combine like terms.

$x^2 + 3x - 4 = 0$ Set the quadratic equal to 0.

$(x + 4)(x - 1) = 0$ Factor the quadratic expression.

So $x = -4$ or $x = 1$. Check -4 and 1 in the denominators of the original equation. When you substitute $x = -4$ into the second term's denominator, you get $-4 + 4 = 0$. So -4 is an invalid solution. The only solution to this equation is $x = 1$.

IT'S YOUR TURN

Read each problem. Circle the letter of the best answer.

1. Solve for y.

$$\frac{6}{y-2} = \frac{4}{y}$$

A $y = -16$

B $y = -8$

C $y = -4$

D $y = -1$

2. Solve this rational equation.

$$\frac{4t}{t} - \frac{1}{2t} = \frac{9}{2t}$$

A $t = 2$

B $t = \frac{5}{2}$

C $t = 1$

D $t = \frac{5}{4}$

3. What is the solution to this algebraic proportion?

$$\frac{2x-4}{3} = \frac{3x-5}{7}$$

A $x = -\frac{43}{5}$

B $x = -\frac{1}{5}$

C $x = \frac{13}{5}$

D $x = \frac{43}{5}$

4. What is the solution to this rational equation?

$$\frac{2}{x+2} + \frac{x}{x-5} = \frac{2}{x^2-3x-10}$$

A $x = 2$ or $x = -6$

B $x = -2$ or $x = 6$

C $x = 6$

D $x = 2$

Read each problem. Write your answers.

5. What is the solution to this algebraic proportion?

$$\frac{10 - 2w}{5} = \frac{4 - 3w}{6}$$

Answer: ____________

6. Look at this rational equation.

$$\frac{x}{x - 2} + \frac{1}{x - 4} = \frac{2}{x^2 - 6x + 8}$$

What is the solution to this rational equation?

Answer: ____________

Explain how you know your answer is correct.

____

____

____

____

LESSON 3

Radical Expressions

Standard A1.6.3

A **radical expression** is an expression in which one or more variables appears inside a **radical sign.**

A radical sign can be a square root ($\sqrt{\ }$), cube root ($\sqrt[3]{\ }$), fourth root ($\sqrt[4]{\ }$), or higher nth root ($\sqrt[n]{\ }$).

Simplifying Square Roots

To simplify square roots, look for factors of the number that are perfect squares. Take the square root of the perfect square and multiply by the remaining factors. For example, $\sqrt{45} = \sqrt{9 \cdot 5} = \sqrt{9} \cdot \sqrt{5} = 3\sqrt{5}$.

Perfect Squares

$1^2 = 1$	$6^2 = 36$
$2^2 = 4$	$7^2 = 49$
$3^2 = 9$	$8^2 = 64$
$4^2 = 16$	$9^2 = 81$
$5^2 = 25$	$10^2 = 100$

Now try this question.

S-1 What is the simplified form of $\sqrt{108}$?

A $6\sqrt{2}$

B $6\sqrt{3}$

C $36\sqrt{2}$

D $36\sqrt{3}$

$\sqrt{108}$ simplifies to $\sqrt{36} \cdot \sqrt{3} = 6\sqrt{3}$. Choice B is correct.

Radical Expressions with Variables

Radical expressions that contain variables are simplified the same way. Break down the variables in the same way you break down the numbers.

Remember these rules:

$x^m \cdot x^n = x^{m+n}$

$\frac{x^m}{x^n} = x^{m-n}$

For example, to simplify $\sqrt{18x^4y}$, break down the factors like this:

$$\sqrt{2 \cdot 9 \cdot x^2 \cdot x^2 \cdot y}$$

Then find the square root of each factor:

$$\sqrt{2} \cdot \sqrt{9} \cdot \sqrt{x^2} \cdot \sqrt{x^2} \cdot \sqrt{y} = 3 \cdot x \cdot x \cdot \sqrt{2 \cdot y} = 3x^2\sqrt{2y}$$

Try this sample question.

S-2 Simplify this radical expression: $\sqrt{98a^3b^2}$.

A $7ab\sqrt{2}$

B $7a^2b\sqrt{2}$

C $7ab\sqrt{2a}$

D $7a^2b\sqrt{2}$

Break down the expressions into factors. Look for factors that are perfect squares: $\sqrt{2 \cdot 49 \cdot a^2 \cdot a \cdot b^2}$. Find the square roots of the perfect squares and move them outside the radical sign: $\sqrt{49} = 7$, $\sqrt{a^2} = a$, $\sqrt{b^2} = b$. The 2 and the remaining a stay under the radical sign. So $\sqrt{98a^3b^2} = 7ab\sqrt{2a}$. Choice C is correct.

When finding the square roots of variables, sometimes it is easier to think of them in pairs, instead of writing out the entire factorization. For example, in $\sqrt{b^{20}}$, there are 10 pairs of b, so $\sqrt{b^{20}} = b^{10}$.

Radical expressions with the cube root, fourth root, or nth root sign can be simplified in the same way as those with the square root sign. For example, to simplify $\sqrt[4]{16x^8}$, look for factors that you have four of:
$\sqrt[4]{2 \cdot 2 \cdot 2 \cdot 2 \cdot x \cdot x \cdot x \cdot x \cdot x \cdot x \cdot x \cdot x} = 2x^2$.

Now try this sample question.

S-3 What is the simplified form of $\sqrt[3]{27x^{25}}$?

First note that this radical expression shows a cube root symbol, not a square root. So you will be looking for factors that are perfect cubes, not squares. The number 27 is a perfect cube because $9 \cdot 9 \cdot 9 = 27$. To factor x^{25}, think of how many groups of 3 there are in 25. There are 8 groups of 3 with 1 left over. So the simplified form of this expression is $(9x^8)\sqrt[3]{x}$.

When simplifying radical expressions with variables, you will usually be told to assume that the variables represent non-negative real numbers. This is because you cannot find the square root of a negative number. The factors of a negative number are always one positive and one negative.

IT'S YOUR TURN

Read each problem. Circle the letter of the best answer.

1. What is the simplified form of $\sqrt{54x^5y^9}$?

   A $3x^2y^4\sqrt{6xy}$

   B $6x^2y^4\sqrt{3xy}$

   C $9x^4y^8\sqrt{3xy}$

   D $9x^4y^8\sqrt{3}$

2. Simplify the radical expression $\sqrt[3]{32a^3b}$?

   A $4a\sqrt{2ab}$

   B $4a\sqrt{2a}$

   C $2a\sqrt{4b}$

   D $2a\sqrt{4ab}$

3. What is the simplified form of $\sqrt{250g^{26}h^{19}}$?

   A $5g^{13}h^9\sqrt{5h}$

   B $5g^{13}h^9\sqrt{10h}$

   C $10\sqrt{5g^{26}h^{19}}$

   D $25g^5h^3\sqrt{10gh^{10}}$

4. Simplify $\sqrt[4]{324x^{12}y^{22}}$?

   A $(3x^6y^{11})\sqrt[4]{4}$

   B $(3x^2y^2)\sqrt[4]{4x^3y^2}$

   C $(3x^4y^4)\sqrt[4]{4y}$

   D $(3x^3y^5)\sqrt[4]{4y^2}$

Read each problem. Write your answers.

5. What is the simplified form of $\sqrt{96x^6y}$?

   Answer: ____________________

6. Simplify this radical expression.

   $$\sqrt[3]{135a^9b^{29}}?$$

   Answer: ____________________

LESSON 4

Solving Radical Equations

Standard A1.6.4

Radical Equations

A **radical equation** is an equation in which one or more variables appears inside a **radical sign.** To solve a radical equation with a square root sign, square both sides of the equation to eliminate the square root. Then solve.

> A radical sign can be a square root ($\sqrt{\ }$), cube root ($\sqrt[3]{\ }$), fourth root ($\sqrt[4]{\ }$), or higher nth root ($\sqrt[n]{\ }$).

For example, to solve $\sqrt{3x} = 6$, square both sides, then solve for x:

$(\sqrt{3x})^2 = 6^2$
$3x = 36$
$x = 12$

If the radical in an equation is an nth root, remove the radical by raising both sides of the equation to the nth power. Then solve for the variable. In this example, raise both sides of the equation to the 3rd power:

$\sqrt[3]{k + 2} = 4$
$(\sqrt[3]{k + 2})^3 = 4^3$
$k + 2 = 64$
$k = 62$

Try this sample question.

S-1 What is the solution to the equation $\sqrt[4]{2a + 3} = 3$?

A $a = 0$

B $a = 3$

C $a = 39$

D $a = 42$

Raise both sides of the equation to the 4th power to eliminate the radical sign: $2a + 3 = 81$. Subtract 3 from each side: $2a = 78$. Divide each side by 2 to get the solution: $a = 39$. Choice C is correct.

Isolating the Radical Sign

To solve a radical equation, you may need to start by isolating the radical on one side of the equation before raising both sides to the appropriate power. For example, to solve the equation $3\sqrt{y + 2} - 5 = 7$, use inverse operations to get $\sqrt{y + 2}$ by itself on the left side of the equation. Then square both sides as before:

$$3\sqrt{y + 2} - 5 + 5 = 7 + 5$$

$$\frac{3\sqrt{y + 2}}{3} = \frac{12}{3}$$

$$(\sqrt{y + 2})^2 = 4^2$$

$$y + 2 = 16$$

$$y = 14$$

Try this sample question.

S-2 Solve for t.

$$4 - \sqrt[3]{9t} = 0$$

A $t = \text{-}\frac{64}{9}$

B $t = \text{-}\frac{16}{9}$

C $t = \frac{16}{9}$

D $t = \frac{64}{9}$

> To isolate the cube root, subtract 4 from each side to get $\text{-}\sqrt[3]{9t} = \text{-}4$. Then divide both sides by -1 to get $\sqrt[3]{9t} = 4$. Now raise each side to the 3rd power to eliminate the radical sign: $9t = 64$. Finally divide both sides by 9 to get the solution: $t = \frac{64}{9}$. Choice D is correct.

Radical Equations with Quadratic Equations

When you eliminate the radical sign from a radical equation, the result may be a quadratic equation. Solve the quadratic equation by factoring, completing the square, or using the quadratic formula.

In the example below, squaring both sides of the radical equation gives you a quadratic equation that can be solved by factoring.

$\sqrt{3x + 4} = x$	
$(\sqrt{3x + 4})^2 = x^2$	Square both sides.
$3x + 4 = x^2$	
$x^2 - 3x - 4 = 0$	Write in standard form.
$(x - 4)(x + 1) = 0$	Factor.
$x = 4$ and $x = \text{-}1$	Solve for x.

> When you raise both sides of a radical equation to an even power, **extraneous solutions** (false solutions) may appear. Check the solutions in the original equation to make sure they are actual solutions.

Check each solution in the original equation:

$x = 4$: $\sqrt{3(4) + 4} = 4$ $\quad$ $\sqrt{16} = 4$

$x = -1$: $\sqrt{3(-1) + 4} = -1$ $\quad$ $\sqrt{1} \neq -1$

So $x = -1$ is an extraneous solution, and the only solution is $x = 4$.

Try this sample question.

S-3 What is the solution to the radical equation below?

$$\sqrt{9y + 10} - 7 = y - 5$$

A $y = 1$

B $y = 6$

C $y = -1$ or $y = 6$

D $y = -1$ or $y = -6$

Isolate the radical by adding 7 to both sides of the equation:

$\sqrt{9y + 10} = y + 2$

Square both sides. Then write the quadratic equation in standard form.

$(\sqrt{9y + 10})^2 = (y + 2)^2$

$9y + 10 = y^2 + 4y + 4$

$y^2 - 5y - 6 = 0$

Solve by factoring.

$(y + 1)(y - 6) = 0$

$y = -1$ or $y = 6$

Check both solutions by substituting them into the original equation:

$y = -1$: $\sqrt{9(-1) + 10} - 7 = (-1) - 5$

$\sqrt{1} - 7 = -6$

$1 - 7 = -6$

$-6 = -6$

$y = 6$: $\sqrt{9(6) + 10} - 7 = 6 - 5$

$\sqrt{64} - 7 = 1$

$8 - 7 = 1$

$1 = 1$

Both $y = -1$ and $y = 6$ are actual solutions. Choice C is correct.

IT'S YOUR TURN

Read each problem. Circle the letter of the best answer.

1. Solve this radical equation for x.

$$\sqrt{2x + 1} = 3$$

A $x = 1$

B $x = 4$

C $x = 5$

D $x = 8$

2. What is the solution to this radical equation?

$$5\sqrt{n} - 6 = 14$$

A $n = 2$

B $n = 4$

C $n = 10$

D $n = 16$

3. Solve:

$$\sqrt{y \quad 5} = 4$$

A $y = 9$

B $y = 11$

C $y = 13$

D $y = 21$

4. What is the solution to the radical equation below?

$$\sqrt{7x - 10} = x$$

A $x = -2$

B $x = 5$

C $x = -2$ or $x = -5$

D $x = 2$ or $x = 5$

5. Solve this radical equation for t.

$$\sqrt{24 - 5t} = t$$

A $t = 3$

B $t = 8$

C $t = -3$ or $t = 8$

D $t = 3$ or $t = -8$

Read each problem. Write your answers.

6. Solve this radical equation for x.

$$8 = 6 + \sqrt[4]{3x}$$

Answer: ____________

7. What is the solution to the radical equation below?

$$4\sqrt{13y - 3} = 8y$$

Answer: ________________________

Rational and Radical Expressions and Equations Review

Read each problem. Circle the letter of the best answer.

1. Simplify:

$$\frac{3w - 15}{w^2 - 3w - 10}$$

A $\frac{3}{w + 2}$

B $\frac{3}{w - 2}$

C $\frac{3}{(w - 5)(w + 2)}$

D $\frac{3}{(w + 5)(w - 2)}$

2. What is the solution to this rational equation?

$$\frac{x + 1}{6} = \frac{7}{3}$$

A $x = 13$

B $x = \frac{41}{3}$

C $x = \frac{43}{3}$

D $x = 15$

3. What is the simplified form of $\sqrt{60x^2y^7}$?

A $2xy^2\sqrt{15y}$

B $2xy^3\sqrt{15y}$

C $4x^2y^6\sqrt{15y}$

D $4xy^3\sqrt{15y}$

4. Add: $\frac{4z}{4z^2 + 12z + 9} + \frac{6}{4z^2 + 12z + 9}$.

A $\frac{4z + 6}{8z^2 + 24z + 18}$

B $\frac{4z + 6}{2z + 3}$

C $\frac{1}{z^2 + 11}$

D $\frac{2}{2z + 3}$

5. Solve for z.

$$\sqrt[3]{4z} + 5 = 7$$

A $z = 1$

B $z = \frac{3}{2}$

C $z = 2$

D $z = \frac{9}{4}$

Read each problem. Circle the letter of the best answer.

6. Which expression has the same value as the expression below?

$$\frac{w^3 + 5w^2 - w - 5}{w^2 - 6w + 5}$$

A $w + 1$

B $\frac{w^3 - w}{-6w + 5}$

C $\frac{(w + 1)(w - 5)}{w + 5}$

D $\frac{(w + 1)(w + 5)}{w - 5}$

7. Find the solution this rational equation:

$$\frac{x}{x + 3} + \frac{2x}{x - 6} = \frac{27}{x^2 - 3x - 18}$$

A $x = 3$

B $x = 9$

C $x = 7$

D $x = -3$ or $x = 7$

8. Simplify this radical expression.

$$\sqrt{192m^8n^2}$$

A $2m^2n\sqrt{48m^2}$

B $8m^2n\sqrt{3m^2}$

C $8m^4n\sqrt{3}$

D $2m^4n\sqrt{48}$

Read each problem. Write your answers.

9. What is the simplified form of the expression below?

$$\frac{y^2 - 9y + 14}{8y - 16}$$

Answer: ____________

10. Solve this rational expression.

$$\frac{x^2 - 9}{x} \div \frac{x + 3}{x + 2}$$

Answer: ________________________

Read each problem. Write your answers.

11. What is the solution to this rational equation?

$$\frac{3}{m} + \frac{1}{2m} = \frac{m + 8}{2m}$$

Answer: ____________

12. Solve this radical equation for w.

$$\sqrt{w + 2} = w - 4$$

Answer: ____________

Unit 7
Data Analysis

In our daily lives, we encounter many forms of numerical data. These data can summarize important measures of averages and spread, like details on a favorite sports team's performance. Data also can be used to make predictions about future events, such as a college predicting the number of new students expected to enroll in two, five, or ten years based on past years' enrollments. Data is presented in many forms. Displays such as bar graphs, scatterplots, tables, box-and-whisker plots, and circle graphs all summarize data. Being able to read and interpret these different graphical representations is a valuable skill, not only for understanding current information and events, but also for analyzing past events in order to make educated conjectures about future events.

There are four lessons in this unit:

1. **Statistical Measures of Data** reviews using appropriate statistics to communicate information about the data and using these notions to compare different sets of data.
2. **Representing and Interpreting Data** reviews selecting and interpreting an appropriate graphical representation for a set of data.
3. **Sampling and Predicting** reviews describing and explaining how the relative sizes of a sample and the population affect the validity of predictions from a set of data.
4. **Use and Misuse of Data** reviews how to evaluate the validity of graphs and claims based on statistics.

LESSON 1

Statistical Measures of Data

Standard A1.7.1

When you read a magazine, watch sports, or surf the Internet, it is not uncommon at all to encounter statements like "compact disc sales in Europe are slower than expected" or "Rogers is the best player in the league right now." What these statements have in common is that they present conclusions that are based on data. Frequently these kinds of conclusions are based on the mean or median of a set of data.

Mean

The **mean** (also called "average") is the most common measure of central tendency. To find the mean of a set of numbers, calculate their sum and divide by how many numbers are in the set.

For example, assume that the girls' soccer team scored 0, 2, 6, 1, and 3 goals in its last five games. Then the mean number of goals scored is $\frac{0+2+6+1+3}{5} = \frac{12}{5} = 2.4$.

Now assume that the girls' team scores 1, 4, 3, 2, and 4 goals in its next five games. Then the mean number of goals for these five games is $\frac{1+4+3+2+4}{5} = \frac{14}{5} = 2.8$. A sportswriter might use this information to report that the team is improving in its ability to score goals.

Now try this question.

S-1 A transportation agency was deciding between two different routes for a new bus line. On six different days, the agency conducted tests to see how long it took the bus to complete each route. The results are shown in the table.

Compute the mean times for both routes.

Which route is faster?

BUS TIMES

Day	Route 1 (minutes)	Route 2 (minutes)
1	45	49
2	54	51
3	42	48
4	52	56
5	53	48
6	48	51

First calculate the mean for each route. The mean time for route 1 is $(45 + 54 + 42 + 52 + 53 + 48) \div 6 = 49.0$ minutes. The mean time for route 2 is $(49 + 51 + 48 + 56 + 48 + 51) \div 6 = 50.5$ minutes. To find which route is faster, compare the data: 49.0 , 50.5. So route 1 is 1.5 minutes faster than route 2.

Median

The **median** is the middle value of a set of numbers, when organized from least to greatest. If there is an even number of values in the data set, then the median of the set is the mean (average) of the middle two numbers.

> Before finding the median, be sure that you arrange the numbers from least to greatest.

For example, assume that a veterinarian weighs five cats. The weights, in pounds, are 7, 11, 3, 16, and 8. These numbers can be arranged from least to greatest:

3, 7, **8,** 11, 16

Since 8 is the number in the middle, 8 is the median of the set of numbers. The median weight of the cats is 8 pounds. Notice that no computations were necessary to find the median.

> The mean and median *may* be equal, but usually they are different.

Now assume that a sixth cat, weighing 10 pounds, is included in the group of cats. Now, in order, the weights become:

3, 7, **8, 10,** 11, 16

Since there is an even number of cats, there are two middle numbers—not one. To find the median of the set, you need to take the mean of the middle two numbers, 8 and 10.

$(8 + 10) \div 2 = 9$

The median weight of the six cats is 9 pounds.

Now try this question.

S-2 The selling prices of 5 houses in a neighborhood were $114,096, $150,000, $223,000, $198,999, and $138,900. What was the median selling price?

> The prices, arranged in order, are:
>
> $114,096, $138,900, $150,000, $198,999, $223,000
>
> The middle value is $150,000, so this is the median selling price.

Mode

The **mode** is the number or the data item that occurs most frequently in the data set.

For example, Jennifer surveyed some of her classmates to find out how many times they had watched a new television show. Their responses were 3, 10, 7, 7, 3, 4, 7, 7, 2, 5, and 6. The mode of this data is 7 because it appears the most, four times.

Now try the question on the following page.

S-3 The coach measured the heights of the women on the basketball team. They were 6'1", 5'9", 5'11", 5'10", 5'8", 5'11", 5'10", 6', 5'6", 5'9", and 5'10". What height was the mode?

A 5'9" **B** 5'10" **C** 5'11" **D** 6'0"

The most frequent height is 5'10" because it appears three times. Therefore, the mode is 5'10". Choice B is correct.

Note that some sets of data may have more than one mode or no mode at all. For example, in the set of numbers below, both 4 and 9 are modes.

2, 4, 6, 4, 9, 9

Both 4 and 9 occur twice, so they have equal frequency. The other numbers each occur only once. Now look at this set.

1, 5, 8, 12, 19

This set has no mode because each value occurs only once. No number occurs more frequently than any other.

Look at the set of data below showing the birthday months of each person in Sarah's family.

January, March, May, January, April, April, January, August

In this data set, the mode would be January, since that occurs more times than any other month listed.

When data are not numerical, the mode is the best measure to use.

Range

While mean and median are measures of central tendency, **range** is a measure of dispersion, or spread. When the range of a set of data is large, the data are very spread out. When the range is small, the data are very close together. To compute range, find the difference between the highest and lowest numbers in a data set.

Among the 30 people at a picnic, the youngest person is 3 years old, and the oldest person is 79 years old. Then the range of the ages is $79 - 3 = 76$. At another picnic, the youngest person is 10 years old, and the range is 21. What can you say about the oldest person? That person must be 31 because $10 + 21 = 31$.

Arranging the numbers in order or making a tally chart can help you find the range.

Now try this question.

S-4 A company asked seven employees to turn in receipts for their travel expenses. The expenses were separated into transportation (plane travel, car rental, taxi) and lodging (hotel rooms, meals).

TRAVEL EXPENSES

Employee	Transportation	Lodging
Watkins	$460	$534
Sawamura	$912	$350
Jensen	$794	$483
Stolzfus	$329	$311
McManus	$409	$612
Escobar	$211	$543
Chang	$902	$433

What was more spread out, the transportation expenses or the lodging expenses?

The company is planning to send another employee on a business trip. About how much money, in all, should the company expect the employee to spend on the trip?

The best way to measure spread is to calculate the range. The range of transportation costs is $912 – $211 = $701. The range of lodging costs is $612 – $311 = $301. Therefore, the transportation costs are more spread out.

One way to predict how much it will cost to send another employee on a business trip is to use medians. The median transportation cost in the table is $460. The median lodging cost in the table is $483. Combined, the total is $460 + $483 = $943. The company should expect to spend about $943 for the employee's business trip. You can also use the mean to make this prediction.

Standard Deviation and Variance

The **standard deviation** of a set of data is a measure of how spread out the data are. The **variance** is the average of the squared differences from the mean. These measures help you understand how far each data value is from the average.

To find the **variance,** first find the mean of the data. Then, for each number, subtract the mean and square the difference. Finally, find the average of the squared differences.

To find the **standard deviation,** find the square root of the variance.

For example, the heights of five brothers are 65 in., 72 in., 69 in., 74 in., and 70 in. Find the variance first, and then you can calculate the standard deviation.

$\frac{65 + 72 + 69 + 74 + 70}{5} = 70$	Find the mean of the data.
$65 - 70 = -5; (-5)^2 = 25$ $72 - 70 = 2; 2^2 = 4$ $69 - 70 = -1; (-1)^2 = 1$ $74 - 70 = 4; 4^2 = 16$ $70 - 70 = 0; 0^2 = 0$	Calculate the difference of each height from the mean. Then square the difference.
$\frac{25 + 4 + 1 + 16 + 0}{5} = 9.2$	Find the mean of the differences.

So the variance is 9.2 inches.

$\sqrt{9.2} \approx 3.03$	Find the square root of the variance.

So the standard deviation is about 3.03 inches.

The average height of the brothers is 70 inches. The heights 69 in. and 72 in. are within one standard deviation (3.03 inches) of the average. The heights 65 in. and 74 in. are within two standard deviations of the average.

Try this sample question.

S-5 A scientist measured the heights of five different tomato plants. The heights, in centimeters, are listed below.

53 49 66 52 65

What is the variance of this set of data?

What is the standard deviation of this set of data?

To find the variance, first find the mean of the heights: $\frac{53 + 49 + 66 + 52 + 65}{5} = 57$. Then find the difference between the mean and each data value; square the difference: $53 - 57 = -4$, $(-4)^2 = 16$; $49 - 57 = -8$, $(-8)^2 = 64$; $66 - 57 = 9$, $9^2 = 81$; $52 - 57 = -5$, $(-5)^2 = 25$; $65 - 57 = 8$, $8^2 = 64$. Find the mean of the squared differences: $\frac{16 + 64 + 81 + 25 + 64}{5} = 50$. So the variance is 50.

To find the standard deviation, find the square root of the variance: $\sqrt{50} \approx 7.07$.

IT'S YOUR TURN

Read each problem. Circle the letter of the best answer.

1. The prices of the 5 most popular big screen television sets at an electronics store are listed below.

   $2,499 $1,359 $2,299
   $2,999 $1,789

   If the price of the next most popular television set is included with this data, the range in prices increases by $800. What could be the price of the next most popular television set?

   A $2,159
   B $2,199
   C $3,799
   D $3,859

2. The hourly pay rate of each employee at a bookstore is listed below.

$7.15	$7.50	$7.50	$7.75
$7.90	$8.00	$8.00	$8.00
$8.25	$8.60	$8.80	$9.00
$9.00	$10.20	$11.00	$11.15
$11.75	$16.00	$16.75	$19.25

   Which statement is best supported by this data?

   A One-fourth of the employees have an hourly pay rate less than $7.95.

   B Half of the employees have an hourly pay rate between $8.00 and $9.60.

   C One-fourth of the employees have an hourly pay rate greater than $11.15.

   D Half of the employees have an hourly pay rate between $8.85 and $19.25.

3. Which situation is best described using the mode?

   A the favorite book on a summer reading list

   B the distance students travel to and from school

   C the amount of time some friends used the Internet yesterday

   D the names of each student at school who has a driver's license

4. Eight judges rated a slam dunk on a scale of 1 to 10. Their ratings are given below.

   6, 8, 9, 10, 6, 9, 9, 8

   What was the median of their ratings?

   A 4
   B 8
   C 8.5
   D 9

Read the problem. Fill in your answer on the response grid.

5. An office building has spaces for lease. The areas of the spaces, in square feet, are listed below.

950 1,000 1,125 1,160 950
1,250 1,200 1,240 1,025

What is the mean area of these spaces?

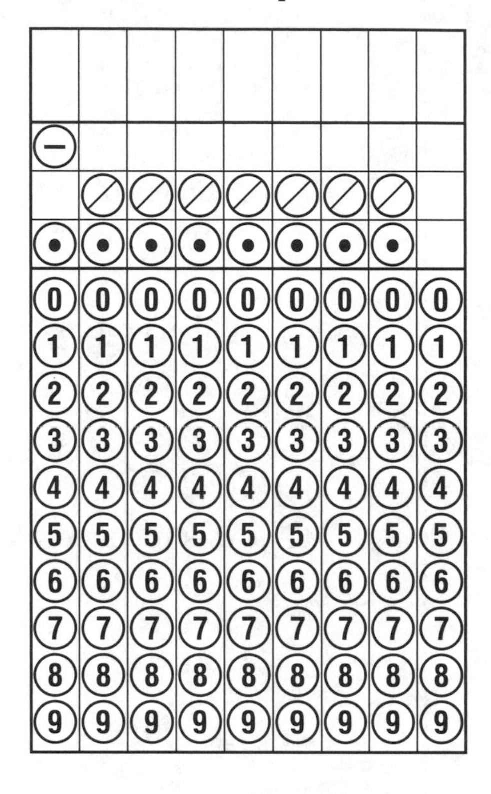

Read the problem. Write your answer.

6. The scores Terrence got in the last ten video games he played are listed below.

400 900 -250 -150 500
650 1,200 -100 1,350 950

What is the range of these scores?

Answer: ____________

Read the problem. Write your answers.

7. A marine biologist weighed sea otters. The results are shown below.

SEA OTTER WEIGHTS

Sea Otter	Weight (lb)
1	70.1
2	99.0
3	85.6
4	79.4
5	73.6
6	62.7

What is the variance for this set of data? Give your answer to the nearest hundreth.

Answer: ____________

What is the standard deviation of this set of data? Give your answer to the nearest hundreth.

Answer: ____________

Read the problem. Write your answers.

8. The chart below shows the ages of the members of two popular musical bands.

TWO BANDS

Band Name	Ages of Members
NBINX	13, 13, 17, 19, 28
Polite Boys	16, 16, 16, 21, 24

A magazine article suggested that NBINX is more popular among high school students because its members are older than the Polite Boys. Use a measure of central tendency to justify the statement from the article.

Answer: ____

____

____

____

In a third five-member band, the median of the members' ages is 18, and the range is 3. What could the five ages could be?

Answer: ____________________

Read the problem. Write your answers.

9. Allen's bowling scores for April are shown below. His mean score after all five games was 221.

ALLEN'S BOWLING SCORES

Game	Score
1	225
2	245
3	222
4	230
5	?

What was his score in game 5?

Answer: ____________

Was Allen's mean score or median score for the five games greater?

Answer: ________________________

Allen bowls a sixth game and his median score changes to 227. What must be true of Allen's score on the sixth game?

Answer: ____

____

LESSON 2

Representing and Interpreting Data

Standard A1.7.1

Bar Graphs and Histograms

Visual representations provide a good way to summarize data from studies or surveys. Two types of visual aids are **bar graphs** and **histograms.** Both types of graphs use bars to display and summarize data. The bars on a bar graph represent individual pieces of data and are separate from each other. Sometimes two sets of data are represented on one bar graph. This graph is known as a **double bar graph.** A sample of a double bar graph is shown at the right.

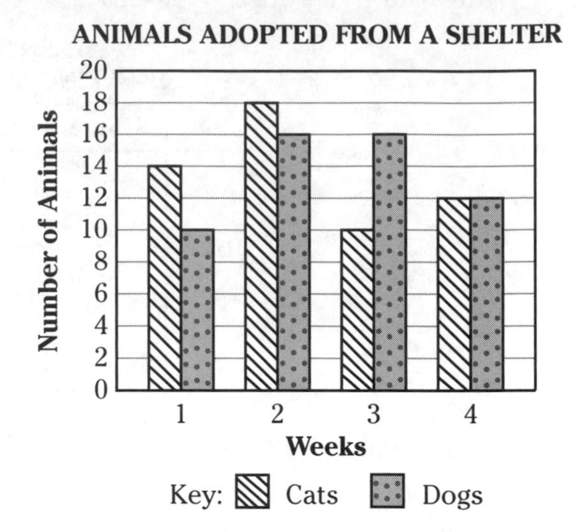

Bars on a histogram represent a range of data and are joined together. Histograms are useful for summarizing a large range of data that can be grouped together easily.

The sample problem below shows how to read and interpret a histogram.

S-1 The histogram below shows the times, in seconds, it took students in Ms. Gorman's swim class to complete one lap in the pool.

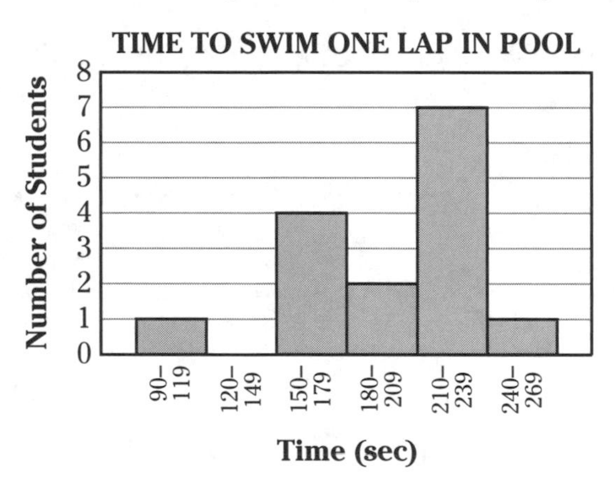

What fraction of the students took fewer than 180 seconds to complete one lap in the pool?

Each bar on the histogram represents students whose swim times were within a specific 30-second interval of time. Count the number of students whose times fell in the intervals less than 180 seconds. This includes 5 students altogether: 1 student with a time between 90 and 119 seconds and 4 students with times between 150 and 179 seconds. Now count the total number of students represented by each bar in the histogram: $1 + 4 + 2 + 7 + 1 = 15$ total students.

Since 5 of the 15 total students had times under 180 seconds, the fraction is $\frac{5}{15}$ or $\frac{1}{3}$.

Line Graphs and Line Plots

Line graphs and **line plots** are two additional representations that summarize data visually. Line graphs are useful for showing how data changes over a period of time. Points on a line graph show a relationship between quantities on the horizontal and vertical axes.

Line plots display data points above a horizontal line showing a range of values. For example, the line plot here shows the ages of 20 people surveyed at the mall. Each X represents one person surveyed.

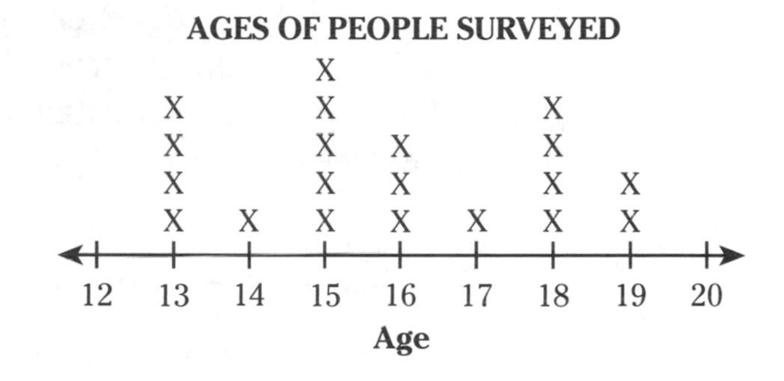

Try this sample question dealing with line graphs.

S-2 The line graph below shows how Ana's hourly rate of pay changed during the past eight years.

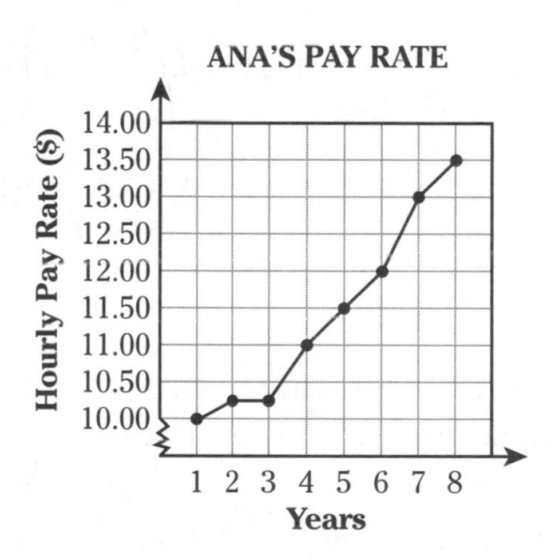

Between which two years did Ana's hourly rate of pay change the most?

A between years 2 and 3

B between years 3 and 4

C between years 6 and 7

D between years 7 and 8

To identify the rates of pay for each year, locate the pay rate on the vertical axis that corresponds to the point for each year on the horizontal axis. Then find the approximate differences between each pay rate from year to year:

Hourly pay change from year 2 to year 3: $10.25 − $10.25 = $0.00.
Hourly pay change from year 3 to year 4: $11.00 − $10.25 = $0.75.
Hourly pay change from year 6 to year 7: $13.00 − $12.00 = $1.00.
Hourly pay change from year 7 to year 8: $13.50 − $13.00 = $0.50.

The greatest increase in hourly pay was $1.00 between years 6 and 7. Choice C is correct.

Circle Graphs

A **circle graph** is a visual representation that divides data into sections. Each section of a circle graph represents a fraction or percentage of a whole amount. For example, in the circle graph at the right, all the numbers together represent 100% of the house numbers on Hilltop Street. House numbers from 200 to 399 represent 50%, or half, of the house numbers on that street.

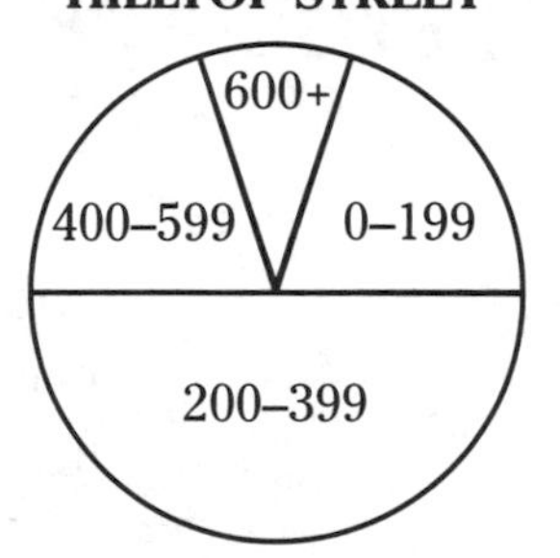

Try this sample problem.

S-3 The circle graph below shows the number of students in the marching band at each grade level in Washington High School.

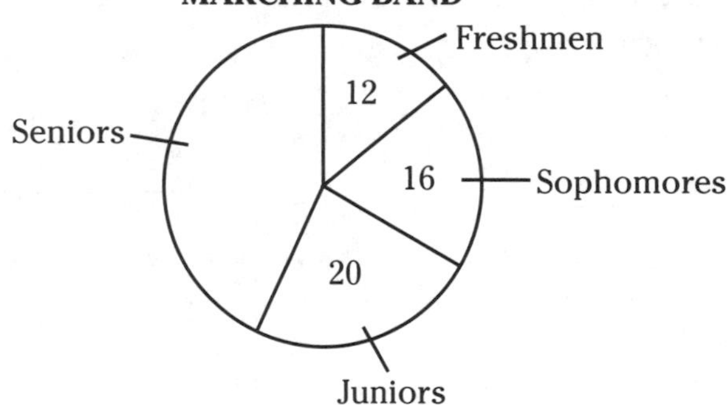

There are 80 students altogether in the marching band. What fraction of these students are seniors?

A $\frac{1}{4}$

B $\frac{3}{10}$

C $\frac{1}{3}$

D $\frac{2}{5}$

First find the number of seniors that are in the marching band. Since there are 80 students in the band altogether, there are $80 - (12 + 16 + 20)$, or 32 seniors in the marching band. So $\frac{32}{80}$ or $\frac{2}{5}$ of the band members are seniors. Choice D is correct.

People who use statistics often find it valuable to divide data into fourths. When data are divided this way, the divisions between groups of data are called **quartiles.**

- The **first quartile** is the median of the lower half of the data.
- The **second quartile** is the median of all of the data.
- The **third quartile** is the median of the upper half of the data.
- The **interquartile range** is the range between the third and first quartiles.

Box-and-Whisker Plots

One type of data display that uses quartiles is the **box-and-whisker plot.** Quartiles are used to create box-and-whisker plots as follows:

- The minimum value is the left-most whisker.
- The first quartile is the left edge of the box.
- The median (or second quartile) is the middle line in the box.
- The third quartile is the right edge of the box.
- The maximum value is the right-most whisker.

For example, the box-and-whisker plot below represents data with a median of 70 and an interquartile range of $85 - 50 = 35$.

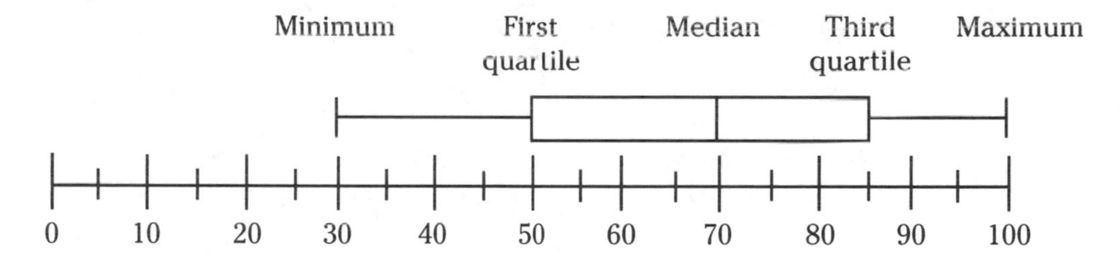

Now try this question.

S-4 The box-and-whisker plot below shows the number of touchdowns scored each year by a football player.

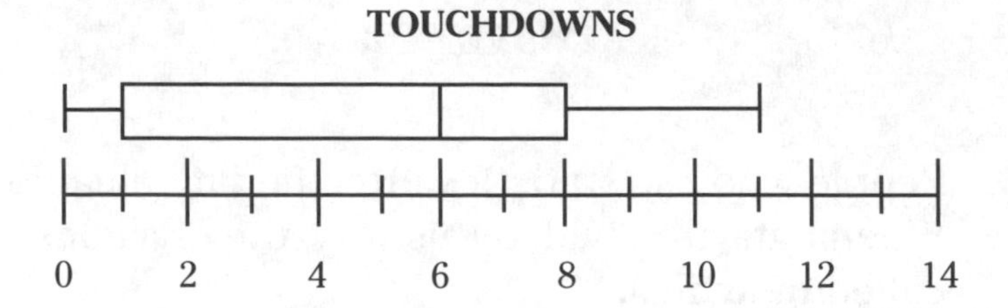

What was his median number of touchdowns?

A 1 **B** 6 **C** 8 **D** 11

In a box-and-whisker plot, the median is represented by the middle line in the box. This line matches up with 6 on the scale. The median number of touchdowns was 6. Choice B is correct.

Stem-and-Leaf Plots

Another way data can be organized is in a **stem-and-leaf plot.** To make a stem-and-leaf plot, the left digit or digits of each data value are lined up in the "stem" of the plot. The right digit is placed in the corresponding "leaf" of the stem.

For example, the ages of each cast member in a play are 19, 35, 16, 24, 22, 37, 60, 34, 57, and 19. The stem-and-leaf plot shown here organizes these data values. Notice that the tens digits are the stem in this plot, and the ones digits are the leaves.

AGE OF CAST MEMBERS

1	6 9 9
2	2 4
3	4 5 7
4	
5	7
6	0

1 | 6 means 16

Measures of central tendency (mean, median, and mode) and measures of dispersion or spread (range and quartiles) can be determined based on the data in a stem-and-leaf plot. For example, in the stem-and-leaf plot showing the ages of the cast members, the first and last data values can be used to find the range: $60 - 16 = 44$. Also, the mode can be found by locating digits that repeat most often for a particular stem. The mode in this stem-and-leaf plot is 19 since there are two leaf 9's corresponding to the stem 1.

The sample problem below shows how to interpret a double stem-and-leaf plot.

S-5 The stem-and-leaf plot below shows the number of copies made on the two copiers in the school library during a two-week period.

COPIES MADE EACH DAY

Copier 1		Copier 2
	2	
8 3	3	
9	4	8 9
2	5	1 6 6
1	6	
8 8 6 5	7	
2	8	0 4 8
	9	3
	10	7

means 52 → 2 | 5 | 1 ← means 51

Which statement can be concluded from this data?

A The range for copier 1 is greater than the range for copier 2.

B The range for copier 2 is greater than the range for copier 1.

C The median for copier 1 is greater than the median for copier 2.

D The median for copier 2 is greater than the median for copier 1.

To find the range for each copier, first identify the smallest and largest data values. For copier 1, the range is $82 - 33 = 49$. For copier 2, the range is $107 - 48 = 59$. The range for copier 2 is greater than the range for copier 1. So, choice B is correct.

Note that the medians for each data set can be found by calculating the mean of the two middle values. The medians for the data sets are both 68, so the medians are equal.

Scatterplots

A **scatterplot** shows the relationship between two sets of data. To make a scatterplot, the two sets of data are written as ordered pairs. Those ordered pairs are then graphed as points on a coordinate plane.

Try this sample question.

S-6 The table below shows the average miles per gallon some new cars travel in the city and on the highway.

AVERAGE GAS MILEAGE

City (mpg)	Highway (mpg)
22	30
34	40
30	34
49	51
20	24
15	21
22	26
20	29

Which scatterplot best shows this data?

A

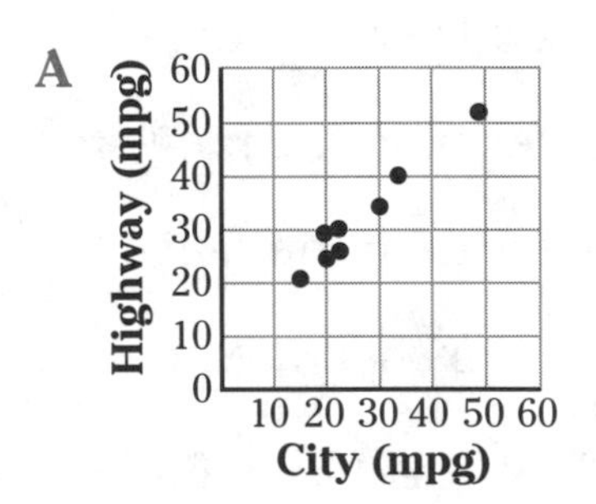

C

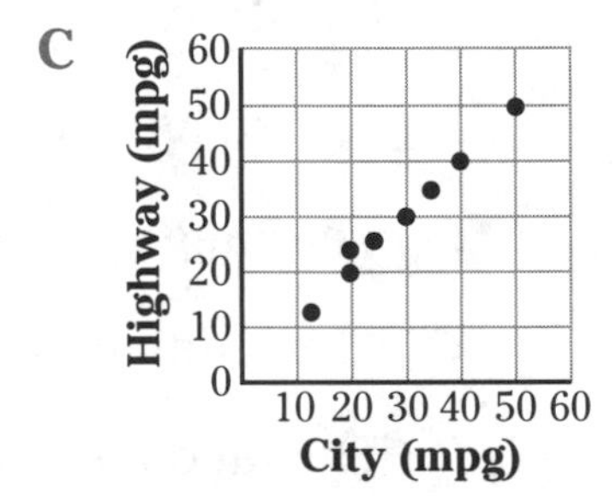

B

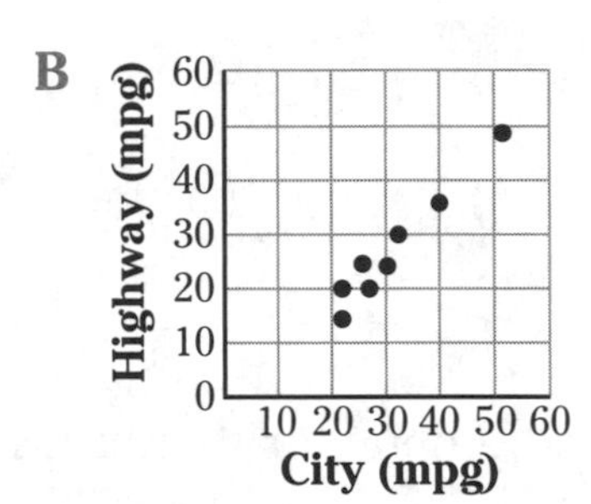

D

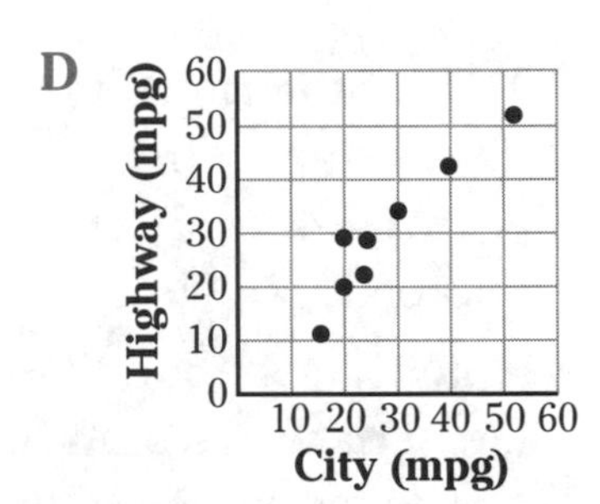

Rewrite each point in the table as an ordered pair. Then graph each ordered pair, marking the first coordinate on the horizontal City axis and the second coordinate on the vertical Highway axis. Choice A shows these points plotted correctly.

IT'S YOUR TURN

Read the problem. Circle the letter of the best answer.

1. The bar graph below shows the number of people registered for classes at the local gym.

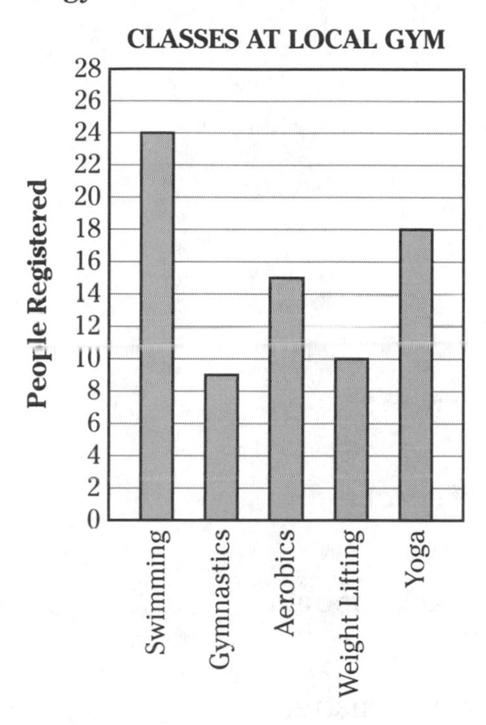

Which of the following can be concluded from this data?

A One-fourth of the people are registered for aerobics.

B One-fifth of the people are registered for weight lifting.

C More than half the people are registered for swimming and aerobics.

D More than twice as many people are registered for yoga than weight lifting.

Read the problem. Fill in your answer on the response grid.

2. The circle graph below shows the number of hours Theresa worked last week.

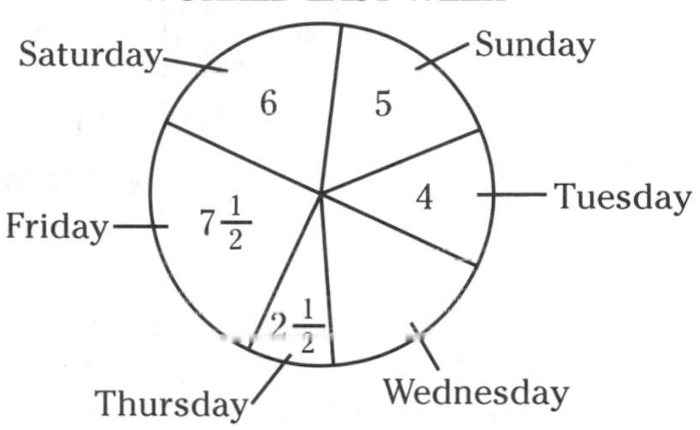

One-fifth of the hours Theresa worked last week were on Saturday. How many hours did Theresa work on Wednesday last week?

Read each problem. Circle the letter of the best answer.

3. The scatterplot below shows the relationship between the number of snacks bought at a game and the cost of the snack.

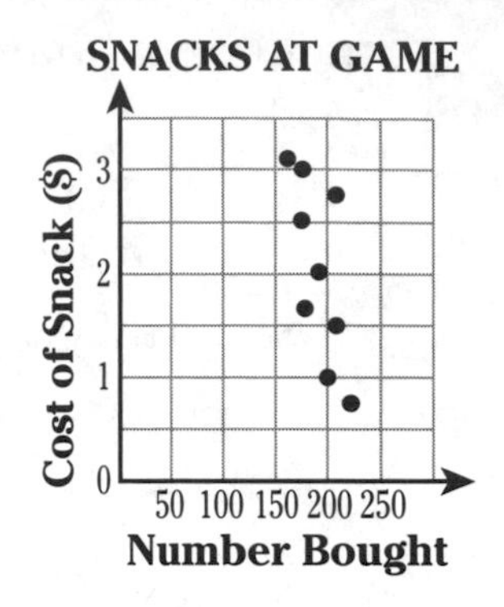

Which statement best describes this relationship?

A As the price of the snack increases, the number of snacks bought tends to increase.

B As the price of the snack increases, the number of snacks bought tends to decrease.

C There is no relationship between the number of snacks bought and the price of the snack.

D The number of snacks bought tends to be the same no matter what the price of the snack is.

4. The box-and-whisker plot below shows the weight, in pounds, of each package a shipping company delivered one day.

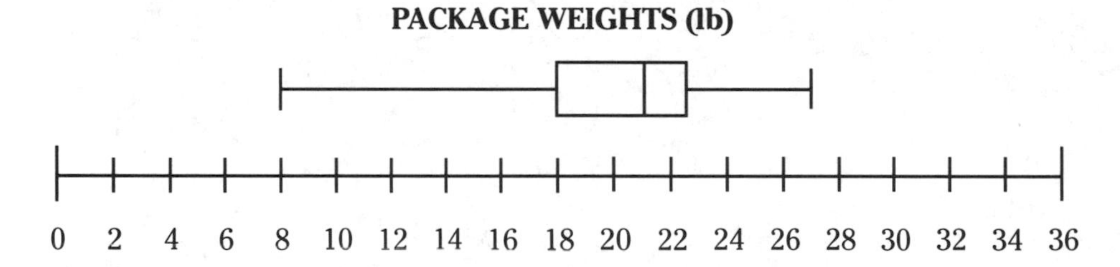

Which statement is best supported by the data in the box-and-whisker plot?

A The median package weight was about 18 pounds.

B The range in package weights was about 19 pounds.

C More than half the packages weighed less than 18 pounds.

D About one-fourth of the packages weighed between 21 and 27 pounds.

Read each problem. Write your answers.

5. The number of chin-ups each of the 25 students in Mr. Donaldson's gym class completed is shown in the line plot below.

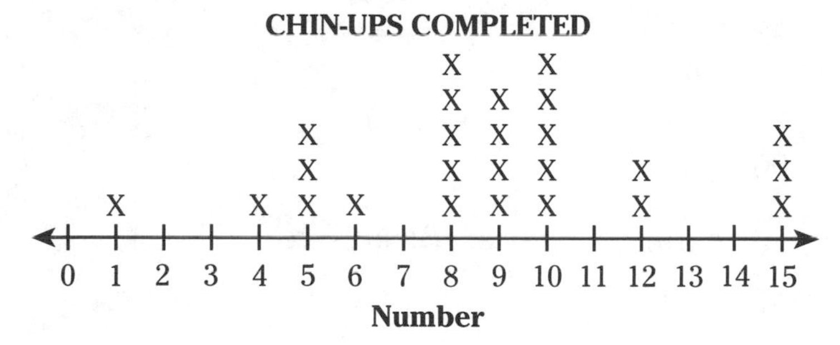

How many of these students completed more than 9 chin-ups?

Answer: ___________

6. Luke developed 40 sets of digital pictures one weekend. The number of digital pictures developed in each set is shown in the stem-and-leaf plot below.

DIGITAL PICTURES DEVELOPED

Stem	Leaf
0	
1	3 5 6 6 8
2	5 5 7
3	0 2 4 4 4 8 8
4	4 6 7 8 8
5	0 0 2 2 2 2 5 7 9 9
6	1 3 4 4 5 5
7	0 2 4
8	5

1 | 3 means 13 pictures

What is the median number of digital pictures Luke developed that weekend?

Answer: ___________

Read the problem. Write your answers.

7. Listed below are the grades each student received on a practice driving test.

75	78	83	75
90	85	70	92
88	78	80	83
83	80	90	85

Make a stem-and-leaf plot to organize the test scores. Be sure to include a key.

What is the range in test scores?

Answer: ___________

Describe how the median and mode of this data compare.

Answer: ____

____

____

____

LESSON 3

Sampling and Predicting

Standard A1.7.2

Businesses, governments, and social scientists rely on surveys to learn accurate information about the wants, needs, and behaviors of the public. Therefore, an important part of their work is knowing how to analyze and interpret the results of surveys. However, an equally important part of their work is in deciding who to survey.

Populations and Samples

There are two terms frequently used when discussing survey methods.

- The **population** is the entire set of individuals about whom you would like information.
- The **sample** is the smaller set of individuals from whom you collect information. The sample is always part of the larger population.

For example, if you were interested in the amount of milk consumed by 10-year-olds worldwide, you might send surveys to various schools or homes around the world. Your population would be all 10-year-olds in the world, but your sample would be only those 10-year-olds who responded to your survey.

Now try this question.

S-1 A scientist is interested in the number of hours that polar bears sleep each day. She watches 12 different polar bears for a period of one month and records their sleep patterns. What is the sample in her experiment?

A the polar bears she watches

B all polar bears in the world

C all animals in the world

D all bears in the world

The scientist is interested in all polar bears, so choice B describes the population. The scientist is only gathering information from 12 specific polar bears. These 12 polar bears are her sample. Choice A is correct.

Representative Samples

Since information from a small sample is used to make predictions or draw conclusions about the entire population, it is important that the sample be as similar to the population as possible. This kind of sample is called a **representative** sample. It is often difficult to ensure that a sample will be exactly like the population. However, it is easy to avoid samples that are likely to differ substantially from the full population.

Suppose that a toy company is interested in learning whether a new action figure will be popular among children in the United States. The following are examples of survey samples the company should avoid:

- 100 randomly selected boys from around the United States
- 100 randomly selected children in Indiana
- the first 100 children who respond to a mail-in offer for a free action figure

The first example is not representative because it only includes boys, while the population includes both boys and girls. The second sample is not representative because it only includes children in Indiana, while the population includes children from all over the United States. Finally, the third sample is not representative because children in this sample are probably more interested in action figures than typical children around the United States. A more representative sample would come from selecting 100 children randomly from all over the United States.

Now try this question.

S-2 An Indiana county government is interested in learning whether county residents favor the conversion of a wilderness area into a business park. Which of these samples would provide the most reliable information?

A 100 randomly selected residents of the county

B 100 randomly selected residents of Indiana

C 100 randomly selected members of a hunting and fishing club

D 100 randomly selected members of the business community

Choice A is correct because this sample is likely to be most similar to the entire population of the county. Choice B includes residents from other counties, which is inappropriate. Choices C and D are likely to include residents whose special interests are not necessarily shared by all county residents.

Simple Random Samples

One of the best ways to obtain a representative sample is to select the sample at random from among the members of the population. While there's no guarantee that the sample will be just like the population, at least there are no reasons to expect that the sample will be different.

A simple random sample is the best way to obtain a representative sample.

In a **random sample,** all members of the population have the same probability of being chosen. In a **simple random sample,** all members of the population have the same probability of being chosen, and the probability of one member being chosen is not affected by whether or not another member is chosen.

At first, it may be difficult to understand the difference between a random sample and a simple random sample. In fact, any simple random sample is also a random sample. However, it is possible to choose a random sample that is not a simple random sample.

Suppose that there are 200 students at a school, and the principal would like to select 100 students at random. Here are two different ways that the principal might select a random sample of 100 students.

1. Beginning with an alphabetical list of all students, the principal will select either the first 100 students on the list or the second 100 students on the list.
2. Beginning with an alphabetical list of all students, the principal will select 100 students at random, one at a time.

The first example will not be a simple random sample. Here is how you can see this. Assume that the student Jason Alvarez is selected. Then, the probability that Tanya Anderson will be selected is 100%, while the probability that Ronald Zisk will be selected is 0%. The selection of one member of the sample makes it more or less likely that other students will be selected.

Now try this sample question.

S-3 There are 10,000 registered voters in Greendale. A polling firm would like to survey 100 of the voters. The polling firm proposes this method for obtaining their sample.

Begin with a complete list of registered voters that is sorted by voter registration number.

- Use a random number generator to choose 1 voter at random.
- Survey this voter and the next 99 voters on the list. If the end of the list is reached, continue at the beginning of the list.

Will the polling firm's sample be a random sample?

Will the polling firm's sample be a simple random sample?

The population is all 10,000 registered voters in Greendale. The polling firm's sample will be a random sample since any registered voter has an equal probability of being selected. The probability of being selected is 100 out of 10,000 or 1%. However, this will not be a simple random sample. Once you know that a certain voter is included in the sample, it becomes more likely that voters with nearby registration numbers will be selected also. It also becomes much less likely that voters with very different registration numbers will be selected.

Sample Size

A general rule for gathering information is the more information, the better. A large sample will give better information than a small sample. There is an element of randomness in just about any sample. For example, in the polar bear study, how can the scientist be sure that she hasn't studied 12 particularly sleepy polar bears? When the sample is large, this kind of variability is more likely to either cancel out or blend in with other data from the sample.

> The larger the sample size, the more reliable the information.

However, because collecting data requires time and money, agencies frequently use small samples. The practice of using small samples is fine, as long as these agencies recognize that their data are more subject to random variation. When obtaining a large sample is cost-effective and convenient, a large sample should be used.

Now try this question.

S-4 A non-profit organization wants to learn about the study habits of students in Japan. Which of these sampling methods is likely to provide the most reliable information?

A randomly selecting 100 students in Japan

B randomly selecting 100 students in Asian countries

C randomly selecting 500 students in Japan

D randomly selecting 500 students in Asian countries

> Because the study focuses on students specifically in Japan, choices A and C both provide representative samples. However, choice C is better than choice A since it uses a larger sample. Choice C is correct.

Biased Sampling

A random sample is supposed to have an equal chance of sampling every individual in the whole population. When a sample is not random, the data from the sample can lead to faulty conclusions. Here is an example.

Suppose that Mary wanted to know what percent of students in Indiana watch the news in the evening. For convenience, her sample might be the 25 students in her journalism class. Assuming 20 of them watch the evening news, Mary would conclude that 80% of students in Indiana watch the evening news. However, students taking a journalism course might be much more likely to be interested in the news than students in general. Because of this, Mary's sample is said to be **biased** (or **slanted**), and her results are probably not valid.

Now try this question.

S-5 Trevor randomly selected 100 adults visiting a zoo and asked them if they owned a pet. He found that 86 of them did own a pet. Trevor concluded that 86% of all adults own pets. Which of these best describes why Trevor's conclusion is not valid?

A He did not ask what kind of pet the people owned.

B Some of the people probably gave false information to Trevor.

C Trevor should have asked children as well as adults.

D Visitors to the zoo probably like animals more than the average person.

Based on his survey, Trevor can really only draw conclusions about the percentage of adult visitors to this particular zoo who own pets. It is likely that the percentage of pet owners in the general population will be much less. Choice D is correct.

Predictions Based on Data

Data samples and trends found from data are often used to predict outcomes of larger populations or of future events. For example, this graph shows the amount of sales a company earned each year they were in business. This data can be used to draw conclusions about the amount of sales they might expect to earn one year, two years, or five years into the future. From the trend in this data, a reasonable conclusion might be that this company can expect to earn about $1,000,000 in sales by year 7.

Try this sample question.

S-6 The library formed youth and adult book clubs five years ago. The number of members in each book club is shown in the bar graph below.

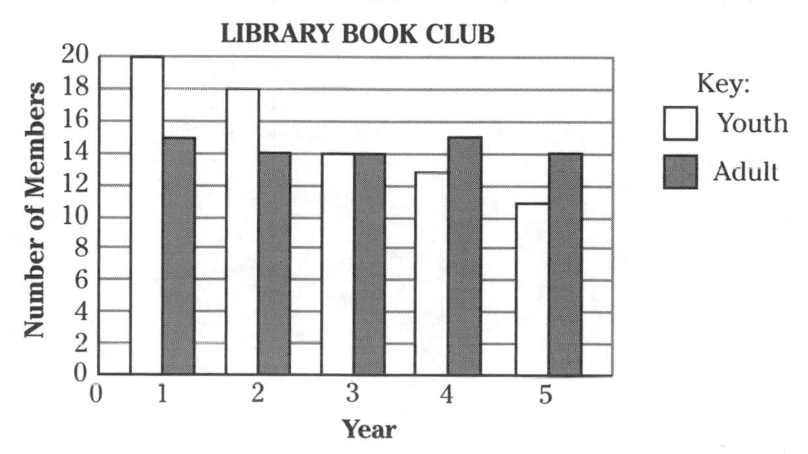

Assuming the trend in number of members in each book club continues, about how many total members would be expected in both book clubs by year 6?

A 8 B 14 C 22 D 28

From this data, the number of members in the youth book club tends to decrease by about 2 people each year. The number of members in the adult book club tends to remain the same from year to year. In year 5, there were about 11 members in the youth club. So, in year 6, about $11 - 2$, or 9 members would be expected. The number of members in the adult club is about 14 each year. So, in year 6, the total number of expected members in both clubs is about $9 + 14 = 23$. Of the choices, 22 is the closest. Choice C is correct.

IT'S YOUR TURN

Read each problem. Circle the letter of the best answer.

1. A professional sports team wants to understand why so few females in the city attend the team's games. Which of these sampling methods should provide the most reliable information?

   A surveying 50 females, selected at random from throughout the city

   B surveying 50 females, selected at random from throughout the U.S.

   C surveying 500 females, selected at random from throughout the city

   D surveying 500 females, selected at random from throughout the U.S.

2. A car company wants to know the three features of cars that are most important to licensed drivers in the United States. The company telephones 100 Florida residents and asks a series of questions. Which of these is the population in their survey?

   A all licensed drivers in Florida

   B all residents of Florida

   C all licensed drivers in the United States

   D all residents of the United States

Read each problem. Circle the letter of the best answer.

3. Andrew wants to know the average height of all 16-year-old males in Indiana. He records the heights of five 16-year-old males at his school. Which of these is the sample in his survey?

   A the five 16-year-olds whose heights he recorded

   B all the 16-year-old males at his school

   C all the 16-year-old males in Indiana

   D all the 16-year-old males in the United States

4. A company executive wants to know what percentage of her employees drive to work. Which of these methods would provide her with a simple random sample?

   A Choose the first 10 employees that arrive at the office.

   B Choose all employees with last names that begins with "A."

   C Assign a number to each employee and then use a random number generator to select employees.

   D Select one department at random and then survey all employees in that department.

5. Arthur wants to know what percentage of drivers in his town favor a new highway project. Which of these samples will provide the most reliable data?

   A 50 drivers randomly selected at a political rally

   B 50 drivers randomly selected from a traffic jam

   C 50 drivers randomly selected at a construction agency

   D 50 drivers randomly selected from a list of licensed drivers

Read each problem. Fill in your answer on the response grid.

6. Lisa asked 50 students in her school how many hours a week they work at an after-school job. The results of her survey are summarized in the circle graph below.

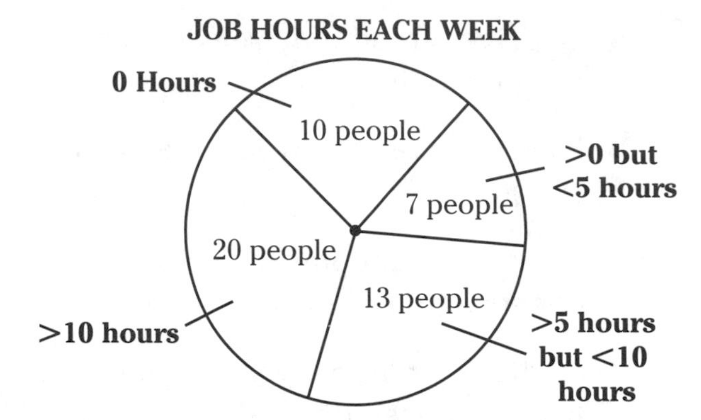

There are 840 total students in Lisa's school. Based on the results of her survey, about how many total students in her school would be expected to work more than 10 hours a week?

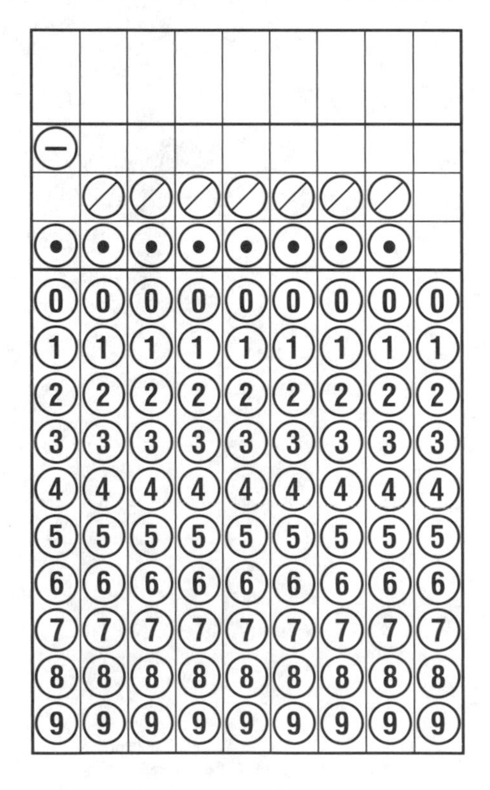

7. On four different days, a research company asked 100 random people if they would be willing to pay a certain price for a ticket to a new amusement park. The results of the survey are shown in the graph below.

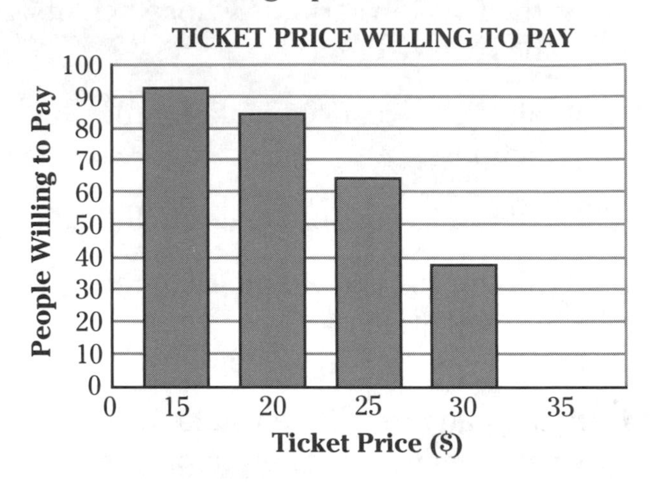

Based on this data, how many people are expected to be willing to pay $35 for a ticket to the new amusement park?

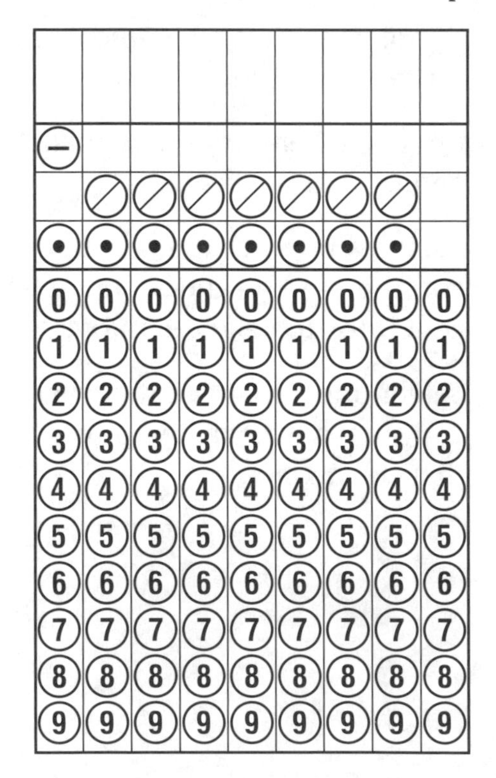

Read the problem. Write your answers.

8. There are 100 residents of a small town. The mayor would like to collect information from a sample of 10 residents. She plans the following method for obtaining her sample.

   1. List the 100 residents alphabetically.
   2. Use a random number generator to select a resident at random.
   3. Choose that resident and the next 9 names on the list as the sample of 10 residents. If the bottom of the list is reached, continue at the top.

   Explain whether the mayor's sample will be a random sample or a simple random sample.

   Answer: ______________________________

   ____

   ____

   ____

   Give at least one reason why a simple random sample would be better than a random sample in this situation.

   Answer: ______________________________

   ____

   ____

   ____

LESSON 4

Use and Misuse of Data

Standard A1.7.3

In a perfect world, statistics and data analysis would only be used to make information more clear and comprehensible. However, statistics and data analysis are often used inappropriately to lead people to a particular conclusion that may not be valid. The more you know about the potential misuses of statistics, the more likely that you will be able to make informed decisions when confronted with data.

Scaling

Similar graphs are often shown side by side to give "at a glance" comparisons. However, the choice of scales used can greatly affect the appearance of the graphs.

Here are two graphs showing the sales for two divisions of a company from 2004 to 2009.

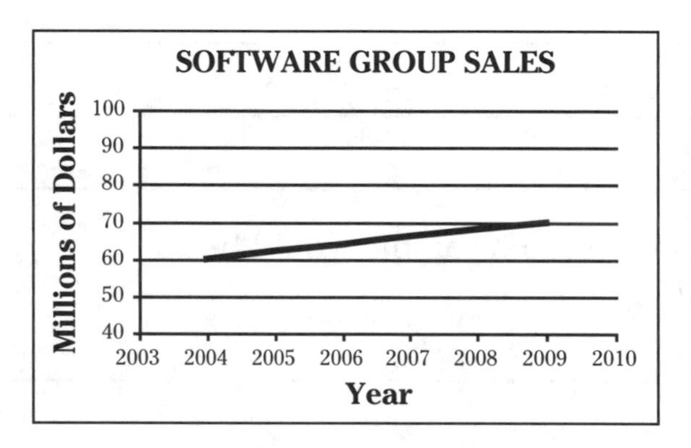

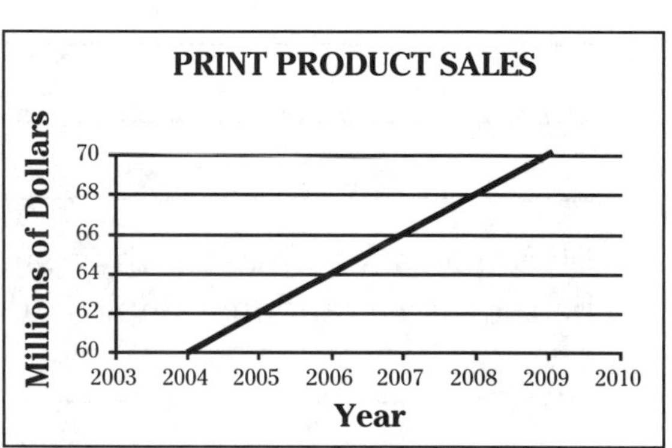

At first glance, the software graph looks flat compared to the print product graph. It is easy to look at the first graph and conclude that sales went up slowly in the software group, while they went up very quickly in the print product group. This kind of conclusion might be used to make important decisions about the company (e.g., fire the software sales manager).

However, the scales on the graphs tell a different story. Notice that the first scale ranges from $40 million to $100 million. The second scale ranges from $60 million to $70 million. Because the scales are different, the graphs appear different. In reality, sales were identical in both divisions. In each case, they rose at a constant rate from 60 million to 70 million.

Now try the question on the next page.

S-1 The table below shows the customer satisfaction rating for three brands of printers, based on the percentage of customers who report being satisfied with their purchases.

CUSTOMER SATISFACTION

Brand of Printer	Customer Satisfaction Rating
Xenon	91%
Versajet	91%
Balsa	94%

Show the same data in a graph that makes it look like all three printer brands have about the same customer satisfaction level.

Show the same data in a graph that makes it look like Balsa is a much better printer than the other two printers.

Which of the two graphs more accurately represents the data?

The key to answering this question is to realize that different scales can affect the appearance of the graph greatly.

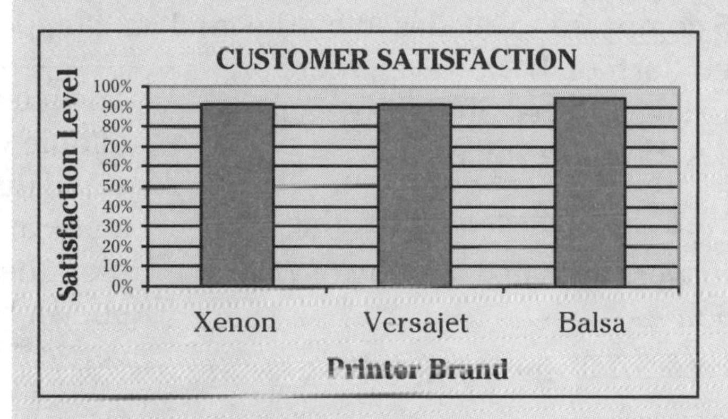

This first graph makes the data appear similar for all three brands of printers.

This second graph makes it appear (at first glance) that Balsa is a far superior printer.

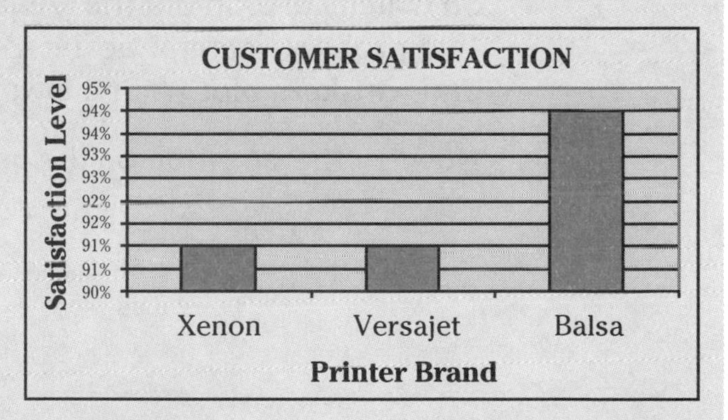

In the second graph, the height of the Balsa bar is four times the height of the other two bars. This suggests that Balsa has four times the customer satisfaction level. However, this is not true since the actual satisfaction levels (91%, 91%, 94%) are actually very close to each other. The first graph more accurately represents the data.

Different Statistics, Different Conclusions

Data can be described with many different statistics. Mean, median, mode, range, and interquartile range are just some of the ways we summarize information. Often, one of these statistics suggests one interpretation while a different statistic suggests another interpretation altogether.

For example, suppose 20 teenagers watched two different cartoons. They rated each on a scale from 0 to 100. The results are shown on the double box-and-whiskers plot below.

CARTOON RATINGS

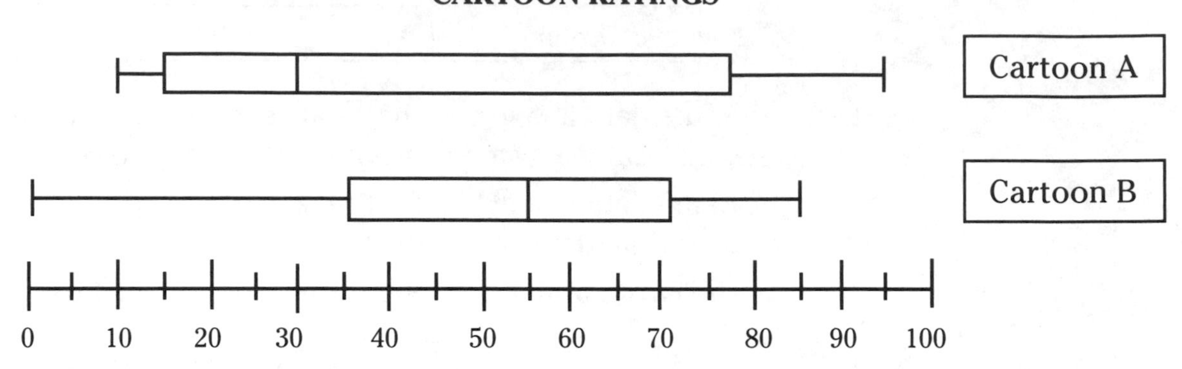

Which cartoon did the teenagers like better? The median for Cartoon B is much higher: 55 compared to 30. Based on the median, it appears that teenagers preferred Cartoon B. However, there are many valid ways to suggest that, in fact, teenagers preferred Cartoon A. Here are some:

- Cartoon A received the highest single rating.
- Over 25% of teenagers assigned a rating of 75 or greater to Cartoon A.
- Cartoon B received the lowest single rating.

> The median is the middle value in a set of numbers. In a box-and-whiskers plot, the median is shown by the middle vertical bar.

So which cartoon did the teenagers really like better? In fact, this is something that probably cannot be determined based only on the data in the double box-and-whiskers plot. Your answer depends on how you look at the data.

Now try the question on the next page.

S-2 The table below shows the salaries of six circus employees.

CIRCUS SALARIES

Employee	Profession	Annual Salary
Jean	Acrobat	$14,000
Louis	Acrobat	$14,800
Bertrand	Acrobat	$22,000
Isabelle	Clown	$15,200
Jamal	Clown	$16,900
Desiree	Clown	$16,900

Jean claims that the acrobats make less than the clowns. How could Jean use statistics to show this?

Isabelle claims that the clowns make less than the acrobats. How could Isabelle show this?

Who, if anyone, is correct?

A good strategy for solving this problem is to make a table that shows the mean and median salaries for both professions.

CIRCUS SALARIES

Profession	Mean Salary	Median Salary
Acrobat	$16,933	$14,400
Clown	$16,333	$16,900

Jean could use the median to show that acrobats make less than clowns. However, Isabelle could use the mean to show that clowns make less than acrobats. In fact, the salaries across both professions are not very different, with five of the six employees making between $14,000 and $17,000.

Evaluating Validity

When you read statistics and graphs in printed form, it is important for you to be able to evaluate their validity. This helps you decide if you can draw trustworthy conclusions from the data.

Try these sample questions.

S-3 A toothpaste company asked 100 customers to vote for their favorite brand of toothpaste. There were 36 votes for CleanBrite, 41 votes for DynaMint, and 23 votes for Freshen. Which of the following is a valid claim based on this data?

A CleanBrite received over one-third of the votes.

B CleanBrite received more votes that DynaMint.

C DynaMint received over one-half of the votes.

D DynaMint received twice as many votes as Freshen.

Since one-third of 100 is approximately 33.3, choice A is correct.

S-4 An advertisement for this Web site made this claim: "The number of visitors to our new Web site is doubling every month!" Why is this claim misleading?

Web Site Visitors

Month	Number of Visitors
April	10
May	20

A It should say "…increasing by 10% every month."

B It should say "…multiplying by 10 every month."

C The number of Web site visitors will decrease in June.

D The Web site has been active for only two months.

The best answer is choice D. After just two months, it's too soon to claim that there is a pattern of doubling.

IT'S YOUR TURN

Read each problem. Circle the letter of the best answer.

1. The table below shows the value of a rare coin over many years.

RARE COIN

Year	Value
1985	$120
1990	$160
1995	$280
2000	$300
2005	$340

For which of these years would it be least reliable to predict the value of the coin?

A 1983 C 1993

B 1987 D 2014

2. The table below shows the profits of a technology firm over several years.

TECHNOTECH PROFITS

Year	Profit
2000	$1.1 million
2002	$1.4 million
2004	$1.9 million
2006	$2.2 million
2008	$2.6 million

For which of these years would it be least accurate to estimate the profits of the firm?

A 2001 C 2007

B 2005 D 2013

3. The bar graph shows how many students belonged to two clubs in 2009 and 2010.

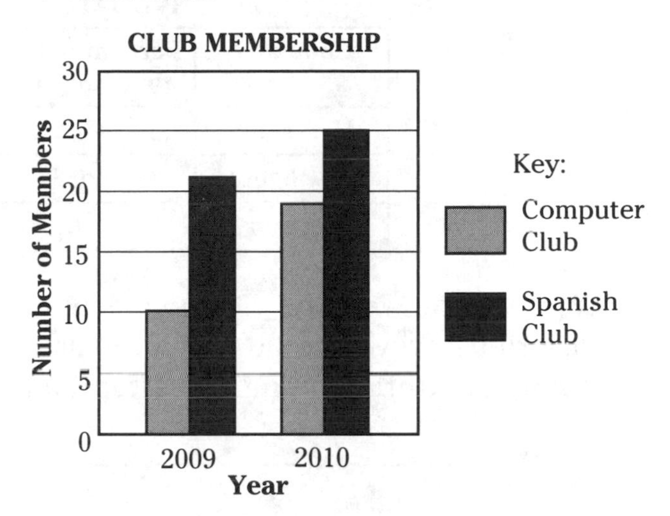

Which of the following is a valid claim according to the data shown in the graph?

A The Spanish Club had more members in 2009 than in 2010.

B The Spanish Club will have more than 40 members in 2011.

C The Computer Club had more members than the Spanish Club in 2010.

D The Computer Club grew more than the Spanish Club between 2009 and 2010.

Read the problem. Write your answers.

4. The table below shows three different companies and the percentages of their batteries that are defective.

DEFECTIVE BATTERIES

Company	Percent of Batteries that Are Defective
Marksman	1.2%
Twilight	0.8%
Jopson	1.1%

Suppose you were the vice president of marketing for Twilight. Describe how you could graph the data to make it appear that Twilight batteries are much better than the other two brands.

Answer: ______________________________

____

____

____

Now suppose that you worked for one of the other companies. Describe how you could graph the data to make it appear that all three companies are about the same.

Answer: ______________________________

____

____

____

Which graph more accurately represents the data?

Answer: ______________________________

Read the problem. Write your answers.

5. Ten students at Monet High School rated two shoe stores on a scale of 1 to 10. The results are shown below.

   Ratings for Shoe Junction: 3, 4, 4, 6, 6, 7, 7, 7, 7, 10
   Ratings for Cover Your Socks: 1, 1, 5, 5, 5, 5, 10, 10, 10, 10

   Marnie claims that students liked Shoe Junction better than Cover Your Socks. How could Marnie use a measure of central tendency to support this?

   Answer: ______________________________

   ____

   ____

   ____

   Ellie thinks that the opposite is true. How could Ellie use a measure of central tendency to support this?

   Answer: ______________________________

   ____

   ____

   ____

Data Analysis Review

Read each problem. Circle the letter of the best answer.

1. The cost for each continuing education class Joanne wants to take is shown in the table below.

CONTINUING EDUCATION CLASSES

Class	Cost ($)
Dance	120
Cooking	40
German	60
Yoga	80
Computer Programming	250

What is the mean cost of these continuing education classes?

A $60 C $110

B $80 D $210

2. Daisy gathered information on annual car insurance rates in her area. These data are shown in the box-and-whisker plot below.

ANNUAL CAR INSURANCE RATES ($)

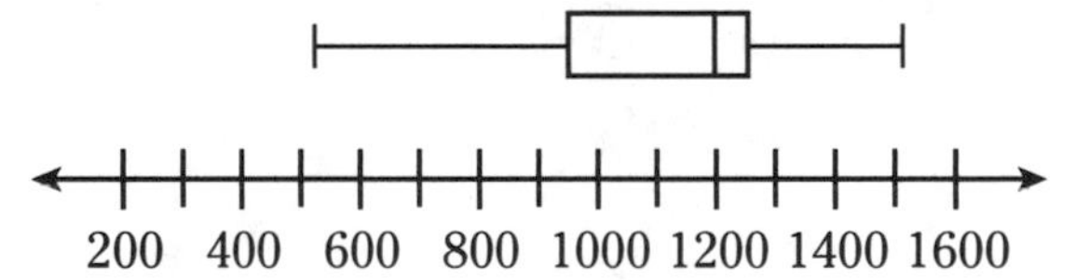

Which amount is closest to the interquartile range of these rates?

A $300 C $675

B $525 D $950

3. The box-and-whisker plot below shows the typing speed, in words per minute, of the students in Mr. Carroll's typing class at the beginning of the year.

TYPING SPEED

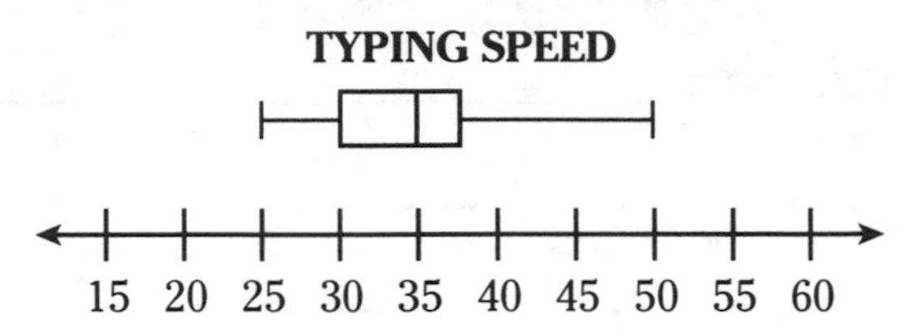

Based on this plot, which of the following statements must be true?

A Exactly one student types 35 words per minute.

B Exactly one student types 37 words per minute.

C Half of the students type 35 words per minute or less.

D Half of the students type 37 words per minute or less.

Read each problem. Circle the letter of the best answer.

4. A company executive wants to know what percentage of her employees own a home. Which of these sampling methods should provide her with the most accurate results?

   A surveying all employees in one particular department

   B surveying the first 30 employees that arrive at the office

   C surveying all employees whose last name begins with the letter "A"

   D assigning a number to each employee and randomly selecting 30 employees

5. The bar graph below shows the number of customer service calls an appliance company received during the first six months of the year.

   Based on this trend, about how many customer service calls can this company expect to receive in month 8?

   A 8,000 C 10,000

   B 9,250 D 11,500

6. A salesperson used the graph below to show the number of sales he made each month.

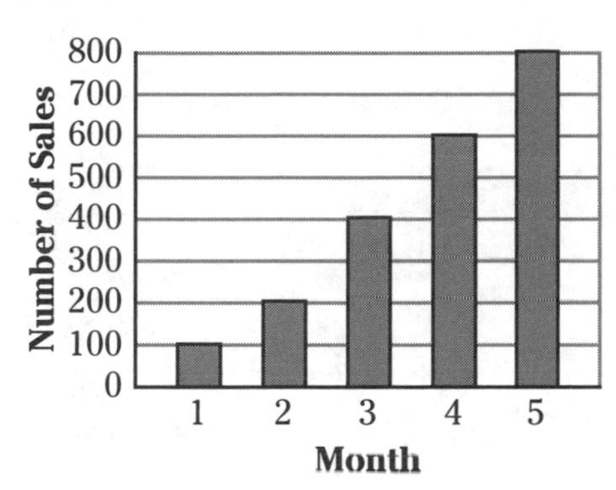

   What is a valid claim the salesperson could make based on this graph?

   A The number of sales he makes increases each month.

   B The number of sales he makes doubles each month.

   C He made more sales in month 5 than in months 3 and 4 combined.

   D He made more sales in months 1 and 2 than in months 3–5.

Read each problem. Fill in your answer on the response grid.

7. The university library subscribes to 16 nursing journals. The line plot below shows the number of issues each nursing journal prints each year.

NURSING JOURNAL ISSUES

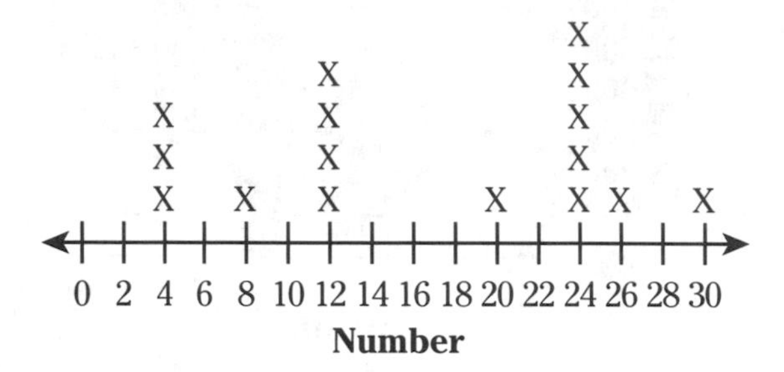

What is the median number of issues printed by these nursing journals each year?

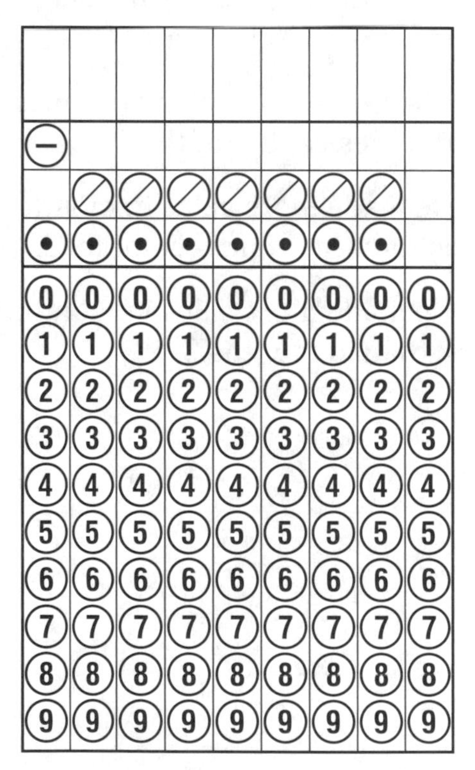

8. Jonas recorded the weight of some rock samples in the stem-and-leaf plot below.

ROCK SAMPLE WEIGHTS (kg)

Stem	Leaf
1	5
2	2 6 7
3	
4	0 3 9
5	7
6	1 1 4

1 | 5 means 1.5 kg

What is the mode weight of these rock samples?

Read the problem. Write your answers.

9. There are 500 students at Karen's school. She wants to find out how they feel about the school's new Algebra requirement. She considers the three survey methods below.
    1. Ask 25 students in her school's mathematics club, selected at random.
    2. Ask 25 students at other schools, selected at random.
    3. Ask 25 students at her school, selected at random.

    Which method will give Karen the most representative sample?

    Answer: ____________

    Explain why the other two methods will not give Karen as representative a sample.

    ____

    ____

    ____

    ____

    ____

    ____

    For the method you selected, suggest a way that Karen could obtain this sample.

    Answer: ______________________________________

    ____

    ____

    ____

Read each problem. Write your answers.

10. The stem-and-leaf plot below shows the length, in minutes, of each movie playing at the local theater complex this week.

MOVIE LENGTHS (minutes)

Stem	Leaf
8	5 8
9	3 4 7 9
10	0 8
11	2 5 6 8 8
12	0 4 5
13	3

8|5 means 85 minutes

What is the range, in minutes, for these movie lengths?

Answer: ______________________

11. The line graph below shows the number of minutes Eli used on his cell phone last year.

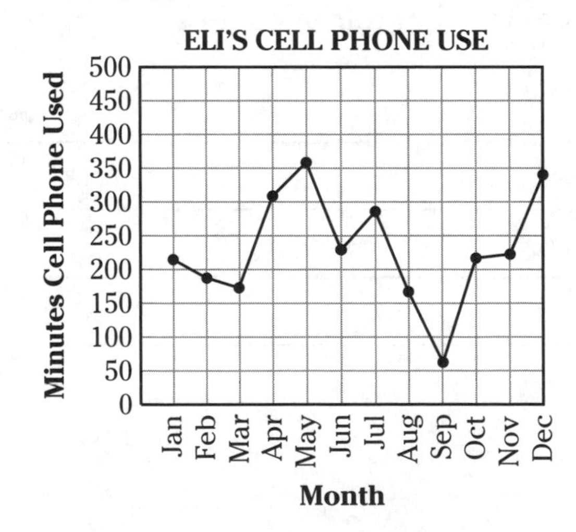

How many months did Eli use his cell phone less than 200 minutes?

Answer: ___________

Read the problem. Write your answers.

12. The box-and-whisker plot below shows the interest rates charged by credit card companies.

INTEREST RATES

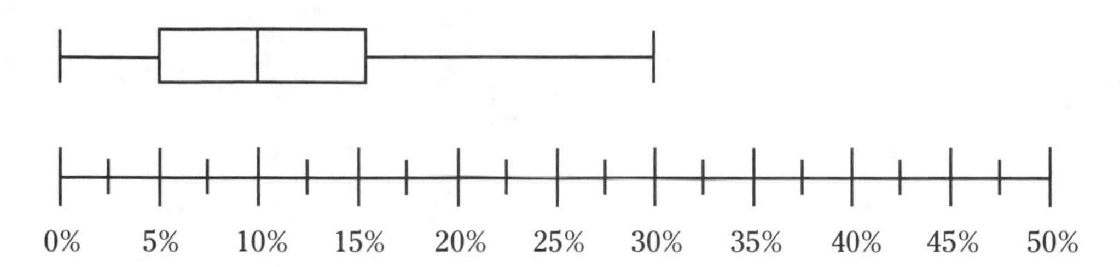

Estimate the median interest rate charged by credit card companies.

Answer: ____________

A credit card company that charges 6% interest claims that their rates are lower than 75% of all other credit card companies. Is this claim correct?

Answer: ____________

Explain why your answer is correct.

____

____

____

____

____

____

Algebra I Reference Sheet

Equation of a Line

Slope-Intercept Form:

$y = mx + b$

where m = slope and b = y-intercept

Point-Slope Form:

$y - y_1 = m(x - x_1)$

where m = slope and (x_1, y_1) is a point on the line

Standard Form of a Linear Equation:

$Ax + By = C$

where A and B are both not zero

Slope of a Line

Let (x_1, y_1) and (x_2, y_2) be two points in the plane.

$$\text{slope} = \frac{\text{change in } y}{\text{change in } x} = \frac{y_2 - y_1}{x_2 - x_1}$$

where $x_2 \neq x_1$

Standard Form of a Quadratic Function

$f(x) = ax^2 + bx + c$

where $a \neq 0$

axis of symmetry: $x = -\frac{b}{2a}$

Quadratic Formula

$$x = \frac{-b \pm \sqrt{b^2 - 4ac}}{2a}$$

where $ax^2 + bx + c = 0$ and $a \neq 0$

Pythagorean Theorem

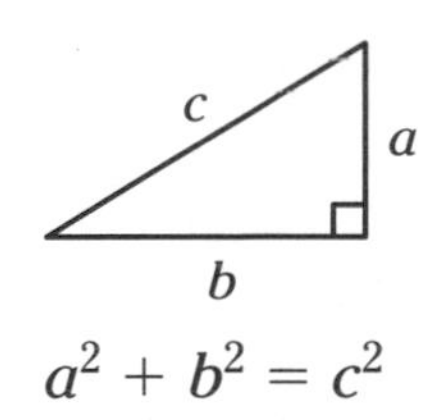

$a^2 + b^2 = c^2$